C000240653

GWR ENGINEERING WORK 1928–1938

R. TOURRET

ISBN 0-905878-08-6

Published by Tourret Publishing, 5 Byron Close, Abingdon, Oxon OX14 5PA, GB.
Typeset and printed by The Alden Press, Oxford

CONTENTS

INTRODUCTION

In reviewing the engineering works, civil and mechanical, carried out by the Great Western Railway in the decade 1928–38, it sometimes seems that they were rebuilding the whole system. Bearing in mind that these years covered more or less the years of depression with trade down and unemployment up, it is all the more surprising that the GWR accomplished so much.

In 1929, there were over one million men out of work, a frightening figure at that time. The Government of the day took action. The House of Commons considered and passed the following motion, to authorise the Treasury to guarantee the payment of the principal of and the interest on any loans to be raised for the purpose of meeting capital expenditure to be incurred under schemes for development, reconstruction or re-equipment in connection with public utility undertakings in Great Britain, also to make at any time grants for the purpose of carrying on any of the same public utility undertakings in defraying the interest payable on any loan. This Bill became known as the Development (Loan Guarantees and Grants) Act of 1929.

Mr J.H. Thomas, as Lord Privy Seal, piloted the motion for the Government, and as a former railwayman he naturally looked to the railways for support in these efforts to relieve unemployment. When the plan was developed in detail it became clear that the railways were to be the main participants. However, no railway company could accept the first provision. The borrowing powers of the private railway companies were limited at that time by their legislation to a certain proportion of their share capital, and in 1929 all of them had exercised those powers to the limits prescribed. They all said that a loan was no good, but the second provision was entirely another matter. By its provisions, the Government could pay the interest for some years on the capital expended on a scheme of development, and the railway companies welcomed it.

As remarked in 1933 by Sir James Milne, then General Manager of the GWR, on the passing of the Development (Loan Guarantees and Grants) Act of 1929, the company decided to embark upon a comprehensive programme of works. By the end of 1929, proposals had been made for capital expenditure of £4,500,000 estimated to afford direct employment for 200,000 man-months. By the end of 1933, there were 35 separate schemes, involving a total expenditure of about £8,000,000 spread over five years. The GWR took advantage of the 1929 Act to put in hand this programme in anticipation of actual requirements and in the expectation that, when trade revived, there would be increased demands for efficient railway transport facilities.

The financial assistance afforded under the provisions of the Act took the form of annual grants of interest at rates up to 5% on the company's capital expenditure for periods of from five to fifteen years, the rate of interest and the period of grant varying in accordance with the speed of carrying out the respective schemes and the estimated period for which the expenditure on the works would not be fully remunerative.

The GWR programme covered all sections of railway and dock operations throughout the system and included the improvement of the station facilities at Paddington, Bristol, Taunton and Cardiff; the construction of avoiding lines at Westbury and Frome to permit accelerated running of express passenger and goods trains to and from the West of England, and also to relieve congestion at the respective stations; and the quadrupling of lines in areas of dense traffic, such as the approaches to Bristol, Cardiff and Birmingham. The lines leading to Taunton were also quadrupled, while further west four lines were laid through a number of stations so as to facilitate the operation of both through trains and local services. At a number of points such as, for example, Birmingham, Cardiff, Swansea, Swindon and St Austell, the facilities for handling and warehousing goods and merchandise traffic were augmented, while new and up-to-date engine sheds were provided at Pantyffynnon, Landore, Cardiff East Dock, Radyr, Duffryn Yard, Port Talbot and Treherbert. At Wolverhampton the locomotive repair shops were reconstructed on modern lines. Other features of the programme were the extension through the main lines of automatic train control, and the installation of colour-light signalling in place of semaphore arms at certain places. Dock facilities in South Wales were improved, in particular by equipping all the docks with appliances capable of dealing with 20-ton wagons for the transport of coal for export. In addition, some other both large and small repair and maintenance works were also carried out, either on GWR's own account, or in cooperation with local County Councils and the like.

All permanent way in connection with the various works was laid with 95 lb/yd British Standard bull-headed rail, generally in 60ft lengths, where running lines and heavy traffic were concerned, although second-hand material was used for certain of the sidings. All the fittings were of GWR standard design, with chairs fixed to the sleepers by through bolts. In fast-running junctions, switch diamonds were generally incorporated. New formations had a bottom ballast of ashes, and ample permanent way drainage, with open jointed earthenware pipes laid down. The top ballast was broken slag or stone or crushed gravel, according to circumstances.

The GWR standard type of fencing was generally used, consisting of concrete posts and eight strands of high-tensile galvanised steel wire. The posts were generally at 12ft or 18ft centres, with pressed-steel droppers at intervals to keep the wire spacing even. Modifications of the type of fencing to suit local conditions consisted of posts and rail, unclimbable iron, close-board screen fencing and special railings. Platform walls as a rule were constructed with the standard pre-cast sections, as described for the Paddington platform extensions scheme, or of concrete block construction. The paving was generally pre-cast concrete slabs where it was covered, or of asphalt on the open sections. All the pre-cast concrete items were manufactured at the GWR concrete plant at Taunton.

Most of these schemes, when completed, were the subject of press releases together with photographs and plans. They therefore appeared in the specialised technical journals of the day, especially the Railway Gazette and the Great Western Railway Magazine, and sometimes also Engineering and The Engineer, often in rather similar terms being based on the press releases. This book concentrates on these contemporary accounts, with thanks to the authors and/or anonymous press officers of the day. It makes no attempt to cover subsequent events, which would not be possible without a large increase in size of this book.

For convenience of presentation, each engineering work has been allocated to a particular year. For smaller works, they were generally started and finished in that year. However, most of the larger schemes took several years to complete, and in these cases the year of completion is generally chosen.

All photographs and drawings are from the author's collection.

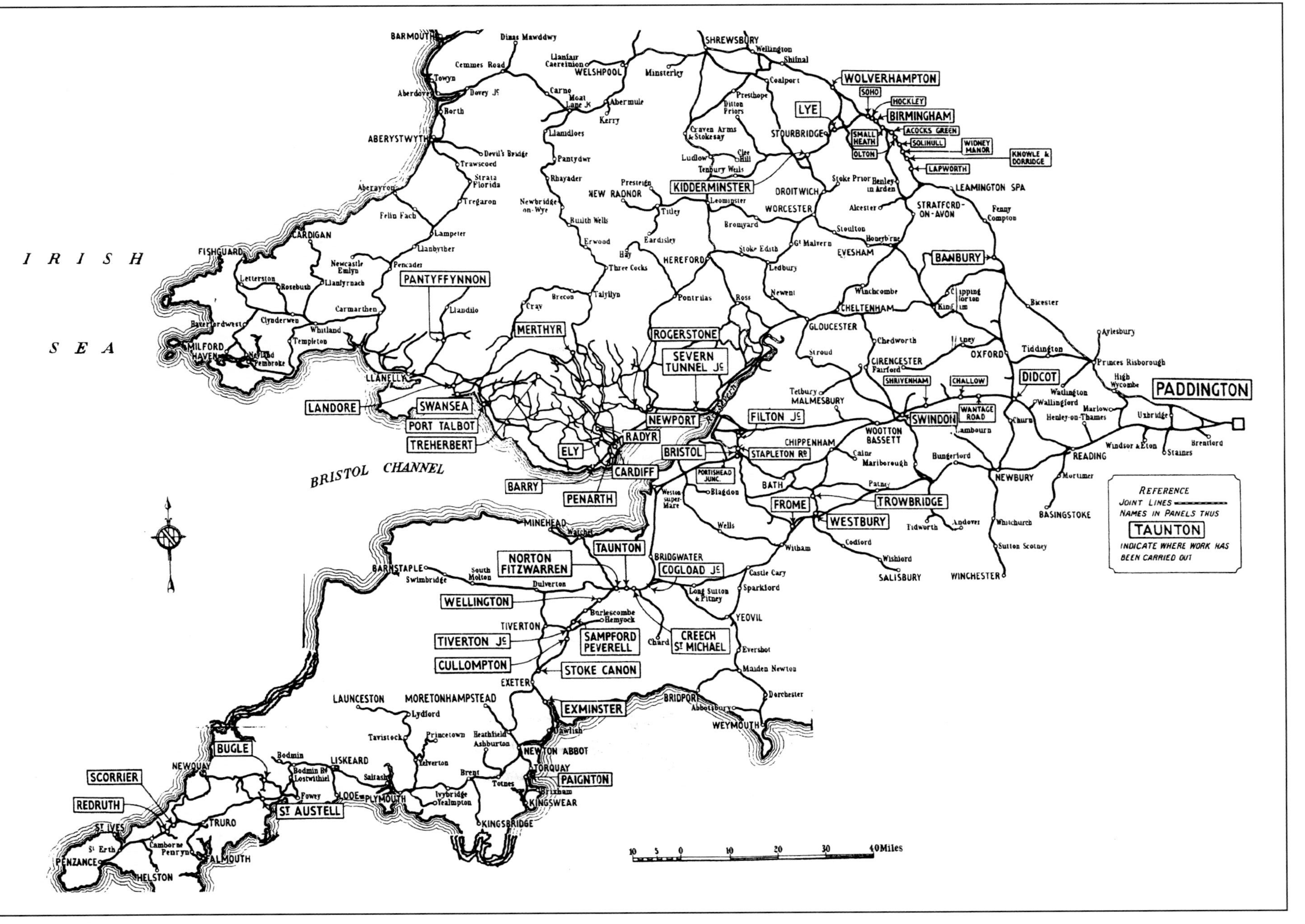

Map 1. The GWR system, indicating where work was being carried out in December 1933.

1928 NEW GOODS FACILITIES AT NEWPORT

It had been apparent for some years that the goods handling facilities at Newport (High Street) station were inadequate for the growing volume of traffic flowing into and out of Newport by goods train. The position was the more difficult because handling goods had to be done at two separate sheds, one a stone and wood structure which served as a warehouse as well as transit shed, the other a temporary structure made entirely of wood. In April 1926, construction of a new combined goods shed and its attendant warehouse began and was expected to take just twelve months to build, but owing to additions and improvements being made to the original plans, and to industrial troubles which held up delivery of steelwork, the work was not completed until March 1928 (thus just bringing it into the scope of this book!).

The new warehouse was constructed entirely of reinforced concrete, some 150 tons of steel being used, together with many thousands of tons of crushed stone, sand and cement. There were three floors; cellar, ground or platform level and first storey warehouse. The space available for the storage of goods was about 14,000 square feet. Each floor was served by an electric goods lift with a platform 9ft 3in by 8ft 1in, and a capacity of two tons. There was an office for twenty clerks and an inspector's office, both centrally heated.

The new goods shed, separate but adjoining the warehouse, consisted of some 300 tons of steelwork, 26,500 square feet of glass and 34,800 square feet of asbestos sheeting. It contained two straight platforms 400ft long, between which were two sets of rails, which allowed for the berthing of 40 wagons. As many as 120 horse or motor vehicles could be positioned under cover along the outsides of the platforms, which were of concrete construction, with covering of oak 4ft wide at the edges and asphalt over the remaining portions. The two platforms were served by a counter-balance lifting bridge, which could be operated by one man, to facilitate the transfer of goods from one platform to the other. Electric capstans were installed to work wagons on the shed roads, which were provided with a crossover to enable wagons to be transferred from one siding to the other without interfering with work on other wagons. Overhead runways provided the staff with means of moving articles, weighing up to a ton, from point to point throughout the building or to and from road vehicles.

1928 CAERPHILLY LOCOMOTIVE WORKS

The late Rhymney Railway was one of the great coal-carrying railways in South Wales and, considering that the ultimate maximum length of its system was only slightly more than 50 miles, it was a remarkably prosperous one. The railway received its Act of Incorporation on 29 July 1854, originally for a railway nine miles long from the town of Rhymney to a junction with the Taff Vale extension of the Newport, Abergavenny and Hereford Railway at Hengoed. Next year, an extension was authorised to join the Taff Vale Railway at Walnut Tree Junction, six miles north of Cardiff. The railway opened on 25 February 1858 for mineral traffic and on 31 March 1858 for passengers.

This remained the Rhymney Company's route to Cardiff until 1 April 1871, when a new independent line from Cardiff to Caerphilly via Llanishen was opened. This new route had the advantage of shortening the distance between Rhymney and Cardiff by $1\frac{1}{2}$ miles. In 1900, it was considered desirable to move the repair shops away from Cardiff Docks, to make room for stabling the RR locomotives there. Accordingly, $17\frac{1}{2}$ acres of land adjoining the main line to the west of Caerphilly Tunnel were purchased for the construction of a new works. The contract for building the workshops was allocated to Mr T.W. Davies, which were completed in February 1901, although difficulties experienced with positioning machinery delayed the start of operations until December 1901.

These new workshops provided appropriate facilities for the Locomotive, Carriage, Wagon and Engineering departments, employing 320 men.

Plate 1 The new goods facilities at Newport, the concrete warehouse in the foreground and behind it the new goods shed.

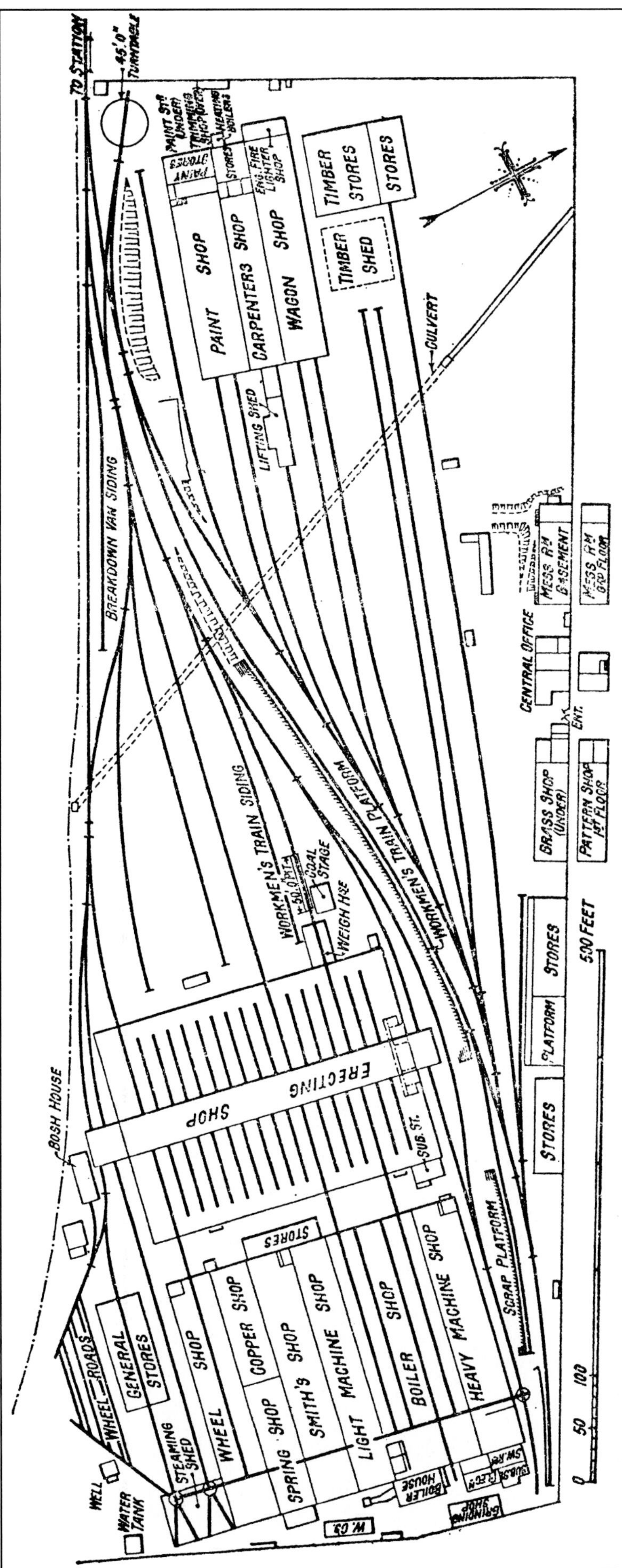

Map 2. Caerphilly Works. Layout of shops as modernised.

The shops comprised erecting, machine, smiths, boiler and engine testing shops on the east side; carriage, wagon and paint shops on the west side; messroom, pattern shop, stores and general offices on the north side. The whole works were designed to be self-contained and they had their own electric generating plant for power and lighting purposes and also a well sunk on the premises to provide water supply. For the workmen, the Rhymney Railway provided a service of workmen's trains between Cardiff and the Works, a distance of 7 miles, with just a nominal fare. In the first year of operation, the locomotive works carried out heavy and light repairs to 17 and 42 locomotives respectively.

From the commencement, these works were improved and added to. Although initially only repairs to rolling stock were undertaken, carriages and wagons were later constructed there. By 1918, the following shops existed: machine shop 10,500 sq ft, erecting shop 20,500 sq ft, coppersmiths 8750 sq ft, smiths 10,500 sq ft, steel & iron stores 8750 sq ft, boiler shop 10,290 sq ft, wagon & wood mill 9240 sq ft, carriage & carpenters 7700 sq ft and paint shop 9240 sq ft. By 1921, the number of workmen was reduced to 250 because the Engineering Department had been moved to Salisbury Road in Cardiff. The next alteration was taking electricity from the South Wales Power Distributing Company instead of generating their own.

The Rhymney Railway became a constituent company of the GWR on 1 January 1922. After grouping, the GWR had as one of its principal objects the cutting out of duplicated services and facilities. One of the consequences was the disestablishment of certain smaller repair centres and the centralising of work at larger ones. Within South Wales, dotted about the various systems were several small repair works, in which also a certain amount of new work was undertaken. To amalgamate these interests, it was decided that the relatively modern workshops at Caerphilly would, with suitable extensions and improvements, provide a convenient centre at which operations on a larger scale could be carried out. This involved repairs to the many different classes of locomotives previously maintained by the constituent companies at their own works.

Therefore, between 1923 and 1928, the old Rhymney works were considerably enlarged, and the machinery and equipment brought up to date. A large

Plate 2 Exterior view of the Locomotive Works at Caerphilly in 1928.

Plate 3 The erecting shop at Caerphilly Works, showing the traverser.

new erecting shop laid out in three bays was constructed, having a floor space of 60,000 sq ft with a capacity for 60 locomotives, supplied with two electric overhead gantry cranes with a lift of 80 tons, with two 40-ton hoists to each gantry so that a complete locomotive could be carried the entire length of the shop. The old boiler shop was converted to a wheel shop. The original erecting shop, with two electric gantries of 30 tons lift, became the boiler and tank repairing shop. The coppersmiths shop, now occupying 10,290 sq ft, was equipped with suitable hydraulic machinery. The smiths shop now contained 22 hearths, complete with various types of steam hammers and two furnaces, one being gas-fired which gave more regular heating. A number of workmen, previously employed at the other centres, were transferred to Caerphilly, so that employment was now over 500 men.

The Caerphilly Works, as reorganised, were modelled upon Swindon lines and it was said that Caerphilly was referred to locally as the Swindon of South Wales. It had become a self-contained factory in which tank locomotives of various sizes, types and weights were completely overhauled. The work was carried out in accordance with a carefully organised plan of operations which achieved a steady flow of work through the shops, thus improving the output of repaired locomotives. In 1927, 87 heavy and 74 light overhauls were completed, while in 1928 the figures were 153 heavy and 67 light. In 1929, 213 heavy and 38 light engine repairs were completed and the general tendency had become

Plate 4 Boiler shop at Caerphilly Works.

to concentrate on heavy repairs. In these early days, work was concentrated on rebuilding engines of the constituent companies with standard GWR boilers, and repair of the new standard heavy South Wales 56XX 0-6-2T class.

1928 REPAIRS TO SWANSEA NORTH DOCK DRAWBRIDGE

One of the two principal main roads, known as the Port Tennant road, leading from Neath to Swansea and West Wales, was carried over the lock entrance to the North Dock Swansea by a roller draw-bridge, over which also passed a double tramway track and a single line of railway, giving access on the low level between the South Dock and the main dock system, formerly owned by the Swansea Harbour Trust and by this time forming part of the extensive dock system owned by the GWR.

This bridge was constructed in 1903 by the SHT and was 122ft long with a clear width of 28ft between the main girders, each of which carried on cantilever brackets a footway 7ft wide. The total weight was about 450 tons. Movements were actuated by hydraulic rams which lifted the bridge to the level of the top of the rollers, of which there were eight, each 3ft 6in in diameter, running in bearings fixed in the roadway. Hydraulically operated chains drew the bridge over the rollers back clear of the lock.

Owing to the heavy increase in weight and volume of motor traffic since the bridge was designed, to the heavy stresses and racking effects set up when the bridge was operated, and to the corrosive effect of the humid atmosphere and of gases from near-by works, it became necessary to carry out an extensive overhaul of the structure. As a preliminary step, arrangements were made for the diversion of traffic, both vehicular and pedestrian. To provide for the safe passage of heavy lorries, extensive repairs were carried out to the Pottery Swing Bridge crossing the lock at the northern end of the North Dock, and the bridge crossing the Swansea Canal was reconstructed and strengthened. The route followed by the diverted traffic is shown on the accompanying diagram. A floating gangway, constructed on a timber barge, enabled pedestrians to cross the lock; this barge was unmoored and withdrawn by hand when vessels passed through the lock. Some 24,000 persons passed over this gangway in 24 hours, during which period 2,500 vehicles were diverted round the upper end of the North Dock. Trams worked up to the lock bridge from either side, passengers passing over the gangway to rejoin trams on the other side. Low-level rail traffic to and from the South Dock, the Prince of Wale's Dock, and King's Dock, was passed over the high-level rail system, transfer from high to low being effected by the existing wagon hoist at the western end of the South Dock.

The repairs comprised the cutting out and renewal of some 40 tons of steelwork in plates, angles, etc including the renewal of the greater part of the roller path attached to the underside of the main girders, and the provision of about 45 tons of cast iron in kerbing etc as well as the renewal of the whole of the timber decking. Additional stiffening plates were rivetted to the existing web plates and bottom angles of the main girders.

On stripping the bridge it was found that, owing to the condition of the web plates, which for considerable lengths were cracked through, the depth of the new plates would be insufficient to provide the necessary rivet attachment through sound metal. To avoid further cutting away of existing members, it was decided to make use of electric welding to provide efficient attachment of the new plates to the old, the first use of this method for bridge repair work on the GWR. During the repair work, over 2,000 rivets were cut out and replaced by similar or larger ones, some 1,400 holes in steelwork were drilled or enlarged, and about 100 cuts were made through steel work (angles, plates, roller track, etc). A petrol-driven compressor actuated the riveting, boring and various other tools.

Plate 5 The coppersmiths shop at Caerphilly Works.

Plate 6 The smiths shop at Caerphilly Works.

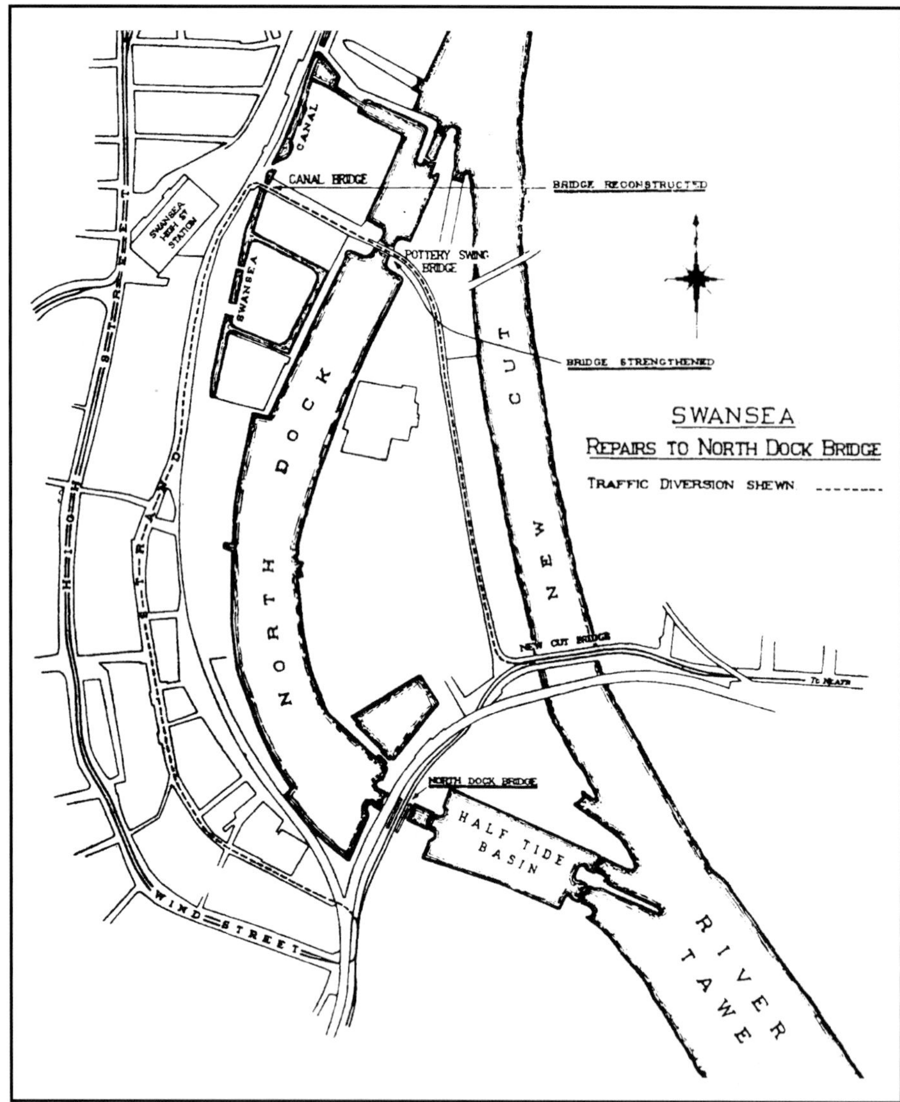

Map 3. Map showing the North Dock, with diversions marked.

1928 ALTERATIONS AT CARDIFF QUEEN STREET STATION

The incorporation of the railways of South Wales into the GWR in 1923 led the GWR to consider ways in which the combined system could be improved. At Cardiff, the GWR wished to coordinate the passenger services of the former Taff Vale, Rhymney and Barry Railways with those of the GWR in one large station at Cardiff General. The Barry trains already had running powers into the GWR station, but the Taff Vale and the Rhymney both had their own stations. There was a connection from Queen Street at East Bridge Junction, whereby Taff Vale trains could proceed by a flying junction over the GWR main line and enter the General station from the east, but from the Rhymney there was no direct connection. The connection between the Taff Vale and the GWR had originally been on the level but this proved such a nuisance that a flying junction was constructed in 1896 to bring the Taff Vale trains across the GWR main line and to the south side.

Cardiff Queen Street station, the former headquarters of the Taff Vale line, and Cardiff Parade station, the terminus of the Rhymney section, adjoined, but there was no direct junction between the two stations. Consequently, a large number of passengers from the Rhymney and

Plate 7 General view of the Swansea North Dock Lock drawbridge.

Plate 8 Temporary floating gangway across the lock.

Plate 9 Bridge blocked up above the street level for repairs.

Cardiff Railways, travelling to and from the docks area, had to change from one station to the other, or to proceed by tram, which many preferred to do rather than to rebook by railway.

In 1928 work was completed on a direct link between the Rhymney and Taff Vale lines just north of Queen Street station. By this Rhymney trains were diverted from their old line that went into Cardiff Parade station, and took instead the new spur into the Taff Vale station, and could continue over the GWR line into the General station. These alterations included the abolition of the Parade station and improved accommodation at Queen Street station, to provide for both the former Taff Vale and Rhymney lines. Thus, it was possible to close the Rhymney station and to effect substantial economy.

Considerable alterations were carried out at Queen Street station, involving the lengthening of the old down Taff Vale platform, its conversion into an island platform, and the demolition of an old screen wall and a portion of the existing roof. A new column was provided to support the roof at the north end of the station, where the end was previously carried on the screen wall. A new roof covering was supplied for the new half of the station. It consisted of rolled steel joist columns, supporting cantilever beams projecting out to carry the valance at one end, and connected to the existing roof columns at the other end. A new down relief platform was constructed, and the existing passenger subway extended to serve it.

Plate 10 The east end of the drawbridge, showing the new end girder, relieving horns, and temporary packing blocks.

1928 RECONSTRUCTION AND WIDENING OF ABERBEEG BRIDGE

The old overbridge at Aberbeeg, which carried the main road to Ebbw Vale, near its junction with the Abertillery road, over the GWR Western Valleys line, was on a gradient of 1 in 6, and only 15ft wide. The approaches to the bridge on both the high and low level sides were narrow and very irregular. The road was, in fact, 55ft higher at the Newport end than at the Ebbw Vale end, this height being attained in the short distance of 468ft, the average gradient of the road, including the bridge, being about 1 in $8\frac{1}{2}$. In view of these conditions, the Abertillery Urban District Council had desired for a long time to improve the situation, and the Council and the GWR agreed to reconstruct the bridge, with 25ft between parapets, and to widen and considerably lessen the gradient of the road approaches.

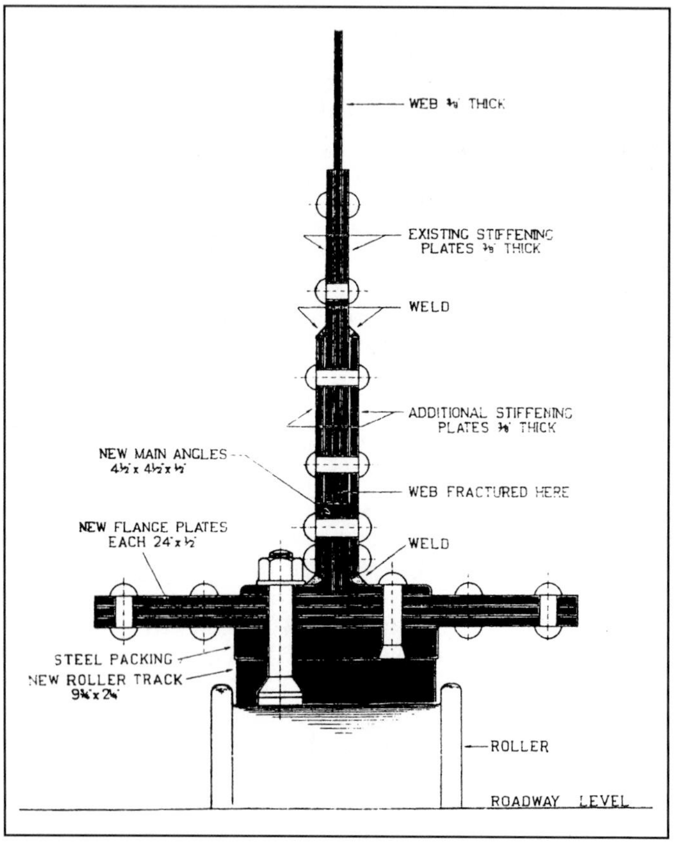

The railway ran at the foot of a mountain, and the Abertillery road ran parallel with, but about 60ft above it. The old Ebbw Vale road left this road at its junction and crossed the railway with a steep grade running down to the valley. As the Council wanted to make the roadway over the new bridge to the easier gradient of 1 in $13\frac{1}{2}$, the old line of roadway could not be used, and the new junction with the Abertillery road had to be made 400ft back, the new road being carried from the high side of the bridge over the mountain slope to the new junction. This section of the road was constructed on 19 blind arches supported on piers, and formed a masonry viaduct 450ft long, built on the side of the mountain. While the roadway viaduct was being constructed, work was started on the extension of the bridge abutments. About 1,300 tons of rock was excavated and 80 tons of steel and iron erected in bridgework. A feature of the new bridge was the pipe gantry carried on cantilevers. This gantry carried a 12in storm water drain, 9in sewer, also the water main, electric cables, etc, and enabled examination

Fig 1. New stiffening plates electrically welded to the old plates.

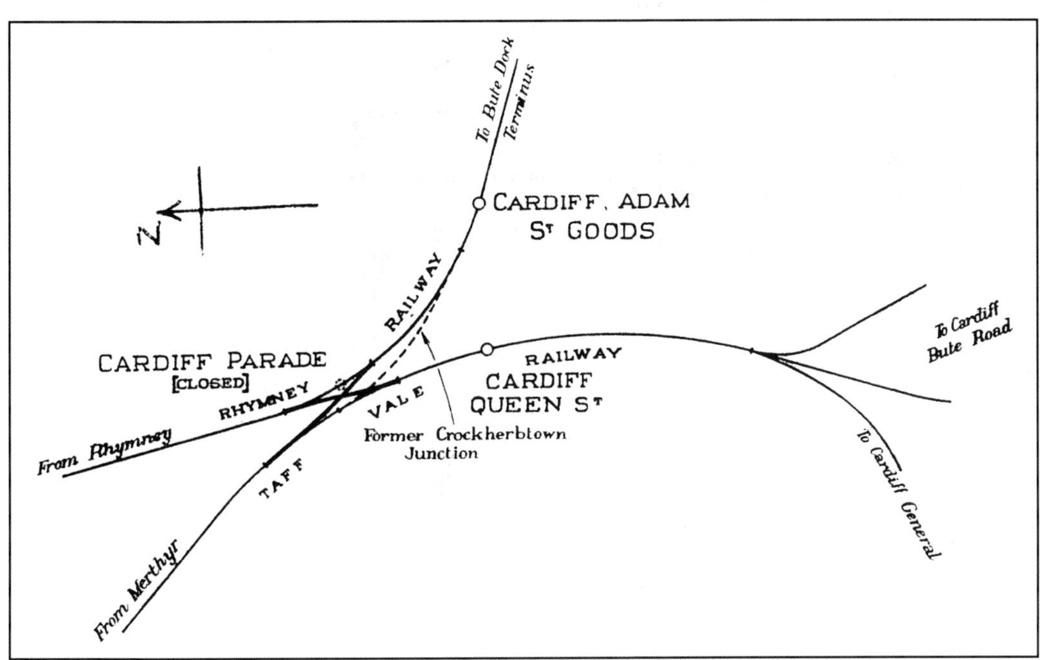

Map 4 New junctions between former Rhymney and Taff Vale Railways and stations.

Plate 11 General view of the new permanent way connections joining the former Rhymney and Taff Vale Railways, showing the new North signal box, with Cardiff Queen Street station in the background as marked by an arrow. The position of the former and now closed Cardiff Parade station is also marked.

Plate 12 The exterior of the new Cardiff Queen Street North signal box.

Plate 13 The interior of the new Cardiff Queen Street North signal box.

or repairs to be effected without disturbing the surface of the road.

In addition to the works already referred to, a large retaining wall 240ft long was built to support the Abertillery road where the new road came near, but at 24ft below it. Three flights of steps were provided to afford pedestrian access from the new road to the Abertillery road. Two smaller retaining walls were constructed by the GWR in the vicinity of Aberbeeg station to meet the needs of the alterations.

1928 OIL GAS WORKS AT NEWPORT

Prior to the amalgamations under the Railways Act of 1921, the only oil gas works belonging to the GWR in the Newport and Cardiff area were those situated at Canton, Cardiff, and the needs of Newport were met by a service of travelling tanks from that depot. Another oil gas works, however, also at Cardiff, was taken over with the Taff Vale Railway, and as the time arrived when it needed renewal, it was decided to replace this plant with one of modern design, but to locate it at Newport as being the more convenient centre.

In view of the then continual increase in the number of carriages lit by electricity, it may be wondered why it was necessary for an oil gas works to be renewed. The reason was that there was considered to be for some years to come a large number of gas-lit vehicles in service, and a number of dining cars which, although electrically lit, used a large quantity

Plate 14 General view of the improvements at Aberbeeg, showing the reconstructed bridge, and the new roadway carried on 19 arches.

Plate 15 View from Aberbeeg station, showing the reconstructed bridge and relative positions of the new roadway and railway.

of gas for cooking. It was considered that the economies which would be effected by the installation of a modern plant would pay for its cost in a very short time. The whole plant was designed and manufactured by the GWR Swindon Works.

The new works were erected on a site at the south corner of the locomotive depot. The general layout embodied all the latest improvements for the economical and safe production of oil gas. Corrugated asbestos was used for the construction of the buildings, which, therefore, were fireproof.

They consisted of a retort and boiler house, compressor room, storehouse and purifier shed. A siding running along one side of the buildings provided for the accommodation of travelling oil and tar tank wagons and coal and coke wagons.

Oil gravitated from the travelling tanks to an underground reinforced concrete storage tank. From here it was raised by a steam pump into an overhead gravity feed tank, fitted with measuring and safety devices. The oil then flowed to the retort benches, of which there were two types, constructed to meet the varying demands for gas. The gas produced passed through condensing and scrubbing apparatus for the extraction of tar and other by-products, and thence to the oxide purifiers for the elimination of sulphur compounds.

Purified gas was measured, and then stored in a low pressure holder, having a capacity of 2000 cubic feet. From here it was drawn by steam-driven compressors, and compressed

Plate 16 The old Taff Vale Railway oil gas works at Cathays, Cardiff, which were superseded.

Plate 17 View of the new oil gas works at Ebbw Junction, Newport.

Plate 18 The unloading side of the new oil gas works at Ebbw Junction.

to 160 psi, being stored at this pressure in cylindrical steel reservoirs. The latter were connected by supply mains to the carriage shed at Ebbw Junction and to Newport High Street station and carriage sidings, where further holding reservoirs were placed and facilities for gassing travelling tanks and vehicles were provided. The tar produced during the manufacture of the gas was stored in an underground tank, and was either used as fuel in the gas work's boilers or conveyed with other hydrocarbons in specially constructed tanks to Swindon for further treatment.

1928 NEW DEPOT FOR J.S. FRY & SONS AT LADBROKE GROVE

In 1928 the GWR provided J.S. Fry & Sons with a new depot at Ladbroke Grove. This firm, who had just celebrated their bi-centenary, were the GWR's oldest customer.

The founder was Mr Walter Churchman who established a small factory in Narrow Wine Street in Bristol in 1728 making and selling Churchman's Patent Chocolate. One Joseph Fry set up as a medical practitioner in Bristol, but later turned to business and became associated with a china manufacturer, a type-founder and a soap maker. Later, he turned his attention to chocolate, which he manufactured at premises in Small Street and, subsequently, in Narrow Wine Street in Bristol. After a few years he acquired Mr Churchman's business and removed his factory to the then new Union Street. Through the next 100 years, this business was controlled by various members of the Fry family, adopting up-to-date machinery and modern business methods. In 1896, the concern became a private limited liability company.

Meanwhile, with the continued expansion of the business, despite the

Plate 19 The railway side of the new depot, showing railway wagons at the unloading bay. Clearly there was no equipment with which to lift containers from the railway wagons on to road vehicles, the usual way of operating containers, so they were unloaded at this depot as if they were ordinary vans. While one container is on a flat wagon, the other is in a five-plank OPEN wagon, so one can deduce that the containers had side doors which could be opened and accessed through the side door of the OPEN wagon. Finally, the fact that all three vans present had their roofs covered with tarpaulin sheets suggests that someone was not certain about their water tightness.

Plate 20 Unloading packages from the railway wagons.

Plate 21 A busy scene in the interior of the transit shed. The tall structure would be the lift.

progressive extension of the Union Street factory, it became essential to seek larger and less restricted premises. A few years previous to 1928, under the control of Mr Cecil Fry, they built an entirely new factory on an extensive site alongside the River Avon at Somerdale, near Keynsham, to which most manufacturing processes were gradually transferred. This factory was connected by a siding to the GWR at Keynsham.

J.S. Fry & Sons were one of the pioneers of the use of containers, having had a number in circulation since 1893. Their present standard type of container held 5 tons, and a number of them left the firm's factories at Bristol and Somerdale daily, loaded with fresh goods to replenish stocks at their depots in London and other distribution centres. They had a large depot in the City of London for the last half century, but decided to transfer all their distribution work in and around the Metropolis to a railhead depot established on the GWR system.

The firm's new London depot was situated on GWR land adjoining the down main line just west of the carriage sheds at Ladbroke Grove, between West London Junction and Westbourne Park. The accommodation was approached over a wide new roadway leading from Ladbroke Grove. It consisted of a brick building 140ft long by 60ft wide, with two floors, the ground floor of which was used as a transit shed, while the basement was used as the main store or warehouse. The transit shed had a long loading deck protected by a verandah covering on the rail side, at which six wagons could be berthed and discharged simultaneously. On the other side, served by the roadway was a long deck also protected by a verandah where ten road vehicles could berth at a time. The two floors were connected by staircases and a 2-ton electric lift. Offices, mess and rest rooms for the staff were on the ground floor. Both floors were maintained at a temperature most suitable for the firm's commodities by a hot water system connected with a boiler in the basement. A garage 60ft by 35ft equipped with store, shop, examination pit and petrol storage tank and pump, was provided adjoining the main depot, for the use of the firm's delivery vans.

The firm's loaded containers left Bristol and Somerdale late in the afternoon and were placed alongside the

Plate 22 The new GWR 125 ton floating crane.

unloading stage at the new warehouse at Ladbroke Grove early the following morning, the transit period being short and at night to minimise risk of deterioration of the products. The goods were then unloaded direct from rail wagons on to trays each carrying 10 cwt, which were lifted by trolleys to the electric lift for transfer to the basement where the main stocks amounting to upwards of 150 tons of chocolate, cocoa and kindred commodities were held. The fleet of twelve 30 cwt Albion vans subsequently delivered supplies direct to their many customers in London, the home counties and the south-east coast.

1928 FLOATING CRANE FOR SOUTH WALES DOCKS

In 1928, the GWR purchased a large floating crane for use at the South Wales docks. This crane had a lifting capacity of 125 tons, with two tackles on a distance of 25ft to 30ft from the fore side of the pontoon, and a third tackle of 10 tons at a distance of about 10ft from the centre of the main lift. The height of the main lift blocks was about 80ft above the deck of the pontoon. The dimensions of the pontoon were length 83ft, breadth 47ft and depth 9ft.

This floating crane was used for the bodily transfer of a coal hoist from Barry to Cardiff West Dock in September 1929. This hoist weighed about 65 tons and was 84ft high, and special arrangements had to be made to prevent any distortion of the structural members when it was lifted. The Bristol Channel had to be negotiated for some eight miles, and careful arrangements were necessary to minimise the risks involved in handling such an awkward load. The floating crane, with hoist suspended, was towed to the entrance of the Cardiff Docks by two of the GWR tugs. The hoist was landed on its new foundation at Cardiff West Docks about six hours after leaving Barry.

Plate 23 The ex-Barry coal hoist lifted by the 125-ton floating crane, and secured, in readiness for towing to Cardiff West Dock.

Plate 24 The 125-ton floating crane loaded with the hoist from Barry, being towed by a GWR tug and guided by another GWR tug, on its voyage from Barry to Cardiff West Dock.

1928 REBUILDING THE LAND SPANS OF THE ROYAL ALBERT BRIDGE

The Royal Albert Bridge, spanning the River Tamar at Saltash, is admired by engineers throughout the world and is a worthy example of the genius of Isambard Kingdom Brunel, the first engineer of the Great Western Railway. It was opened in 1859, converted from broad gauge to narrow gauge in 1892 and was fitted with 401 additional cross girders in 1905 to carry heavier axle-loads. In 1908, the two land spans adjacent to Saltash Station at the Cornish end were reconstructed to allow the double line from the station to be extended on to the bridge.

In 1927 it was decided in view of the ever increasing weight of modern locomotives and the onset of corrosion of some of the iron plates, to renew the main girders of the fifteen remaining land spans. This involved removing the original cross girders while retaining the 1905 replacements. The main girders of the seven Devon approach spans were renewed from April to July 1928 and the remaining eight Cornish approach spans were replaced from September 1928 to January 1929, retaining the general contour of the structure as designed and built.

Owing to traffic requirements, occupation of the single line could be obtained by the Engineering Department only for limited periods. Even so, the Traffic Department had to rearrange the times of some through trains on Sundays, while the local services to Saltash were run between Plymouth and St Budeaux station, from where passengers were carried by GWR road coaches to the ferry which crossed the Tamar to and from Saltash.

Because of the limited occupation, a special method of girder replacement had to be devised. The replacement operation for each span was therefore undertaken using a specially designed erection wagon formed by a lattice girder 95ft long, 9ft 0¾in deep and 4ft 3¼in wide, weighing about 18½ tons and carried on two demountable bogies. This wagon was equipped with special cross traversing beams, capable of carrying the new main girders from the site siding to the span to be reconstructed. In more detail, attached to the top boom were transverse girders forming four cross members, through each of which was centrally fixed a vertical pintle shaft, enabling them to pivot and so bring the girders within the load gauge while being moved by locomotive power over the bridge. Within each pair of cross girders were fixed lifting screws, each about 8ft long and 2 5/8in diameter, with Whitworth square thread fitted with ball bearings, each tested for a working load of 15 tons. Traversing gear was controlled by similar screws, about 12ft long, and upon the top booms of the transverse girders 24 lb/yd rail of bridge section was provided. Attached to the underside of this girder, at each end, were box girders, 12ft long, which were adjustable as their positions varied on each span. These girders rested on stools and carried the total weight during the time the replacement of each of the girders of each span was carried out. The top cross members were spaced approximately above each of the cross girders of the bridge, and from them screwed steel rods were suspended with wire cables for raising each cross girder. Similar attachments were connected to the lower boom, by which the permanent way timber decking, and staging were temporarily raised. The erection girder was provided with two standard engine bogies, with special frames, enabling it to travel at slow speed. The total weight of the erection wagon when carrying the old and new girders, and other items, was about 80 tons.

The new main girders, varying in weight from about 15 to 21 tons, were conveyed by ordinary freight train from the manufacturer to the site on CROCODILE D wagons. The cross girders of the bridge which were provided in 1905 were reused and rivetted to the new main girders. A temporary constructional yard with the necessary siding accommodation was provided on which to stable the erection wagon. The construction work was divided into two parts to avoid having occupations of the main line during the summer traffic, the first part dealing with the seven land spans on the Devon side and the second with the eight spans on the Cornish side.

Preliminary work started in February. Close-decked scaffolding was suspended under each of the seven spans, a longitudinally supported track was laid in place of the former cross-sleeper road, oxy-acetylene plant was used to separate the original cross girders which had been left in place at the time of the new cross girders being added in 1905, the tops of the abutment and piers were levelled, building up a recess in the former and strengthening the latter.

On the first and succeeding alternate Sundays when possession of the main line was obtained, the original cross girders were removed, the old timber decking renewed and the new main girders unloaded from the CROCODILE wagon and placed in position alongside the erection girder in the siding. On the second and every other Sundays, when the main girders of each span were renewed, the occupation of the line extended from about 0900 to 1400 hours. The erection girder, with the new main girders suspended therefrom,

Plate 25 The erection girder resting on the bogies, with the traversing cross beams on top.

was drawn slowly out of the siding by a locomotive on to the main line, and thence propelled on to the bridge over the span to be renewed. The steel stools for the erection girder were then fixed in position over the piers and the girder itself lowered on to them. The bogies having been run out clear of the work, the permanent way and cross girders were then attached to the erection girder and the new main girders lowered on to temporary packing on each pier, thereby removing their weight from the erection girder. Having attached the shackles to the old main girders, allowing a clearance of 6in, the erection girder was lifted by four 40-ton hydraulic jacks and set on cross timber beams inserted on top of the stools, this lift raising the cross girders sufficiently to clear their supports on the new girders and to draw the shackles tight on the bottom flanges of the old main girders. Everything now being clear, the old girders were lifted and moved outwards to positions where they would clear everything when drawn off the bridge, the new main girders were then lowered and set on their bedplates in final position. The cross girders were next set in place on the new main girders, steel tapered wedges inserted and the permanent way restored. It then only remained to replace the bogies under the erection girder and to draw it carefully, with the old girders suspended, back to the siding.

The procedure described above covered the first six spans, but the reconstruction of the portal span necessitated additional work, as the ends of the main girders were housed in the casing of one of the main piers, and to enable these to be withdrawn and replaced by the new girders a travelling platform was designed and

Plate 26 Close-up view of the end of the erection wagon in position, with the old girders having been slewed out and the two new main girders being prepared for lifting off.

Plate 27 A view from the Devon main pier of the erection wagon in position on No 4 Devon approach span, showing the old girders moved out and the new girders being placed in their final position, ready for the work of fitting the cross girders, decking and permanent way.

Plate 28 With the work on the span completed, the erection wagon with the old girders slung from the traversing cross beams clear of their replacements is being drawn off the bridge.

Plate 29 The Royal Albert Bridge, Saltash, photographed in 1929 after the land spans had been reconstructed. This famous structure, built at a cost of £225,000, was opened by HRH The Prince Consort on 3 May 1859. The total length of the bridge is 2,200ft, the two main spans being each 455ft, and the seventeen approach spans varying from 70 to 90ft.

fixed at each end of the erection girder. After the old girders had been lifted as previously described, they were transferred to the traverser, drawn out of the portal and connected to the main screws and the new girders run into the final position by similar means.

The new steelwork was supplied by the Fairfield Shipbuilding Co of Chepstow and the lifting and traversing gear by the East Ferry Engineering Works Co. The whole reconstruction was carried out by GWR staff, the average number of men employed each Sunday being about 46.The average time taken in reconstructing a span was about 3½ hours.

1928 IMPROVEMENTS AT OSWESTRY

At the time of the railways amalgamation in 1922, the town of Oswestry was served by two stations, some distance apart, and there were no physical connections, such as covered footways or through passenger lines, between them. The former Cambrian Company's station was on the Whitchurch to Aberystwyth section of the Cambrian main line, and the GWR terminal station on the Oswestry to Gobowen branch line. The situation involved considerable delay and inconvenience to passengers in changing from one station to the other, specially those with luggage.

To reduce expenditure and afford better facilities for passenger travel and goods transit, a scheme was carried out whereby the Oswestry to Gobowen branch station was closed for passenger traffic. This gave increased facilities for goods traffic on that side, the line being extended to serve the Cambrian main line station and connections laid in to enable through running between Birkenhead and Aberystwyth. The up and down platforms of the former Cambrian station were extended 300ft, the up platform extension forming an island platform for the up main line and the Gobowen branch bay line. This involved demolishing the Cambrian goods warehouse and offices and the Central signal box. Extensive additions and alterations were made to the siding accommodation. The carriage shed, with its three roads and an area of 8500 sq ft, was paved with concrete, glazed side windows were fitted throughout, and washing-down hydrants installed. The siding alterations involved the demolition of an obsolete weightbridge and the transfer to another site of a 60-ton weighing machine.

At the engine shed, the six existing outside engine pits were substituted by new standard brick and concrete pits, 40ft long, the paving outside the engine shed being renewed. A new 120ft inspection pit was built adjacent to a new elevated coaling stage, which replaced the old stage and was surmounted by a new steel water tank of 45,000 gl capacity. A sand drying furnace and hot water washing-out plant was also installed and new offices, workshops and stores constructed. The old 45ft turntable was taken up and a new 65ft table erected. Near to the station, a new water tank of 23,000 gl on steel standards was erected, new mains laid and new columns erected.

Before the alterations, there were five signal boxes, GW Branch Station, GW Branch North Level Crossing, Cambrian North Level Crossing, Cambrian Central and Cambrian South. The first four boxes were taken down and a new central box substituted. The locking frame consisted of 78 working levers. Track circuiting was installed in the up and down middle roads through the station. The verandah on the up platform was extended and a new verandah erected on the down platform.

Extensive repairs were carried out to the roof covering, floors etc of the Locomotive, Carriage and Wagon Department factory, and new concrete inspection pits were constructed in the paint shop and engine bays. Electric lighting replaced gas in the yard, engine shed, engineering workshops and offices.

1929 NEW SWING BRIDGE AT CARDIFF DOCKS

A new double-road steel swing bridge, hydraulically operated, was brought into use over the East Dock lock at Cardiff in 1929. The bridge consisted of two main plate girders,

Plate 30 The verandah extension on the up platform and the new verandah on the down platform.

Plate 31 A view of the platform extensions at Oswestry Station.

Plate 32 The new Central signal box at Oswestry.

with the usual cross girders and timber flooring. It was of the centre-pivot type, and was built by Horseley Bridge & Engineering Co of Birmingham to GWR design. The advantage of the centre-pivot design of swing bridge is that in the event of the hydraulic pressure failing at any time, the bridge can be swung clear by means of ropes from adjacent capstans, so as to enable the lock to be worked, whereas in the case of the centre-ram type of bridge, failure of the operating gear may stop the lock working. The dimensions of the bridge were overall length 118ft, width of double-track roadway 18ft 6in with footpath 3ft 2in wide on each side, span across the lock 55ft. The hydraulic pressure was 800 lb/sq.in, and the total weight of the bridge about 320 tons.

Plate 33 The new double-road swing bridge at Cardiff East Dock.

Plate 34 The new Appleford Viaduct.

1929 RECONSTRUCTION OF APPLEFORD VIADUCT

The old viaduct structure at Appleford, between Didcot and Culham, was erected about 1860. It comprised two separate bridges side by side, having seven spans, two of 30ft 6in and five of 41ft 3in, of which four were over the River Thames and the remainder over the land at the river sides. The spans consisted of continuous wrought-iron plate girders and timber decking, strengthened by cross girders and rail bearers which were added about 1878. The structure rested on cast-iron columns, 2ft 6in diameter, filled with concrete. The foundations for the columns on the land consisted of brick piers; and those in the water were provided at the base with a screw flange, and the columns were screwed down into the river bed.

In order to minimise single-line working during the reconstruction work, the new bridge was designed so that the down line portion could be built outside the existing bridge, and the up line portion on the site of the up line. The new bridge consisted of four brick arches of 18ft span each on the Didcot side, a single central span of 167ft over the River Thames, and one brick arch of 14ft span on the Oxford side. The central span consisted of steel lattice main girders, supported on roller bearings, steel cross girders and rail bearers, and had a steel plate floor. To facilitate the structural work, a large derrick crane was erected on the up river side with a jib 100ft long, which enabled any part of the new structure to be reached. The brickwork in the new abutments, piers and brick arches was built for the width of the new down line, the outside and centre main girders erected, and the superstructure completed for that side of the viaduct. The embankments on both sides of the bridge had previously been widened, allowing the down line to be slewed to its new position. This enabled the old down line structure to be dismantled and removed, and work to proceed with the construction of the remaining width of the brick arches, to erect the other outside main girders, and to complete the erection of the remaining steelwork. The up line was then slewed over the new bridge and the old up line portion dismantled and removed.

1929 REMOVAL AND REPLACEMENT OF LOCK GATES

In Great Britain, and particularly at the Bristol Channel ports, the range of tides is so great as to make it imperative to provide lock gates to retain a more or less permanent water level inside the docks. It follows that a great deal depends on the sound condition and satisfactory operations of these appliances. If the gates were to fail, the whole of the dock working would come practically to a standstill.

In times gone by, the lifting out (termed the "unstepping") of lock gates was a tedious process, and entailed the manufacture and erection of temporary structures (known as "catheads") on the quay side. These were fixed derricks or cranes, and were capable of lifting the gates almost bodily out of the lock, placing them on or alongside pontoons for removal to a dry dock, grid or slipway for inspection and repair, and in the reverse operation, of replacing (termed the "stepping") the gates when the repairs were completed. In later years, large floating cranes proved of service in dealing with the large modern steel gates, and even the old wooden ones where they still existed. The GWR's giant floating crane proved its worth in the removal and replacing of lock gates at Cardiff, and other South Wales ports.

At Swansea, and also in changing the very heavy and deep lock gates in the Lady Windsor deep sea lock and the basin gates at Barry Docks, the operations were carried out without the aid of catheads or cranes, the gates being unstepped by taking advantage of their natural flotation; in other words by so adjusting their displacement as to cause them automatically to float off their "pintles", that is the bottom portion of their hinges, and, at the same time, governing their movements by means of ropes and the adjacent capstans only. Modern steel lock gates consisted of an entirely closed box, divided into numerous compartments by watertight horizontal decks and vertical partitions, with necessary access shafts; but these constituted the component parts of only two main, and distinctly independent, chambers, upper and lower, separated by a horizontal watertight deck, the full length of the gate. The upper was known as the "ballast chamber" and the lower one the "air chamber".

The bottom of the ballast chamber was in communication with the outside by means of a number of small bent pipes, termed "scupper holes", so that when the rising tide reached the level of the top of the air chamber, it commenced to fill the ballast chamber. Therefore, at high water, the ballast chamber was nearly full of water, that is the level of water inside the gate coincided with the level of the tide, except when the tide was below the top of the air chamber. The latter chamber was free from water at all states of the tide, whether high or low. The effect of this arrangement was that when the tidal water level was just below the scupper holes, the displacement of the gate (that is, the weight of a quantity of water equivalent to the space occupied by the still immersed portion of the gate) would be a little less than the total actual weight of the gate itself. In other words, the scupper holes were placed at a point just below the tidal water line level at which it was calculated that the total weight of the gate, as an entirely closed vessel, would equal the weight of water displaced by the immersed portion of the gate. That is to say, these holes were placed just below the point at which the gate would become buoyant. The gate therefore preponderates slightly when the tide was at or near the scupper holes.

As the tide continued to rise, the water poured through the scupper holes into the ballast chamber, and the weight of this water counteracted the lifting tendency of the tide on the outside of the gate. The advantage of this very valuable flotation effect of the air chamber was that even at about half-tide level there was very little dead weight on the pintle, the wear and tear being thereby considerably reduced, and, further owing to the gate being almost buoyant at most states of the tide, comparatively little power was necessary to operate the gate.

When it was necessary to remove gates for repairs, the procedure was, first of all, to release all the top anchorages, and afterwards to plug the scupper holes, so that as the tide rose, the gate gradually became buoyant and eventually floated off its hinges, when ropes were used to guide its movements while it was towed into dry dock or elsewhere. When the repairs were completed, the gate was floated back into its recess, and sufficient water ran into it to "up-end" it into a vertical position, when it was adjusted over its anchorage. Afterwards, more water ballast was added or the gate permitted to fall with the tide (whichever was more convenient) until it came to rest on the bottom pintle, when the top anchorage was fixed, and the scupper plugs removed.

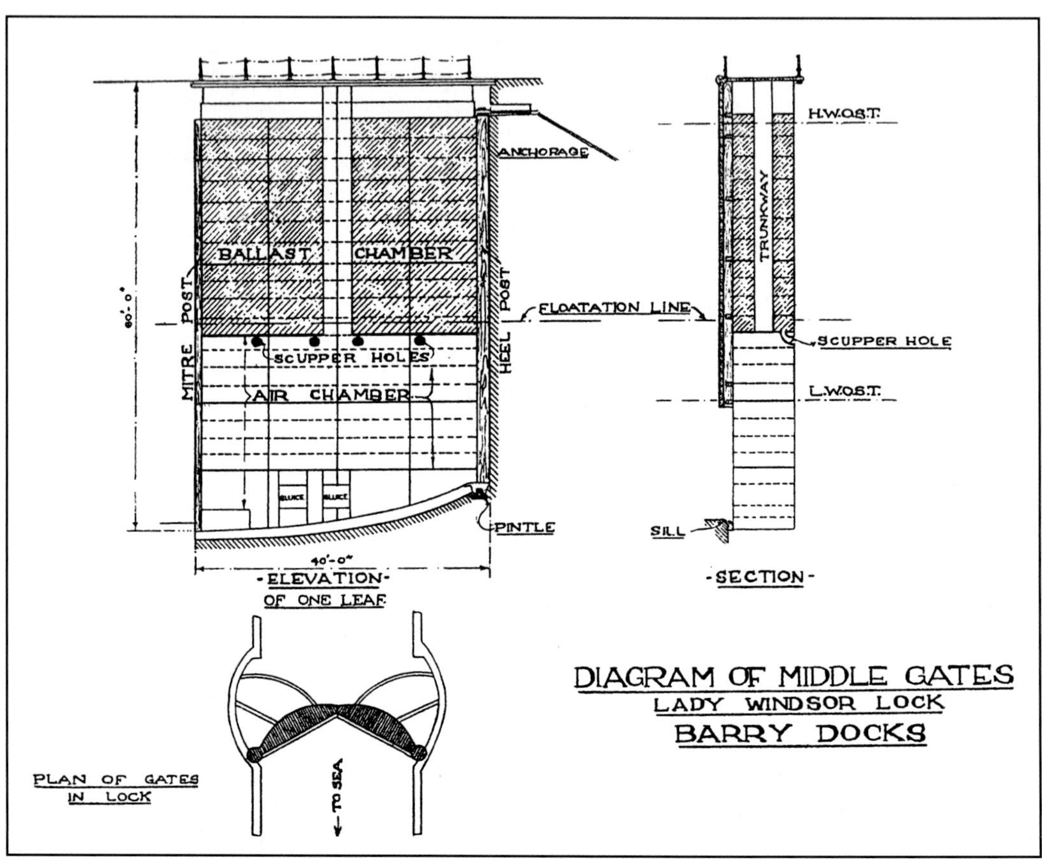

Fig 2. Diagram of the Middle Gates at Lady Winsor Lock at Barry Docks, showing the air and ballast chambers, and scupper holes.

Plate 35 Side and front views of a small lock gate being lifted and conveyed by the GWR's 120-ton floating crane.

Plate 36 A lock gate, having been lifted out and let down in the water to float, ready to be towed into dry dock.

Described in this way, it may seem a simple and easy process, but in fact, great care and experience was necessary to avoid damage, especially as almost all gates differed from others in design, and each pair had their own little idiosyncrasies which demanded both knowledge and vigilance. Many incidental details also had to be watched and provided for, such as calculating for and supplying a certain quantity of water as temporary ballast at the bottom of the air chamber, to stabilize the gate and prevent its becoming over buoyant. If a steel gate was allowed to get out of control, "a bull in a china shop" was a very inadequate simile.

1929 RECONSTRUCTION OF HERONSTON LANE UNDERBRIDGE

The Heronston Lane underbridge was situated on the Vale of Glamorgan section, about $^3/_4$ mile outside Bridgend, and the railway passing over it was the former Barry Railway line between Bridgend and Barry. The Glamorgan County Council was constructing a by-pass road to the main Aberavon and Cardiff road, in order that traffic could avoid passing through Bridgend, as it had to do previously. The new by-pass road was to run under the new bridge, as it cut the country road called Heronston Lane at that point. The new road was to form an important trunk road scheme known as the

Plate 37 One of the lock gates floating off its pintle.

Plate 38 The lock gates afloat and ready for towing away.

Bridgend By-pass, which comprised about two miles of entirely new road, besides several miles of widening to existing roads.

The old underbridge, which was built by the Barry Railway and Docks Company when the line was originally constructed, consisted of a skew five-ring brick arch with masonry abutments, spandrels and parapets. It had a skew span of 26ft 11in and a square span of 25ft 2in. The new bridge was constructed to allow for a road 52ft wide, with footways in addition. The new skew span was 77ft 8in and square span 72ft 0in. The grade of the railway at 1 in 90 was not altered.

The method adopted for the work was as follows. New abutments were built in trenches cut through the railway embankment on each side of the old bridge. At the same time, the new steel superstructure was assembled on temporary wooden trestles alongside the site. When everything was ready, occupation of both lines was obtained. The track was removed, the parapets demolished and the ballast and loose filling excavated. The residual brick rings of the arch were then demolished, partly by gelignite explosives and partly by compressed-air concrete breakers. The main girders of the bridge were lifted on to trollies running on rails laid over the new abutments and timber trestles, the latter erected on the line of the abutments. When sufficient of the arch had been demolished, the steelwork was pulled into position by two hand winches connected by wire hawsers running through snatch-blocks to the steelwork. This sidelong pull was accomplished easily and with only four men on each winch an even speed of six inches per minute was maintained, the 10ft move being accomplished in 22 minutes. Once the steelwork was in position, it was jacked off the trollies and lowered on to the bedstones. The track was then made good over the bridge, and occupation of the lines given up. The new bridge consisted of three main girders, cross girders, rail

Plate 39 An old gate being hauled up a slipway, with the new gate ready for launching behing it.

Plate 40 Repaired lock gate about to be hauled upright by the GWR's floating crane.

Plate 41 The GWR's floating crane assisting in re-stepping the lock gate.

bearers and steel plate floor covered with asphaltic mastic. The remainder of the brickwork and embankment under the new steel bridge was then removed, leaving the way open for the new road to be built.

1929 RECONSTRUCTION WORK AT OLD HILL TUNNEL

Old Hill Tunnel is situated on the Stourbridge extension line between Old Hill and Rowley Regis stations. It is a double line tunnel 2640ft long on a gradient of about 1 in 70. In the past the structure had been considerably affected by mining subsidence. Partly owing to this, and partly owing to the original tunnel having been, for the greater part of its length, constructed without an invert (ie the bottom part of the tunnel), the centre part became so distorted by pressure from the sides and bottom that there was insufficient clearance for two lines of rails. It was therefore decided to rebuild completely, to a larger section, a length of 330ft near the centre of the tunnel, and to provide an invert.

To give clearance for the ribs and centres, the up and down lines were interlaced through the portion of the tunnel being dealt with, temporary signal boxes were provided at each end of the tunnel, and a system similar to single-line working adopted for dealing with the traffic. A telephone box was provided at the site of the work where the man in charge was in communication with the signal boxes at each end of the tunnel, and no train was allowed to enter until the signalmen were informed that all was clear and that the men engaged on the work had been warned. Electric lighting was installed which, on account of the smoky atmosphere of the tunnel, proved of great assistance in carrying out the work.

Four sets of steel ribs were made to support the old arch and the ground above, enabling work to be carried out at four places simultaneously. The steel ribs were erected on movable trestles, and each set comprised four ribs at 3ft 4in or 5ft 0in centres, enabling lengths of either 10 or 15ft to be dealt with.

The actual work of carrying out a length was as follows. The shield, comprising the four ribs on trestles, was moved forward on rollers from the completed length of new brickwork sufficiently to allow the end of the old arch in the next length but one to be supported by props off the end rib. The centre part of the old arch, for a length of 10 or 15ft, was cut out, including the ground over it, to a height of one foot above the level of the top of the new arch, and bars made of old rails inserted to support the roof. These bars were brought forward from the preceding length, and rested at one end on the new brickwork of the last length, and at the other end on the old tunnel arch supported by props off the outside rib. Head boards between the bars completed the support of the roof. The excavation was then continued over and down each side of the old arch, additional bars and boards being fixed as the work progressed down the sides. The material excavated was stacked at the sides of the tunnel, and subsequently loaded up and removed during occupations of the running lines obtained for about two hours at night twice a week.

When the excavation had been completed as far below rail level as was

Plate 42 The old Heronston Lane underbridge, just after demolition and reconstruction had started.

Plate 43 The new Heronston Lane underbridge, just after completion. The steel structure made a striking contrast with the old brick arch and stone abutments.

possible without interfering with the traffic, occupation of the line was obtained on a Sunday; the rails were removed, the material for the centre part of the invert excavated and the invert under the lines concreted. This work, including that of reinstating the permanent way, took about eight hours in a 10ft length, but in the case of a 15ft length this operation had to be spread over two Sundays. The timber ribs for the centres of the new arch were made in two sections and threaded into position between the steel ribs. The brick side walls were then built and the new arch completed. Each length took about one month to complete, two gangs working eight hours each, one by day and one by night. Owing to the bad atmospheric conditions, and the number of trains passing through the tunnel (about 120 in the 24 hours), the work was carried out under considerable difficulty and inconvenience to the workmen.

1929 RECONSTRUCTION OF HOLMBUSH BRIDGE, NEAR ST AUSTELL

Originally erected in 1859, this bridge carried the single line of the Cornwall Railway over the then main County turnpike road. The Brunel structure consisted of two main girders, 80ft long and 8ft deep, with semicircular tops, and curved bottom booms, with cross girders and timber decking. The bridge was manufactured at the Charlestown Foundry, about two miles from the site. When the railway was doubled in 1893, a second bridge of standard design was erected alongside Brunel's structure, and when it was decided to reconstruct, the opportunity was taken to design a standard double-line bridge with three main girders varying in length from 82ft to 92ft and weighing from 21 to 30 tons, with cross girders, rail-bearers, and plate flooring.

Before reconstruction commenced, the Post Office authorities removed their main trunk wires from overhead to a cable under the structure. It was necessary to erect trestles to enable the old bedstones to be removed and new ones placed in position, also to remove the decking and to substitute longitudinal for the cross-sleeper road. The old bridge was removed and the new one placed in position on two Sundays in November 1929, absolute occupation of the road being dealt with being obtained from 2200 hours on Saturday to completion of the work on Sunday, while occupation between trains was in force on the other road. Owing to the angle of skew and the weight of the steelwork, two 36-ton steam cranes were required, which had to be precisely located so that the girders could be lifted from the wagons and set on their bedstones. A 6-ton steam crane was used for setting the cross-girders, rail-bearers, and plates.

1929 DEMOLITION OF WYNNSTAY COLLIERY BRIDGE

The permanent way leading from the Wynnstay Colliery was carried over the Shrewsbury and Chester main line near Ruabon station by a very high girder bridge. By 1929, this needed to be demolished. Previous to the Sunday date scheduled for the removal of the main girders, oxyacetylene plant was used by the contractors, the Horseley Bridge & Engineering Co under contract with the Wynnstay Colliery, to cut through the trough flooring, and the troughs were removed in sections.

Owing to the height of the main girders, it was impossible to reach them with any of the available GWR cranes, so a special derrick was sent to Ruabon for the purpose of lowering the girders. This derrick was made in sections; each section was 20ft long and three sections were used. It was originally constructed for the purpose of erecting high 20-ton girders at Messrs Hickman's yard at Wolverhampton, and when used to its full length consisted of five sections, giving it a total height of 100ft. It was fitted with a revolving cap, to which the hooks of the guides were attached.

The derrick was erected by hauling it up between the two girders, and supporting it by tackle attached to the girders. The first girder was lowered to a siding alongside the main line. The illustration shows the second girder being drawn clear of the abutments. The first girder is lying on the siding, where both girders were cut through with the acetylene plant and loaded on to MACAW wagons by means of a hand crane.

The derrick, being too high to be handled by a crane, was lowered by the use of a second derrick consisting of a telegraph pole 40ft long, the telegraph pole itself being lowered by a hand crane. The whole work was carried out

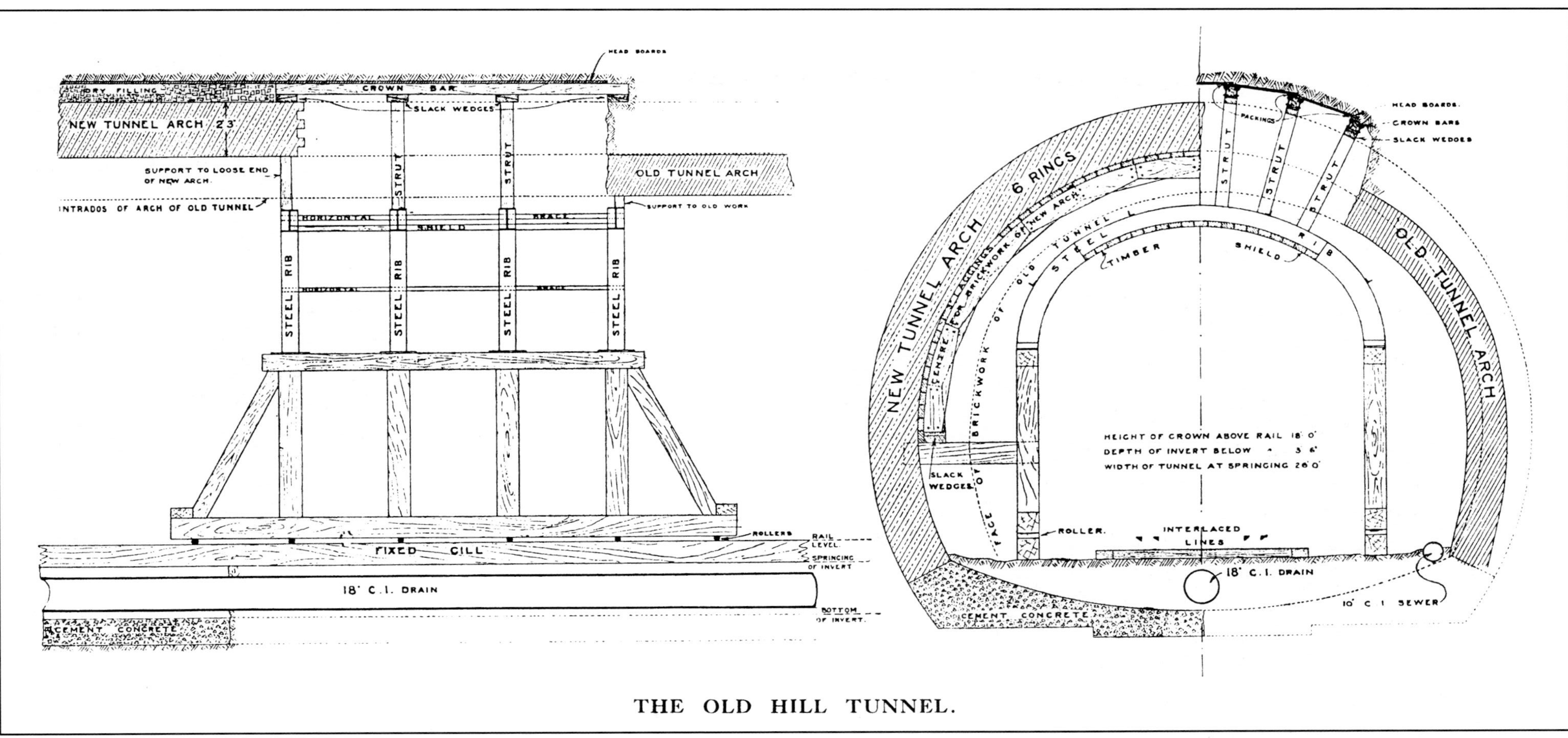

THE OLD HILL TUNNEL.

Fig 3. A longitudinal section, showing the steel ribs in position during the excavation of a length, the movable trestles supporting the steel ribs, and the rail crown bars carrying the roof.
Cross section, showing (on the right hand half) the old arch with the rock and clay above it partly excavated, and (on the left hand half) the new arch completed with the centres in position.

Plate 44 The Old Hill Tunnel under reconstruction, showing one of the sets of steel ribs made to support the old arch and the ground above.

without interruption to traffic, which passed through on the main lines between the various operations.

1929 IMPROVEMENTS AT MORPETH DOCK GOODS STATION IN BIRKENHEAD

In 1928 an important development taking place at Liverpool and Birkenhead was the construction of a road tunnel under the River Mersey. The entrance to the new tunnel on the Birkenhead side was to be near to Morpeth Dock, which led the GWR to decide to remodel and modernise their Morpeth Dock good station, since traffic was steadily increasing and the advent of the tunnel would enable the GWR to reorganise their distribution arrangements.

Morpeth Docks goods station was the GWR's main good depot serving both Birkenhead and Liverpool. It was sited on the eastern side of what was known as the South Reserve between the Morpeth and Wallasey Docks, close to the Woodside Ferry landing stage, and was reached by rail from the GWR system over the joint line from Chester, which joined the Mersey Docks and Harbour Board's lines near the western entrance to the depot.

As far back as 1861, the GWR opened a small goods depot on the site, and eight years later brought into use a fully-equipped goods station and barging depot. Subsequently various minor improvements were made to

Plate 45 Swinging one of the new girders into its position at Holmbush Bridge, near St Austell.

Plate 46 The second of the two girders being removed from the Wynnstay Colliery Bridge.

accommodate the growing traffic. With the exception of the coal and other mileage traffic handled at the four joint goods depots on the Birkenhead side, all the Liverpool and Birkenhead goods traffic passing to and from the GWR went through Morpeth Dock station, the Liverpool traffic being first handled and sorted at the four cartage depots (Langton Dock, Stanley Dock, Manchester Basin and Chaloner Street) which the GWR maintained at convenient points along the river front on the Liverpool side. Traffic carted into these subsidiary depots was taken over the ferries later in the day by the GWR's own motor vehicles for dispatch the same night.

The branch dock, and shed over it, were originally designed to deal with traffic barged across the river, as most of it was then transported locally by these means, but with the change in trade conditions and the increasing

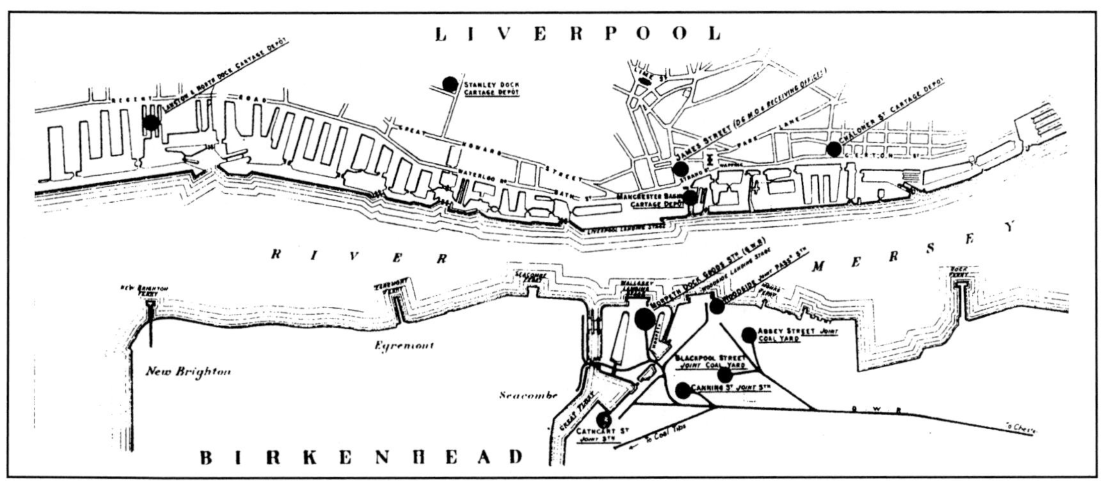

Map 5. The old system of GWR goods depots at Liverpool and Birkenhead as existing in 1928.

need for quicker transits, most of the traffic was now carted to the station, and the branch dock was now used only to a very limited extent. As the main road approach to the depot was over dock bridges which also carried the railway lines serving the station, congestion and difficulties were arising, especially in the afternoon. The following particulars give some indication of the volume of traffic passing through the station daily: an average of 1700 tons, representing over 400 truck loads, were dealt with, in and out; over 160 loads carted into the station, more than half of them after 1700 hours; and on a heavy day 1000 tons of traffic from Liverpool alone was dealt with, 300 road vehicles passing over the ferries.

The site of the station was leased by the GWR from the Mersey Docks and Harbour Board, and a further area was taken over to give possession of the whole of the north side of the main dock, including use of the berths alongside. This gave space for additional holding, marshalling and reception sidings, as well as three sidings served by an overhead gantry crane. The reconstruction involved the complete remodelling of the existing facilities and the provision of the maximum siding, cart road, shed, etc accommodation possible in the increased area available. The previous shed and yard held about 540 wagons, which was increased in the new scheme to nearly 850 wagons; at the same time the layout particularly near the entrance was improved to facilitate the reception and marshalling of trains, and also by widening the present 'bottle-neck' road approach gave more room for road vehicles entering and leaving the station. The branch dock was utilised to form a basement warehouse under the larger transit shed which was erected partly over the site of the previous shed and basin. In this new shed, one end and three long platforms were built for inward traffic, and one long platform for outward traffic. These were connected by a balancing bridge and afforded berthing space for 145 wagons. A considerable length of platform was made accessible to road vehicles. An extra wide cart roadway faced the outwards platform and was designed for container traffic. The channel serving the previous branch dock was filled in so that the existing brick warehouse on this quay could be extended over the site of the channel.

1930 REPAIRS AT DAWLISH

A serious subsidence occurred on Saturday 4 January 1930 between Dawlish and Dawlish Warren stations on the main line to Devon and Cornwall. At about 2200 hours during a heavy gale, a section of the sea wall supporting the main line was undermined by the sea for a length of 50ft, about ½ mile on the London side of Dawlish station. The masonry carrying the public promenade was washed away, exposing the foundations of the main wall which were pierced by the heavy waves. As a result, the earthwork behind the wall carrying the railway was washed out, leaving both lines unsupported.

Repair work was put in hand at once, although under difficulties, as heavy seas continued. It proceeded as continuously as the state of the tide would allow, but heavy seas on the following tide washed out all the repair work; the breaches were enlarged, and the wall showed signs of breaking up. Further steps could only be taken as the tides permitted, but more substantial work was at once put in hand, and the breaches were built up, as practicable, with granite blocks set in quick-setting cement mortar, and concrete backing under the main wall, as well as by other strengthening operations.

By 0600 hours on the following Monday the main wall was thickened for a length of 25ft. The granite blocks had been previously lowered into the subsidence and piled up behind the main wall, with a view to helping to support it against a rising tide and heavy storms. This granite and cement backing behind the main wall proved satisfactory, and was then extended for practically the full length of the subsidence. At every tide, concreting in bags was carried out at the 'toe' of the main wall on the beach, with a view to providing a protection, and also as part of the permanent work in rebuilding the lower pathway in the shape of a new granite-faced 'apron'. The work of filling the large hole under both lines was then taken in hand. It was necessary to support the up main line and then to stand a train thereon from which hand-filling could be discharged. Special gangs worked day and night from the time that the sea wall collapsed, and the repairs, which necessitated taking hundreds of tons of stone and other materials from many parts of the line, were completed in the remarkably short time of three days.

Traffic was at first diverted over the Teign Valley branch, but on Monday it decided that the 'Cornish Riviera' express, amongst others, would run via the Southern Railway route between Exeter and Plymouth. Local service on each side, to Dawlish and Starcross, respectively, were temporarily maintained by road services between those points. On Thursday 9 January, the line between Exeter and Plymouth was reopened for goods train traffic, and on the following day for passenger traffic.

It should be mentioned in passing that the Southern Railway imposed weight restrictions on their line via Okehampton, which meant that of the GWR engines, only Dukes and Bulldogs were permitted, so trains were double-headed by these vintage 4-4-0s, which must have been a fine sight. The Dukes allocated to Laira shed at that time were 3272/84/9 while 3282 of Newton Abbot also worked in. The Bulldogs allocated to Laira were 3368 & 3416/24. According to observation at the time, to deal with the emergency, the following Bulldogs were brought in from other sheds 3302/11/26/36/71/3 & 3404/30/54.

1930 NEW STATION BUILDING AT NEWPORT

In 1930, the GWR brought into use a new station building on the down side at Newport (High Street). The building had five stories and was nearly 80ft high with an impressive facade. The ground floor contained a booking hall, enquiry office, refreshment room and various platform offices. The walls of the main staircase were faced with French stucco and had a marble dado, with fossil skirting and bands. On the first floor were the public dining room and kitchen, smoke room, and writing room, together with lavatory and cloakroom accommodation. The dining room, capable of seating over 200 persons, was panelled in Japanese oak and heated by concealed radiators. The kitchen was equipped with gas cooking apparatus, said at the time to be the largest of its kind in Wales.

The whole of the second floor was designed for use as club premises, and was taken by the County and Monmouth Club. These premises were self-contained, providing ample facilities for the members. The woodwork throughout was mahogany. The third and fourth floors were equipped for the accommodation of the staffs of the

Plate 47 A general view of the GWR Morpeth Dock goods station at Birkenhead before reconstruction.

GWR divisional superintendent and district goods manager.

The passenger, freight and service lifts and the lighting were electric throughout, the electricity being obtained via a new sub-station provided by the Corporation. The new building was heated throughout by radiators and tubes, fed by a low-pressure hot-water system. All important rooms were fitted with electric clocks controlled by a master clock in the station master's office, which also controlled the electrically-operated platform clocks. Communication facilities between the various departments was provided by an automatic telephone installation, and the various departments were connected with the telegraph office by a pneumatic message tube. A large share of the work was carried out by firms from South Wales.

1930 RENEWAL WORK ON CRUMLIN VIADUCT

The Crumlin Viaduct carried the Taff Vale extension line (originally part of the Newport, Abergavenny and Hereford Railway) across the Western and Kendon Valleys, respectively, some 9 miles north-west of Newport in Monmouthshire. The viaduct, which was said at the time to vie with the Royal Albert Bridge at Saltash, as the most important ironwork structure on the GWR, was built in 1853-7. It consisted of ten spans of 150ft and was divided into two sections, between which a hill intervened. The main section, across the Western Valley, was 1000ft long and was borne on six piers; the smaller section across the Kendon Valley was 500ft long and supported on four piers. The height of the structure above the valley, on the longer section, was about 200ft; the shorter section had a maximum height of 100ft.

In 1928 the bottom booms of the two inside main girders were stiffened by the renewal, with angles of larger section, of the angle irons throughout each side of the girders. It was then decided to replace the iron decking of the viaduct, the existing plates having become thin owing to age. This work was of some magnitude and engineering difficulty. It was arranged to close one line at a time over the structure and to work the traffic over the remaining single line, thus enabling one track to

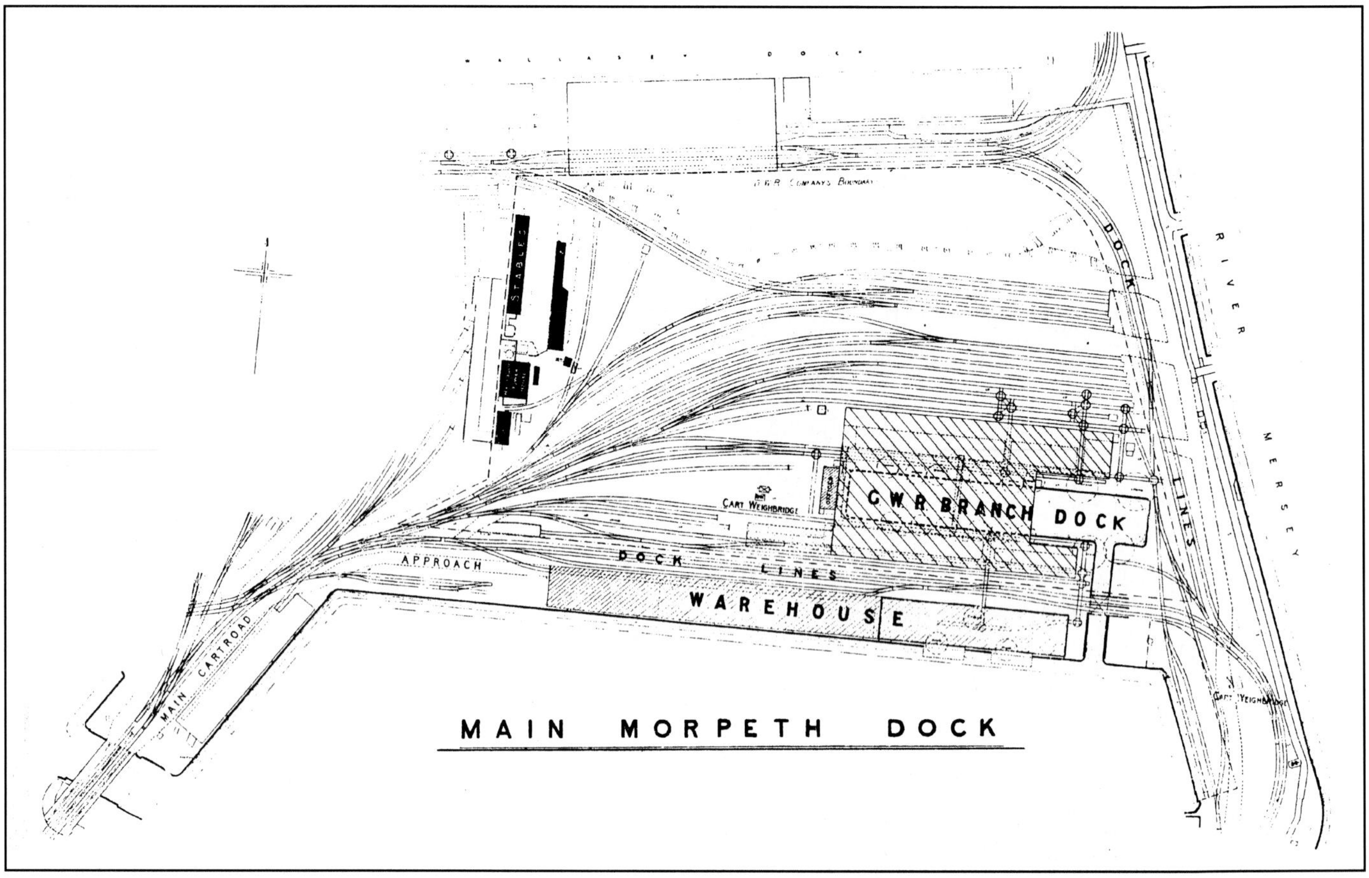

MAIN MORPETH DOCK

Map 6. The old layout at Morpeth Dock goods station, showing the old branch dock and channel leading to it.

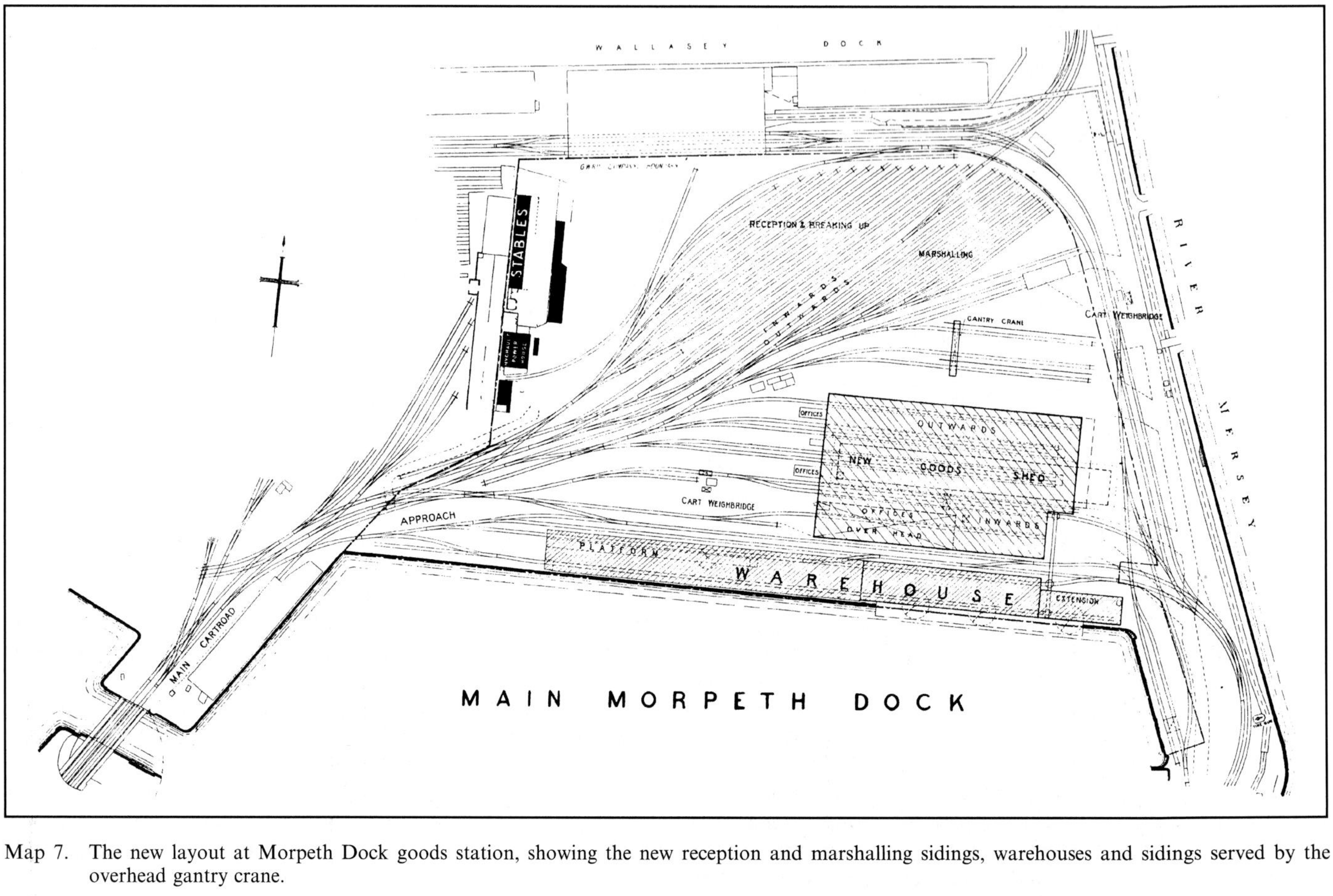

MAIN MORPETH DOCK

Map 7. The new layout at Morpeth Dock goods station, showing the new reception and marshalling sidings, warehouses and sidings served by the overhead gantry crane.

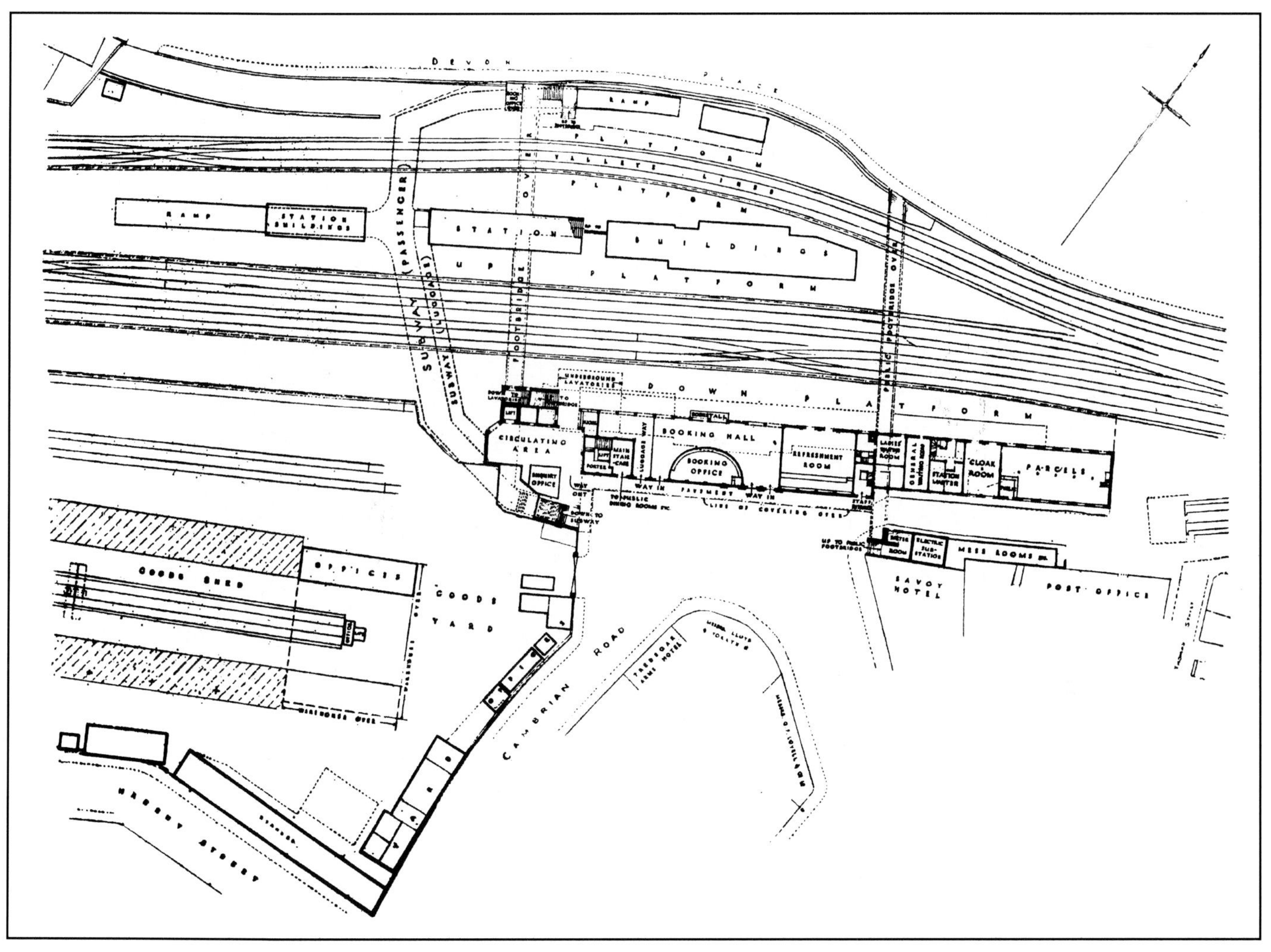

Map 8. General plan showing the lay-out of the new station at Newport (High Street).

be removed entirely, and leaving a clear space for carrying out the renewal. The operation consisted of the removal of the existing old deck iron plating and the lattice fascia girders on the outside, and the replacement of the former by steel plates; rolled steel joists were substituted for the latter, on which the parapet fencing was refixed, instead of as before on timber. Three gangs totalling 30 men were employed, work on the longer section being commenced at each end, and from one end on the smaller length.

Pneumatic tools were used throughout, compressed air being supplied by one steam and two petrol-driven compressors. The total number of plates renewed was 1140, and as each plate differed in size and shape accurate measurement was necessary to enable the contractor supplying the material to cut them to fit. A certain number of holes for the rivets was drilled in these plates before delivery, and the remainder at the site, the total number of holes required being about 90 in each plate. About 110,000 rivets were required in connection with the fixing of the new steelwork. The whole work took about two years to complete.

1930 RECONSTRUCTION OF THE SEVERN BRIDGE AT WORCESTER

Around 1904, the bridge carrying the Worcester to Hereford line over the River Severn, near Foregate Street station, was reconstructed. In the work then undertaken, the arched ribs of the old structure were replaced by two trussed main girders in each of the two spans, which were placed directly underneath the outer rail of the up and down lines. The rails were carried by longitudinal timbers laid in between the cross girders, resting on stools on the top boom of the main girders, the inner rails being supported by longitudinal timbers, which were also let in between the cross girders, and carried by rail bearers.

Considerable difficulty was experienced in maintaining a good top and alignement to the tracks on this bridge, and when in 1930 the time came for the latter to be renewed, the opportunity was taken to effect an improvement by decking the bridge. The new decking was laid transversely on the rail bearers, and upon new 17in by 7in timbers, fixed to the stools on the main girders, enabling ballast to be laid on the bridge, and a standard cross-sleeper track substituted for the previous baulk type.

The work was carried out under six Sunday occupations, three for each track. The down line was taken in hand first, and on the first Sunday, the old longitudinal track was removed and replaced with new sleepers laid direct on the rail bearers and the new

Plate 48 The facade of the new station building at Newport (High Street) while under construction.

17in by 7in longitudinal timbers. This necessitated a lift of the down line on the bridge of some 7in, the gradients on either side having, of course, to be adjusted accordingly. On the following Sunday, the timber decking was laid approximately over two-thirds of the bridge. The decking was completed on the third Sunday, the ballast laid, and the necessary further lift to the track given to meet the new conditions. The operations on the up line proceeded in a precisely similar manner.

1930 RECONSTRUCTION OF GODDARDS BRIDGE NEAR ST FAGANS

This bridge, which consisted of three spans measuring 38ft on the skew and 27ft on the square, carried the up and down main South Wales lines over the River Ely near St Fagans station. It had two outside girders and one centre girder to each span. The girder ends were supported by abutment walls, and in the centre of the river by wrought iron cylinders.

The method of reconstruction consisted of driving piles alongside the cylinders in the river, and 6ft away from them, timber trestles being used where a footing on dry land could be obtained. A timber crosshead between the pile and cylinder cap formed a bearing for launching new girders before the reconstruction work commenced, sufficient space being provided on the crosshead to accommodate two old girders when removed. This arrangement facilitated the operations, and enabled an existing girder to be disposed of before a new girder was placed in position.

In connection with the launching of the new girders, two 12 ton cranes were employed, one stationed on the up road of the St Fagans end of the bridge, and the other retained at the Cardiff end on the down road, by which means girders were manipulated, within the maximum radius of the cranes. Use was also made of the cranes for hoisting and travelling skips of spent ballast from the old bridge; a convenient method of dealing with the latter owing to the large quantities which had to be dealt with.

The old superstructure which was removed consisted of main girders with trough flooring, the track having been carried on longitudinal timbers ballasted up to the correct level. The new bridge was composed of main girders, cross girders, rail bearers and plate floor. The new track was now on cross girders, the level of the floor being arranged so that a minimum quantity of ballast was carried by the bridge. Complete occupation of the bridge was obtained for three week-ends, covering a period from midnight on Saturday to midnight on Sunday. During the time the bridge was out of use trains between Cardiff and Bridgend were diverted via the route Barry to Bridgend. A petrol-driven compressor was used at the site and pneumatic rivetting was employed throughout the operations.

1930 RECONSTRUCTION OF PRINCES ROAD OVERBRIDGE NEAR RUABON

Princes Road overbridge was built at the time when the Shrewsbury to Ruabon line was opened in 1848. Reconstruction became necessary in 1930 owing to the structure having

Plate 49 The facade of the new building at Newport (High Street).

been subjected to severe sulphurous action, by the continual shunting operations carried out under the bridge. Opportunity was also taken to increase the headroom, which had become somewhat restricted owing to mining subsidence. Owing to the position and nature of the old bridge which was on the skew, a restricted view existed for drivers of road vehicles passing over the structure, and arrangements were made with the

Plate 50 The booking hall of the new Newport (High Street) station.

Plate 51 Part of the refreshment room at Newport station.

Plate 52 A portion of the restaurant kitchen, showing the main gas cooking range.

Plate 53 The general office of the Divisional Superintendent at Newport station.

Plate 54 Crumlin Viaduct, the longer section over the Western Valley.

Plate 55 The Severn Bridge at Worcester, showing the new down line track in position, and men working on the old longitudinal up line track.

Denbighshire County Council to improve the road alignement and also to widen the bridge.

A feature of the reconstruction work was that owing to the weight and length of the main girders, which weighed 46 tons each and were 112ft long, coupled with the confined space in which the cranes had to operate, it was necessary for the cranes to be attached to the girders at specially calculated points. One crane was placed to take a lift at a point 18ft from one end, and the other crane to take a lift 30ft from the opposite end, allocating weights to be carried by the cranes at 19 and 27 tons respectively, the cranes, owing to their positions on the road, working at different radii.

1930 RECONSTRUCTION OF THE MILL LEAT BRIDGE AT TOTNES

The reconstruction of this bridge, which carried the main, platform and goods lines over a public footpath and the mill leat at the east end of Totnes station, was interesting as it was the first occasion on which this particular type of construction had been employed on the GWR.

The new structure consisted mainly of a series of units, each of which was composed of three rolled-steel joists, with a filling of cement concrete. The joists were supplied to a site near the bridge, where the units were made up, these being placed in position by steam cranes. The spaces between the units, the largest of which weighed 15 tons, were subsequently filled with mass concrete as shown in the accompanying diagram. A superstructure of this type was considered to be easy to erect and to require a minimum of subsequent maintenance.

1930 CLEANING THE ROOF AT PADDINGTON STATION

Cleaning the glass in the roof at Paddington station was a major undertaking, but in those days carried out with the minimum of scaffolding. Some 6000 panes of glass were cleaned, inside and out. Forty gallons of hydroflouric acid (one hopes a weak solution?) was used to remove around $4\frac{1}{2}$ tons of soot. It was estimated that about 140 cwt of paint, 300 gallons of tar, 50 gallons of turpentine spirits and 20 gallons of linseed oil were used.

1930 PASSING OF THE OLD DOCK AT NEWPORT

The old Town Dock at Newport, which in its youth was a hive of shipping activity, accommodating ships which were then amongst the largest sailing the seas, passed out of active existence in October 1930, after a life of about 88 years. The gates of the lock entrance were opened and fastened in their recesses, so that the dock became a tidal inlet, usable by vessels only at their own risk.

Plate 56 One of the new girders being lifted into position at Princes Road Bridge, Ruabon, showing the different attachment points and working radii of the cranes.

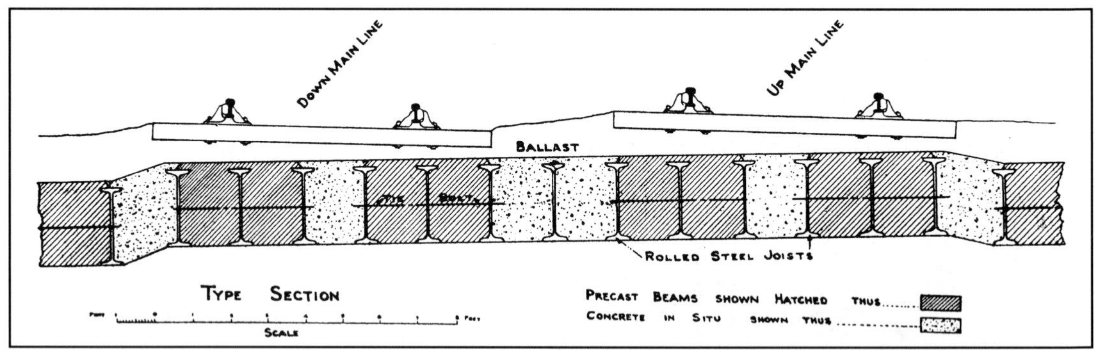

Fig 4. Diagram showing the Bridge units with concrete interlaid.

Plate 57 The site of Mill Leat Bridge, Totnes, with joists in readiness for positioning.

Plate 58 High up beneath the central roof span, a workman fixes a scaffold pole in position at 1134 on 13 October 1930, not apparently using the holes in the iron spans specially provided by Brunel for scaffolding. Far below, a County Tank heads a suburban train.

Situated some 3½ miles from the mouth of the River Usk, the entrance to the Town Dock was on the right or west bank of that river. As shown by the sketch plan, the dock consisted of two basins, the one nearer the river (generally called the outer basin) being the first to be constructed. Comprising about 4 acres of water area, this outer basin, with the entrance lock, was opened in October 1842, under the powers contained in an Act of Parliament of 1835, which also brought into being the Newport Dock Company. Such was the demand for the facilities afforded by the first dock that, in 1854, the Newport Dock Company obtained Parliamentary power to extend the dock, and the inner basin was subsequently built, consisting of about 7½ acres of deep water. This new portion of the dock was opened in March 1858, by the passage into it of the ship "Great Britain".

In the early days, the shipment of coal was effected at the dock by baskets. These were filled by hand labour from the small trucks which brought the coal down to the ship, and were conveyed on board and lowered into the hold by a hand-worked contrivance on board called a "gin", which consisted of an arrangement of windlass, ropes and pulleys. Later on came coal tips, and at one time, in the outer basin, there was erected a movable shipping appliance which was shifted along the quay by a steam engine. It is related that on the first occasion this appliance was worked, not only the coal, but the wagon as well, was shot into the hold of the vessel, which, however, was not such a serious matter in those days, as the trucks were very small and only weighed a few tons.

Besides the shipment of coal, the dock dealt with many other traffics, ore being imported there for the local iron works, and the manufactured iron being shipped abroad. As much as 220,000 tons of iron rails were shipped in one year at the Town Dock in those early days, all destined to America, which was of course

Plate 59 The exterior of the roof, also on 13 October 1930, showing workmen enjoying their lunch on the very edge of the main arched span. The old Departure signal box can be seen on Nos 2/3 platform, just below Bishop's Road Bridge. This signal box was demolished during 1931 when the platforms were extended (see later).

before America started its own iron and steel works. The rails used to be carried in American sailing ships, then among the fastest vessels afloat.

In 1884, the Newport Dock Company was absorbed by the later arrival, the Alexandra (Newport) Dock Company, which by this time had built the Alexandra North Dock (opened in 1875), the commencement of Newport's system of modern docks. The Town Dock served a useful purpose right up to the early 1900s, and even as late as 1909 about 500,000 tons of traffic was dealt with, the bulk of which was coal shipments. Later, however, the traffic dropped off very rapidly, and subsequently the losses on the dock became so serious that the GWR had to abandon it. The use of the GWR appliances for shipping coal, and loading and discharging other cargoes, ceased in July 1928, and since that date such vessels as used the Town Dock have discharged or loaded by their own means.

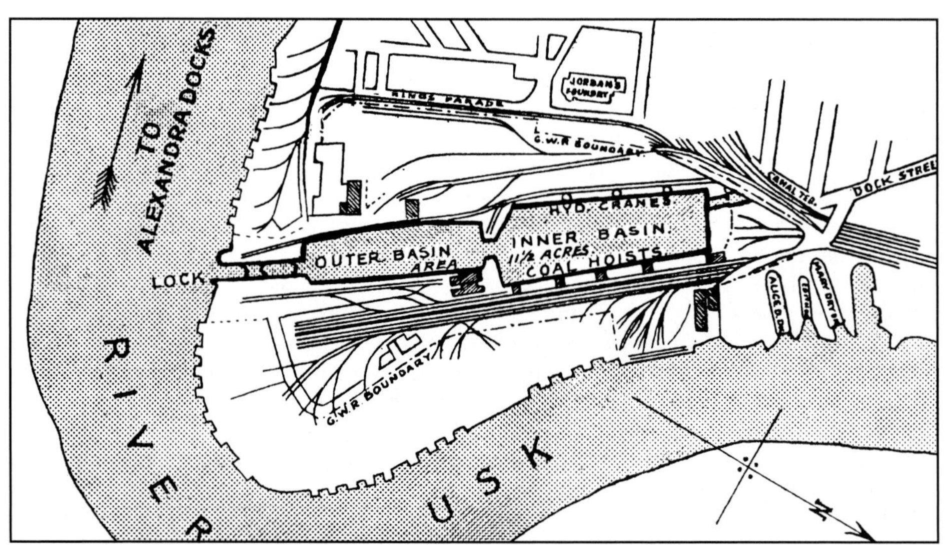

Map 9. Sketch plan showing the site of the old Town Dock at Newport, with its Inner and Outer Basins.

Plate 60 The coal hoists at the Town Dock at Newport, which were subsequently moved to the Alexandra Dock.

Plate 61 The hoist about to be lifted by the 125-ton floating crane at the Town Dock in Newport.

The decline in demand for the use of the Town Dock was due chiefly to the increase in size of ocean-going vessels, which became too large for the lock entrance. In recent years the vessels this dock accommodated had become the smaller class of foreign-going ships, and ships engaged in coastal trade. Having regard to the inevitability of its eventual disuse, the GWR obtained powers to abandon the dock. There were two good coal shipping hoists at the Town Dock, which had been erected in 1907, and these were transferred bodily to the Alexandra Dock by the GWR's floating crane.

Although these hoists weighed between 80 and 90 tons and were 73ft high, by means of the GWR 125-ton floating crane they were lifted off the quay wall, towed from the Town Dock along the River Usk to the Alexandra North Dock, and placed in their new positions in only $6^1/_2$ hours.

1930 NEW LEVEL CROSSING BARRIER AT HAYES

In connection with the construction of a short length of railway at Hayes in Middlesex, from which transport facilities were to be afforded to the British Electric Transformer Co for the carriage of transformers, a road level crossing was necessary at a point where pedestrian traffic to and from the factories and works in the vicinity was particularly heavy. The Middlesex Country Council would not accept the ordinary type of level crossing gates, as these would have involved the erection of posts which would have formed an obstruction in the existing footpaths. For this reason, lifting barriers were

Plate 62 New level crossing barrier at Hayes, shown in the position closed to road and pedestrian but open for rail traffic.

Plate 63 The same new level crossing barrier at Hayes, shown in the position open for road and pedestrian traffic. Separate gates closed off the rail traffic.

Plate 64 The rail side of Cadbury's new depot at Exeter, showing the unloading dock.

Plate 65 The other side of the new depot, which adjoined the main road, showing a lorry departing.

installed, common on the Continent but then rarely seen in the UK.

The barriers, which were known as the 'curtain' type with vertical hanging members, were capable of being raised or lowered in from 20 to 25 seconds by powerful gearing, operating all four barriers. The operating rod passed under the roadway in a 2½in pipe, fitted with special glands, and filled with oil, to ensure easy working. The gearing was fixed on a timber frame carried on concrete walls, the latter forming the pit for a vertical crank, the operating connection being about a foot below rail level.

1930 DISTRIBUTION DEPOT FOR CADBURY AT EXETER

The GWR had a policy of affording special rail-connected accommodation and distributing facilities for the use of important traders whose traffic was regularly passing over the Company's system in large quantities. In pursuance of this policy, in 1930 the GWR provided a depot for Cadbury of Bournville on a site adjoining the down main line at the north end of Exeter St Davids station.

The depot was served on one side by a rail connection from the down main line. The other side had a direct access to the main Cowley Road. The structure was of red brick, roofed with red Roman pattern tiles, and was erected by Messrs Wilkins of Torquay under the supervision of the GWR's divisional engineer, and in accordance with a design prepared by Cadbury's architects. The building measured about 75ft by 60ft. The ground floor was designed for use as a stock room with an area of about 4500 sq ft at platform level, with direct access on the one side to a covered platform serving the rail, and on the other to a covered platform where road vehicles could be berthed. The storage space on this floor had a hard granolithic surface, with a central trolleying way connected with the rail and road platforms which had hard wood blocks.

Offices, waiting room and other accommodation were situated on the upper floor on the Cowley Road side, and behind these were two show rooms, where the firm's commodities could be exhibited to their customers. The building was electrically lit throughout, and heated by a low-pressure hot-water system capable of maintaining a temperature of 60F (15½C) in the stock room and 65F (18C) in the offices, when the outside air was as low as 32F (0C). This system was operated and controlled from a boiler in a basement under the building.

Cadbury's fresh stocks travelled in bulk daily direct from the main factory at Bournville to Exeter, and

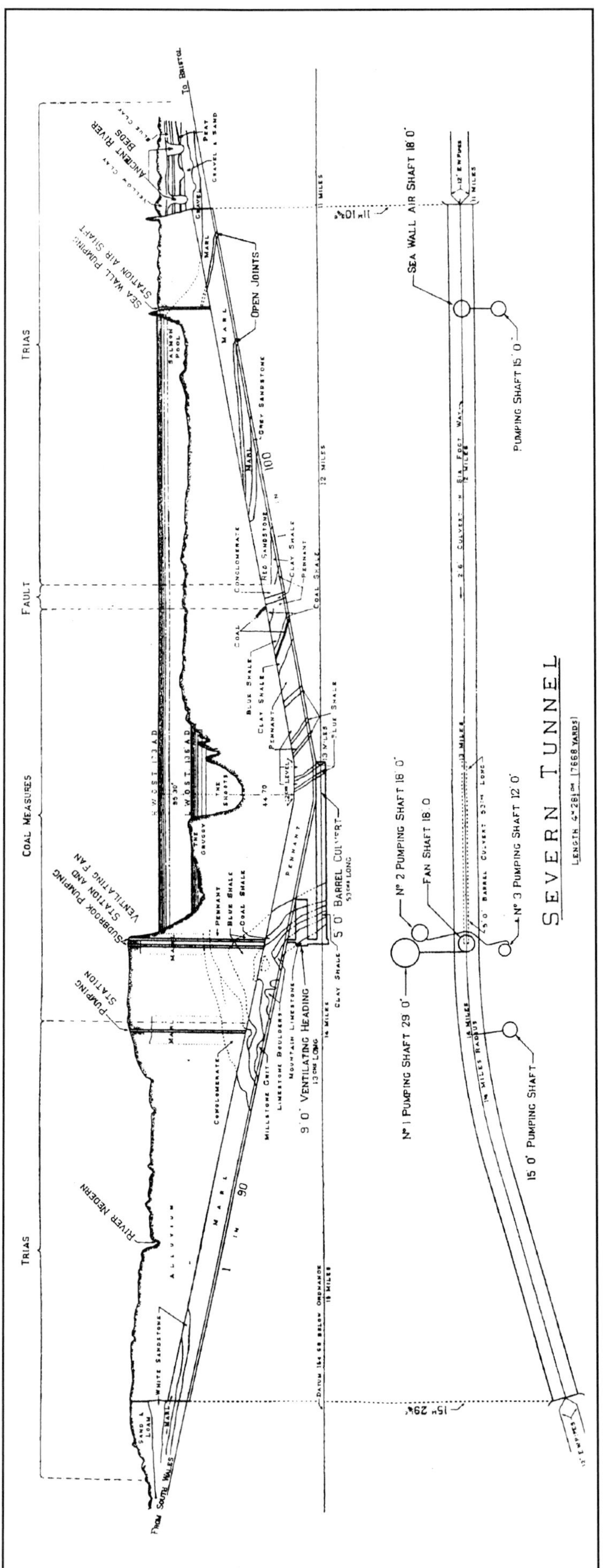

Fig 5. Cross-sectional elevation and plan of the Severn Tunnel, showing the river features, the pumping stations, and the types of soil the tunnel passed through.

the wagons berthed at the depot before noon on the day following despatch. The goods were loaded into specially-designed small containers carried in covered rail vans, to minimise the terminal labour at both ends of the transit. The goods were subsequently delivered by a fleet of road motor vans specially constructed and decorated to Cadbury's requirements, and supplied by the GWR's Road Transport Department. This fleet operated over the chosen delivery area, many miles in extent, which radiated from the new depot. The GWR's railhead distribution service operating from Exeter was also used to some extent as an auxiliary to the main delivery service. Some of the goods were re-despatched by rail to places further away.

1931 CEMENTATION IN THE SEVERN TUNNEL

The Act for the Severn Tunnel was obtained by the GWR in 1872. Owing to the funnel-like shape of the Severn estuary, the tides are very high, the spring tides rising to 50ft above low water. At the chosen site, the estuary is $2^1/_4$ miles wide. Of this distance, starting from the Gloucestershire side, the first $1^1/_2$ mile consists of a level of rough rocks, known as the English Stones, which are exposed at half tide; then comes a deep channel about 1200ft wide and 80ft deep, called the Shoots, through which the strong current of the river runs at low water; and next about $^1/_2$ mile of more half-tide exposed rocks, called the Lady Bench. The railway was designed to pass under the Shoots at a level of 50ft below rock bottom, and from this, its lowest point, to rise in each direction at a uniform gradient of 1 in 100. The total length of the tunnel was just over $4^1/_2$ miles, a little more than half under the river, and about three-quarters of the remainder being under land on the Monmouthshire side.

Water was always a trouble in early days of the Severn Tunnel. There was an inrush of fresh water in 1879, when the heading that was being driven by the GWR, broke through about 800ft from the Bristol mouth. This was subsequently termed the Great Spring. At this point, the GWR asked Sir John Hawkshaw to take charge of the works and he decided to contract the work out and it went to Mr T.A. Walker. Hawkshaw decided to lower the tunnel

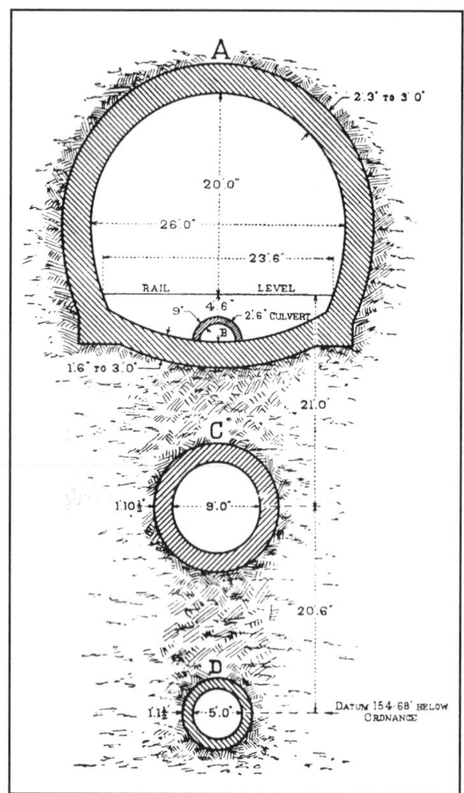

Fig 6. Cross-sectional view of the Severn Tunnel close to Sudbrook pumping station where there were culverts underneath the main tunnel. 'A' marks the main tunnel, 'B' the 2ft 6in culvert in the six-foot way of the track in the tunnel, 'C' the 9ft diameter barrel ventilating heading and 'D' the lowest 5ft barrel culvert.

Plate 66 The work of drilling in progress in the Severn Tunnel.

under the Shoots by 15ft, maintaining the gradient eastward at 1 in 100, 15ft below the former level throughout, and making the westward gradient 1 in 90 instead of 1 in 100, so as to run out into the old levels on the Monmouthshire side. Additional pumps were installed but the works were not clear of water until 1880. Walker's first step was to build a strong wall in the westward heading from the Old Shaft to shut out the water from the Great Spring. In 1882, the works were interrupted by an inrush of salt water near the Sea Wall shaft from the Salmon Pool. This inrush was stopped by pouring concrete in from ground level. In 1883, the Great Spring again burst in, but this problem was overcome. By the end of 1883, $2^1/_4$ miles of tunnel had been completed. Early in 1884, it was decided to reduce the length of tunnel by 800ft by lengthening the cutting at the west end to provide material for making sidings at a new station subsequently called Severn Tunnel Junction. The Great Spring was shut in by two head walls, but to deal with it Hawkshaw drove a side heading parallel with the line of the tunnel to intercept the spring and divert it. In 1886, a new large shaft was sunk at the side of the tunnel, pumps fixed in it, and so the Great Spring was mastered. A special train with Directors aboard made the first journey through the tunnel in September 1885, the first coal train passed through in January 1886, and having been officially inspected passenger trains began to run in December 1886.

In 1924, there was found to be excessive leakage into the tunnel of water from the River Severn, at a point some 3360ft from the Bristol mouth. This part of the river bed being accessible at low water, it was sealed by pouring concrete in at ground level. Similar trouble occurred in 1929 and was cured in the same way. However, this recurrence of infiltration of water tended to indicate the existence of open joints and of broken and faulty strata above the tunnel, and it was felt that special measures should be taken, not only to strengthen the brickwork lining of this length of tunnel, but to fill any voids that might exist between the back of the lining and the surrounding strata, and to consolidate as far as reasonably possible the ground between the tunnel and the river bed. Only one method was available, which was to force liquid cement

Plate 67 The plant and machinery used for cementation in the Severn tunnel.

into and through the brickwork under sufficient pressure to counteract the maximum head of water at high tide.

Machinery was required for compression of air for operating the drills, and for the mixing of the liquid cement and pumping it through the drilled holes into the voids at the back of the brickwork and into the defective joints of the arch ring. It was decided to locate this machinery in sheds to be erected at the Sea Wall pumping station, where the necessary steam supply could be obtained from the existing GWR pumping plant and whence the compressed air and grouting mains could be led down the ventilating shaft. These mains were carried into the tunnel throughout the whole length to be treated, and to them, at appropriate intervals, were fixed valves and connections for flexible pipes to be connected directly to the portable drills and to screwed pipes fitted into the drilled holes for the injection of cement grout. To provide supports for the drilling of the upper holes, travelling stages mounted on trolleys running on the tracks were provided from which drilling could proceed. These could only be used during Sunday occupations.

As an essential feature of the work was that the running lines should, except during these operations, be kept clear, all plant which could not be kept clear during the week had to be brought into and taken out of the tunnel during Sunday occupations. Some of this plant was erected on trucks stored during the week on the Sea Wall sidings, and some was lowered into and hauled out of the tunnel through the Sea Wall shaft, the latter method of transit being that wholly adopted throughout the later stages of the work.

The general programme was to drill a series of holes at intervals throughout the whole length to be treated. Of these, those through the invert were drilled during the week. These holes were bored to a maximum length of 10ft each, reaching points from 4ft to 6ft below the lowest level of the invert. The remaining holes in the arch ring, which varied in thickness from 3ft 0in to 3ft 6in, were drilled to lengths varying from 3ft 6in to 5ft 0in, according to the nature of the ground encountered behind the

Plate 68 Three views of the Guest, Keen and Nettlefold steel sleeper. The top shows the complete sleeper complete with chairs, the middle shows a close-up of the chair cast on to the sleeper, and the lower shows the underneath of the sleeper with the ends of the snugs that secure the chairs.

Plate 69 A section of track, showing the GKN steel sleepers and chairs, with the keys.

Plate 70 The experimental length of steel sleeper track laid at Risca, showing the reverse curves.

brickwork. The diameter of the holes through the ring was $3\frac{1}{8}$in, reducing to $1\frac{7}{8}$in, in the surrounding ground. The injection pipes of $1\frac{1}{2}$in diameter passed right through the holes in the brickwork. All cement injections started at the back of the brickwork, resulting in a final consolidation of the bonding of the latter. Injections of cement commenced through the invert holes and were gradually followed upwards round the arch ring, injections through the crown being undertaken last. A considerable amount of water was tapped during the drilling, and injections were mainly carried out at pressures limited to 25 psi over the pressure due to static head of water. During the later stages, this limit was dispensed with and the maximum injection pressure increased to 100 psi.

The work in the tunnel started in November 1929 and ran until April 1930, 2123 holes being drilled and 3016 tons of cement injected. The work proved to be so successful that it was decided to extend operations to cover the whole length from the Bristol mouth to a point where the marl joined the sandstone rock which was considered to form an adequate barrier. So work recommenced in November 1930 and ran until May 1931. The total work carried out amounted to 4233 holes drilled and 8132 tons of cement injected. In addition to the work in the tunnel proper, similar strengthening by cement injection was carried out on the Sea Wall and Sudbrook ventilating shafts. No difficulty was experienced at Sea Wall, but at Sudbrook it was

Plate 71 Men at work on the new GKN steel sleeper track at Twyford.

Plate 72 Men at work laying GKN steel sleeper track on a stretch of track, just over a mile long, on the main line near Maidenhead, in August 1930.

found necessary to inject and fill numerous voids surrounding the tunnel at the base of the shaft and extending to the 9ft ventilating heading and the 5ft barrel culvert below the tunnel. The work carried out on the two shafts was as follows; Sea Wall 17 holes drilled and 91 tons of cement injected and Sudbrook 85 holes drilled and 455 tons of cement injected.

1931 STEEL SLEEPERS

The position regarding sleepers in the late 1920's was that in the past imported timber sleepers had fulfilled requirements satisfactorily, supplies being sufficiently plentiful and the cost reasonably low. However, conditions in these respects were becoming less satisfactory, and it was considered that the time had come when serious consideration had to be given to the possible advantages of adopting steel as an alternative to timber. Apart from the question of cost, there was an advantage from a national viewpoint in using steel sleepers in that it would creat work for home manufacturers, not only in the actual process of manufacturing the sleepers but also in the production of steel required for the purpose.

At the time there were several types of steel sleepers; GKN Composite, Harvey Patent, Sandberg Patent, Webbs's Patent and Rafarel Patent. The one selected for trial on the GWR was the GKN Composite design, manufactured by Messrs Guest, Keen and Nettlefolds, at Dowlais. The sleeper consisted of a plate 3/8in thick, pressed to trough form, with a bead along the lower edge of the trough for stiffening purposes. It was $9^1/_4$in wide by 4 3/16in deep for a distance of 16in each side of the centre, and was spread to a width of 11in by 3 1/8in deep for the remainder of its length. The ends were turned

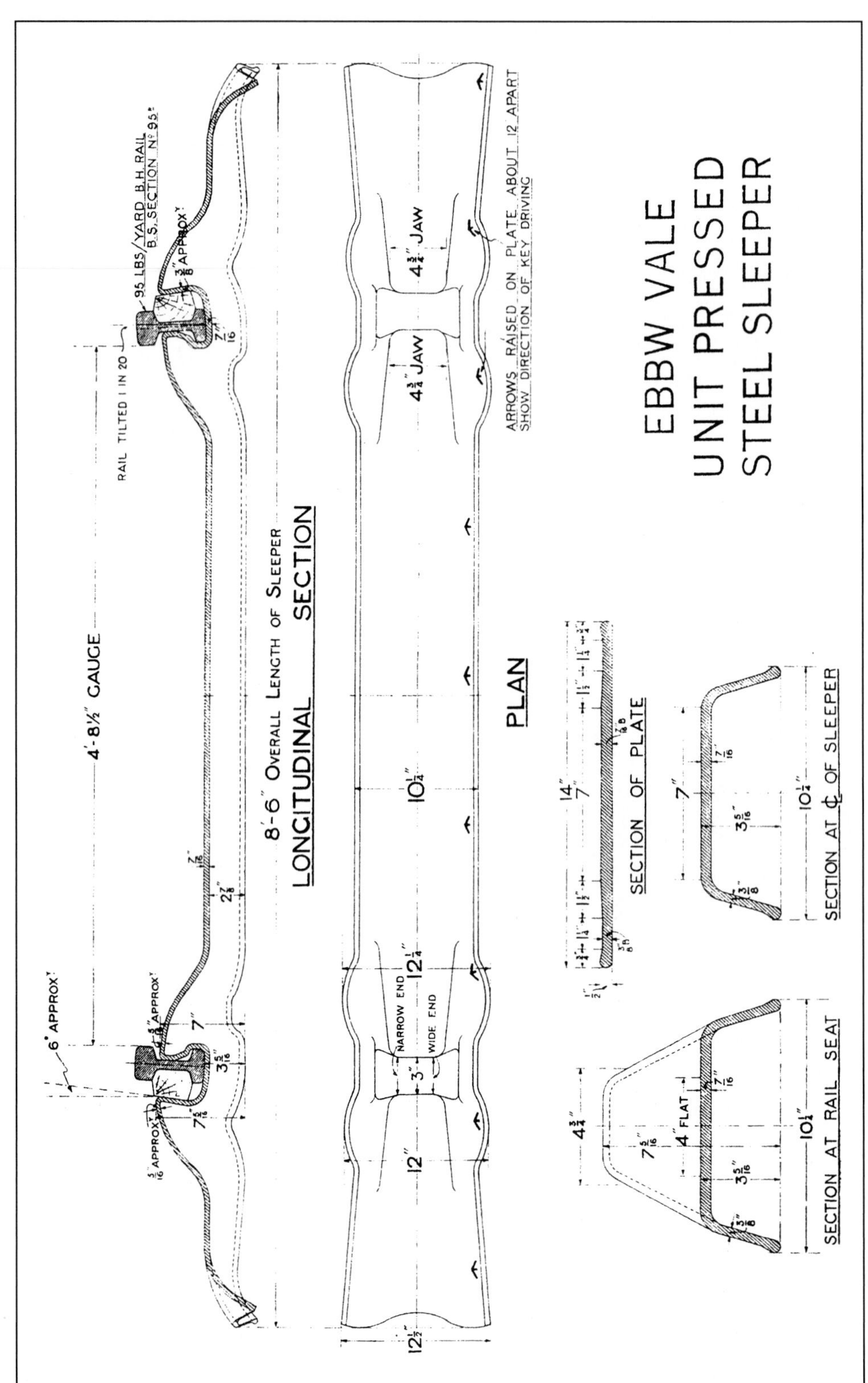

Fig 7. Engineering drawing of the Ebbw Vale unit pressed steel sleeper.

Plate 73 Ebbw Vale unit pressed steel sleeper, resting on a wooden support.

Plate 74 Ebbw Vale unit pressed steel sleepers being laid and the rails fixed at Twyford in November 1931.

Plate 75 A stretch of track laid with the new type of Ebbw Vale unit pressed steel sleepers.

down and splayed to a width of 12in. The fastening of the chair to the sleeper was accomplished by casting the former direct on to the latter and forming, in the process, four snugs (part of the chair) on the underside of the sleeper. By this means the use of chair bolts was avoided. The eight holes to take the cast snugs (equivalent to rivets) for securing the two cast-on chairs in position were first punched small, as a guide, and afterwards flanged upwards, thereby increasing the strength and rigidity of the chair attachment. Severe tests showed that the chair broke before the attachment gave way. Care had to be exercised by the manufacturer in casting on the chairs to ensure proper gauge, this being accomplished to a maximum variation of $^{3}/_{64}$in.

In 1929, the GWR laid experimental lengths of steel sleeper track near Risca and Twyford. At Risca on the Western Valleys line, half a mile of track was relaid with steel sleepers between Risca and Cross Keys, where the traffic was frequent and heavy and the line was formed of comparatively sharp reverse curves. As much as 40,000 tons of traffic, chiefly coal, passed over the line in 24 hours. This, combined with the curves which were as sharp as 725ft in radius, constituted a severe test on the sleepers. The ballast used was South Wales slag, and its possible corrosive effect upon the steel sleepers was to be watched. Near Twyford, the length selected was the down relief line where ordinary high speed was run and the line was on a slight curve. The ballast here was also South Wales slag. At both places, the length of sleeper adopted was 8ft 0in, but a further half mile was laid in the down relief line near Twyford with sleepers 8ft 6in long and with stone ballast.

In addition, an experimental length was laid in the up main line opposite the locomotive shops at Swindon, with 8ft 0in and 8ft 6in steel sleepers and 8ft 6in timber sleepers, to enable comparative deflection tests to be undertaken under fast running conditions on a straight road.

The experience gained with these sleepers was quite satisfactory, the running over them was good, and no special difficulty was experienced in maintaining the line. However, it was appreciated that if steel sleepers were to be laid in lines that were track-circuited, difficulty might be experienced in insulating the rails from the sleepers, and a simple and effective method of doing this was required. Accordingly, during 1930, the GWR ordered 136,000 experimental steel sleepers, sufficient for 60 miles of track.

By the end of 1931, about 198,000 steel sleepers, equivalent to 94 miles of track, were laid in various parts of the GWR system. The types used were the GKN sleeper with cast on chairs (already referred to), the United Steel Companies' sleeper with steel chairs welded on, Dorman Long's sleeper with steel chairs welded on, and the Sandberg sleeper with chair jaws formed by turning up part of the sleeper plate.

In addition, a new type, known as the unit pressed steel sleeper, was designed and manufactured by the Ebbw Vale Steel, Iron and Coal Co Ltd, and the GWR was the first railway company to lay these in the line. There were 264 of these in the up relief line between Taplow and Maidenhead, and 792 in the up relief line near Twyford. The special feature of this new type was that the sleeper and 'chair' for retaining the rails was made integrally from a rolled steel plate, thereby avoiding the necessity for any fastening of the 'chair' by bolts, welding or other means. The rolled steel plates, of which the sleepers were made, were 14in wide and $^{7}/_{16}$in thick, and were cut into 9ft 6in lengths, cold pressed to form two 'waves' near both ends of the plate, these 'waves' eventually forming the 'chair'. The plates were then heated and passed through two hydraulic presses, and again, after reheating, subjected to two more operations, which finished shaping the sleeper section and finally 'nose' the jaws of the 'chairs' over to the correct angle and width. The sleepers were then carried by a conveyor through a bath of tar mixture to give them a protective coating, after which they were ready for use.

The operation of forming the 'chair' jaws resulted in only a very slight reduction in the thickness of the metal. An interesting feature of the 'chair' was that, not only was the key side tapered in the direction the keys were driven, so that the further the key was driven into the 'chair' the tighter it became, but it was also undercut, or inclined towards the rail jaw, for the purpose of holding the rail firmly down on to the rail seat. The gauge, tilt of the rails, and the space between the jaws for the reception of rails and keys, were automatically fixed during the operations of pressing, and careful inspection of the sleepers showed that accurate results were obtained. Various mechanical tests were made to confirm that both the sleeper and the key jaws of the 'chairs' were adequately strong.

1931 IMPROVEMENTS IN THE PAIGNTON AREA

With the increasing popularity of coast resorts in the South-West, and the expansion of the seaside town of Paignton over the 1920s, it became evident that the accommodation had become inadequate. Any improvements would have to be carried out by expanding the passenger facilities over the area occupied by the goods station, which in turn meant finding new accommodation for the goods shed, which in any case needed to be enlarged. Advantage was taken of the Development (Loan Guarantees and Grants) Act of 1929 to improve facilities all round.

At the passenger station, the platforms were lengthened and the old freight mileage accommodation on the down side was converted into carriage sidings. The old good shed at the up side was enlarged and converted into an office to deal with passengers' luggage sent in advance for the Torbay area. Electric lighting was installed in place of the old gas lighting.

Finding another site for the goods station was not easy, but eventually an area of between five and six acres adjoining the up line south of Paignton station near to Goodrington Sands Halt was acquired from the Paignton Urban District Council. It was considered that this location would not only meet the requirements of Paignton itself but also the Brixham, Churston, Kingswear and Dartmouth areas by railhead lorry distribution schemes. As portions of this land were low-lying, filling was needed to bring the site up to the required level, and about 50,000 cubic yards of material that had been excavated from other points, was tipped on to the site. On this ground, the GWR constructed a new goods station. This was brought into use in June 1931, when the old goods shed at the main passenger station was taken over for passengers' luggage.

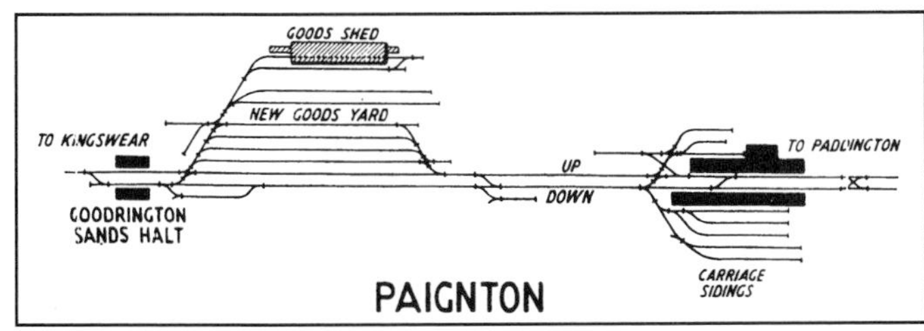

Map 10. New goods yard and station at Paignton, showing relationship to Paignton passenger station and Goodrington Sands Halt.

The new goods station was provided with two dead-end sidings (excluding the goods shed line), which afforded accommodation for about 150 wagons accessible to road vehicles. Between these sidings and the running lines were four loops for running, holding, and general marshalling purposes. Electric floodlights were installed to illuminate this new yard. On the outer siding, a goods shed, nearly 300ft long, was erected, facing the Dartmouth Road. Owing to the soft nature of the ground, it was necessary to pile the foundations, and a number of reinforced concrete piles 25ft long were sunk and connected by reinforced concrete caps to longitudinal and cross beams which carried the platforms and superstructure. The walls were of brick, faced with local facing bricks and artificial Bath stone to give the exterior a pleasing façade. The total width of the shed was 37ft, and an upper floor warehouse 140ft long and 35ft wide extended over a portion of it. This goods shed contained a single platform 395ft long and 25ft wide, of which a length of 295ft was covered by a verandah covering projecting 20ft over the roadway beyond the platform. The platform was equipped with two Pooley 30 cwt weighing machines. A 20 ton vehicle weighbridge with 20ft plate was installed, together with an office, just inside the main entrance gates at the Paignton end of the yard.

The old halt at Goodrington Sands, having became inadequate for the heavy summer traffic, was enlarged so as to consist of two 600ft platforms with shelters, and a timber booking office at the entrance to the down platform. The line between Paignton and the halt was doubled, and a new goods running loop provided on the down side. A new footbridge was built to replace the former foot crossing of the line at the site of the new goods yard, and a new pathway was provided alongside the line from this bridge.

1931 VIADUCTS AT QUAKERS YARD

Underground mining operations for coal and other minerals in the vicinity of railways can cause track subsidence requiring special precautions such as periodical raising of the track. Bridges carrying the railway can also require special treatment to maintain their stability whilst subsidence is in progres.

At Quakers Yard, heavy timbering was carried out on one of the three masonry viaducts formerly forming part of the Taff Vale Railway. Owing to the type of construction of this viaduct, very heavy timbering was

Plate 76 The interior of the new goods shed at Paignton.

Plate 77 Timbering a masonry viaduct at Quakers Yard, showing the centre span over the River Taff where because of the river, specially constructed foundations and steel girders were necessary to support the timbering above the river.

required, some 40,000 cubic ft being used. A similar large quantity was used on two adjoining viaducts, making a total of 82,000 cubic ft. Of particular interest was the timbering of the centre span over the River Taff, to carry which a number of serviceable steel girders were fixed on specially constructed foundations.

1931 BANBURY MARSHALLING YARDS

Under arrangements set up by the Development (Loan Guarantees & Grants) Act of 1929, in order to deal more satisfactorily with the traffic passing southwards from Birmingham and the north, including traffic from other companies' systems, new sidings accommodating around 1000 wagons were provided at Banbury. This enabled traffic hitherto sorted at outlying stations to be concentrated at Banbury and, by means of a new hump yard which was also constructed as

Plate 78 The Quakers Yard Viaduct, spanning the River Taff and its valley. Track subsidence as a result of underground mining operations necessitated the heavy timbering. On the right of the picture is the historic roadway which was the formation of the former Merthyr to Abercynon Railway. The original stone sleepers, as laid in 1802, and over which Trevithick's steam engine ran, were clearly visible in their original positions.

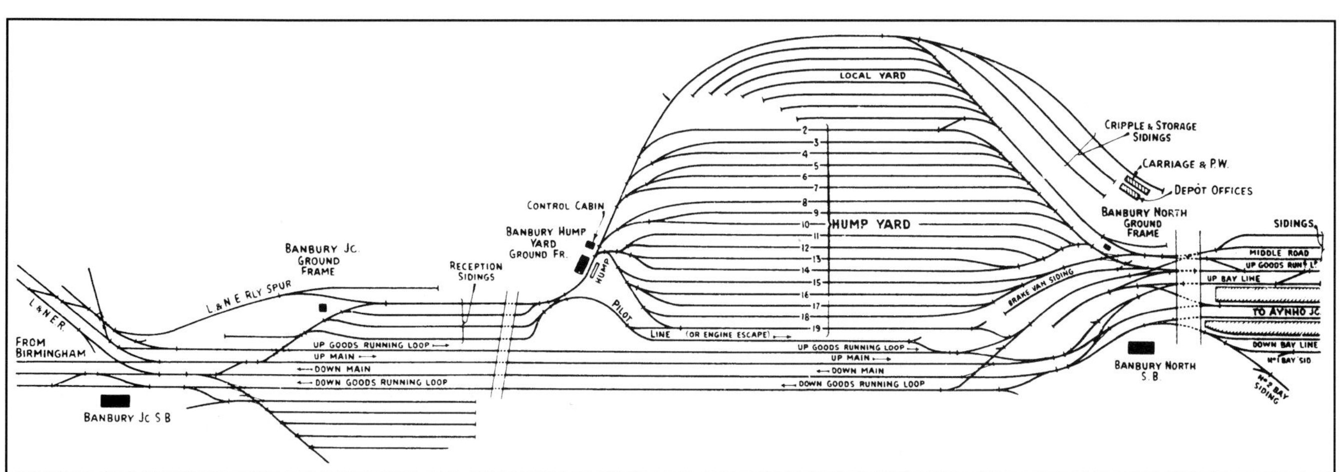

Map 11. The new 'hump' marshalling yards at Banbury.

part of the scheme, wagons could be marshalled more expeditiously.

It will be generally understood that there were two distinct kinds of marshalling yards, known as 'flat' and 'hump' (or gravitation) respectively. The chief difference between them lies in the fact that whereas in a flat yard the sorting and marshalling of wagons was done by both forward and backward shunting, in the gravitation yards the greater part of the shunting was accomplished by forward movements, the wagons being propelled to the summit of the hump, from which point they gravitated on a falling gradient into the various sidings.

The new Banbury 'hump' marshalling yards, which were situated on the up side of the line between Banbury Junction and Banbury station, dealt with most of the GWR traffic passing from north to south, also traffic from the LNER system via Banbury Junction. The wagons arrived unmarshalled at Banbury hump yard, and were sorted there. A considerable proportion of the traffic dealt with over the hump consisted of coal, iron, steel, etc en route from the LNER to various stations on the GWR system, and this was worked into Banbury on pilot trips from Woodford (LNER). Four reception sidings, with a total holding capacity of 265 wagons, were available for accommodating trains and pilot trips requiring to be 'humped'. The hump yard itself comprised 19 sidings, with a total holding capacity of about 1400 wagons.

After a train had been brought to rest in one of the reception sidings, the engine was uncoupled and either crossed to the down side yard for return loading or was sent either to the engine shed via the pilot (or engine escape) line, or to the London end of the yard to pick up a sorted train. Wagons for the down line direction were worked across to the down side yard by train engines. The hump shunting engine was then coupled to the rear of the train, ready to propel it at slow speed, on a rising gradient of 1 in 240, to the summit of the hump.

Before a train from the LNER line passed over the hump, a shunter examined the labels of the wagons from the front of the train to the rear, and filled in a printed slip, known as a 'cut' card, showing the order in which the wagons would be uncoupled at the hump, that is, the number of wagons passing in each movement, and the number of the siding that they were required to run into. In the case of GWR trains, each guard handed a tally of his train to the hump yard head shunter, and the slip was prepared from this document. One copy of the slip was retained by the hump yard head shunter responsible for uncoupling the wagons at the top of the hump, and a copy was handed to the hump yard ground-frame shunter who manipulated the electro-pneumatic push-button frame controlling the points.

When ready to commence shunting operations the "Reception Sidings to

Plate 79 Shunting engine propelling wagons to the summit of the 'hump' at Banbury.

Plate 80 Banbury hump yard, viewed from the centre of the hump.

Hump Yard" starting signal was lowered, and this indicated to the driver of the shunting engine that he could start to push the wagons over the hump. This signal could be placed to 'danger' by the head shunter in charge of the hump, by means of a switch, in case of emergency. During the time wagons were being passed over the hump, this signal was kept in the 'all clear' position, but in the event of the shunting becoming too fast, or in any emergency necessitating shunting being stopped, it was put to 'danger' when the driver of the propelling engine was required to stop instantly. Klaxon horns, manipulated by the shunters, were also provided, whereby the driver could be warned by means of standard codes if necessary. These were also used during periods of fog or falling snow.

Shunters, provided with brake sticks, checked the speed of the wagons as required, by means of the hand brakes, or, if necessary, by using a shunting skid which was placed on the rail. This quickly retarded the speed of the vehicle or vehicles and brought them, when required, to a stand-still. Not more than six wagons, coupled together, were allowed to gravitate over the hump at one time. Wagons with defective brakes, or wagons of live stock, were not allowed to gravitate from the hump. The hump shunting engine could proceed over the hump and into the sidings for the purpose of closing up the wagons, or fetching out a wagon which might have been wrongly shunted. The maximum loads of trains dealt with over the hump varied from 50 to 70 wagons, and the number of 'cuts' to separate them, varied considerably. A train of 60 wagons requiring 40 'cuts' could be disposed of over the hump in 12 minutes.

There were 16 regular GWR freight trains and 14 LNER pilot trips booked to terminate at Banbury hump yard at this time, these services being supplemented by specials as may have been necessary. In addition, eight 'through' GWR freight trains also arrived at Banbury unmarshalled, and these were put off in the reception sidings to be humped, the engines proceeding via the pilot line to the London end of the hump yard, where they picked up marshalled trains in accordance with the schedules.

The wagons having been filtered, by gravitation, from the hump towards the London end of the yard, it was from the latter point that outwards trains in the up direction were despatched. Generally speaking, the train engine picked up a complete load from one siding, but in a few instances, where trains were scheduled to convey traffic for several destinations, it was necessary for the train engine to pick up from two or three sidings. The load having been made up, the train then drew ahead towards the south end. The brake vans were stabled in a short dead-end siding, built on a ramp at the London end of the yard, and after each train had drawn ahead on the loop line, the appropriate brake van was released from the brake-van siding and gravitated on to its train.

'Through' express freight trains, which did not put off wagons for passing over the hump, but had to call at Banbury to pick up or put off traffic, proceeded via the Up Goods loop line, which ran on the level alongside the hump yard, and came to a stand at the London end of the sidings, at which point they detached or attached wagons as required. Immediately after midnight, three express freight trains, each conveying important merchandise traffic from the Birmingham and South Staffordshire districts for the various London depots and formed only in sectional order, ran direct to the London end of the hump yard via the Up Goods loop line. A shunting engine proceeded to shunt these wagons and marshalled those for each depot together, matching them in with other suitable wagons on hand, so that when they were despatched in train loads from Banbury, the traffic for each particular depot was confined to one train.

This was the most intensive period of the night operations, the work at the London end of the yard being carried out simultaneously with the hump operations at the other end. The three express freight trains which worked these wagons forward were partially vacuum-fitted services, and not less than one-third of the load of each train had to consist of vacuum-fitted vehicles formed next to the engine, and coupled by flexible pipe. These trains, which cleared 200 wagons betwen them, left Banbury at intervals of 25 minutes as follows; 0215 direct to Paddington (Goods), 0240 direct to Acton and 0305 direct to Park Royal and thence to Old Oak Common.

Adjoining the hump yard was a group of seven dead-end sidings known as the 'local yard'. There was direct access from the south end of Banbury Yard to these 'flat' sidings, which had a holding capacity of about 235 wagons. Access was also given from the London end of Nos 1, 2 & 3 Hump sidings. The work at this location consisted chiefly of sorting and marshalling traffic for local services, and dealing with traffic for Banbury proper, and LMSR exchange traffic via Banbury. There were also three dead-end sidings, with a holding capacity of 125 wagons, with access off No 1 Hump siding, which were used for stabling and repairing defective wagons, storage of cattle trucks, etc.

During a representative period of 24 hours, the work performed at Banbury Hump Yard may be summarised as 38 trains dealt with, 1862 wagons propelled over the hump and 380 wagons crossed from the hump yard to the down side. Work at the London end of the hump yard may be summarised as 13 through trains called, seven trains and pilot trips terminated, 21 outwards trains despatched, 278 wagons detached and 1720 wagons attached.

1931 PLATFORM EXTENSIONS AT PADDINGTON

In 1931, many platforms at Paddington Station were extended as part of the work undertaken under the arrangements set up by the Development (Loan Guarantees and Grants) Act of 1929. The first platforms to be treated were Nos 6 and 7 which were extended 300 ft in a westerly direction.

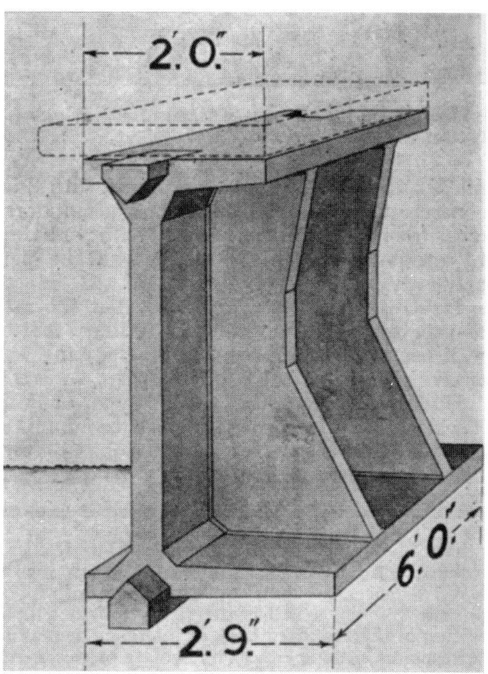

Fig 8. A sketch of one of the blocks, showing the main dimensions.

Particular interest lies in the fact that a new type of pre-cast reinforced concrete wall was introduced. This was designed by the GWR Chief Engineer's office and cast at the GWR's own concrete depot at Taunton. The wall consisted of blocks, or units, in 6ft lengths, complete up to the platform coping, having a 2ft 9in base, face wall 4in thick and a top 2ft wide to take the coping. These units, which weighed 27 cwt each, were interlocked by a reinforced concrete dowel at top and bottom. Small wooden blocks were let into the face of the wall close under the coping for the attachment of supports for gas pipes, electric cables, etc.

To minimise interference to traffic, erection work took place at night between 2200 and 0730 hours. The method was to open out the foundations to about 2ft 2in below rail level and to a width of 3ft, then spread a layer of sand, and level off by means of

Plate 81 End view of one of the reinforced concrete blocks, showing the dowel (on top) for interlocking.

Plate 82 Extension of Paddington Station platforms Nos 6 and 7. The pre-cast concrete blocks are in position, ready for filling between the walls.

Plate 83 The approach lines to platforms 7 (right) and 8 (left) in June 1931, the former having already been lengthened. The covered way on the left would soon be demolished and replaced by an extension of the footbridge which already linked platforms 1-8.

a wooden gauge, after which with the aid of a 12-ton steam crane, the blocks were placed in position, their relation to the running rail being checked by a platform gauge. With such a wide base, the blocks were quite stable and were left to stand until the next occupation, when a train of filling was unloaded and the material spread between the two walls. The coping was next set in concrete, all joints filled, and the space between paved with 2in concrete paving, bedded in sand, as a temporary measure until the filling had had sufficient time to consolidate, when the paving was permanently bedded. With a crew of twelve men, the rate of progress was from 150 to 210 ft per wall per right. This method of construction was considered to give a faster erection with less interference with traffic than any other type of construction.

Ultimately, eight of the eleven platforms were extended, three to more than 1150ft long, one to 1090ft and four to more than 940ft in length, the

Plate 84 Much of the lifting of the track and materials required for altering the layout at Paddington for the lengthened platforms was carried out by one of the GWR's three 0-6-4 crane tanks. Shown here in June 1931 is No 16 "Hercules", being used to position new platform edging.

Plate 85 General view of platform extensions, showing umbrella roofs.

total additional length of platform being 2,200ft. When complete, the parts of the platforms projecting beyond the main arched roof were provided with canopies. To match the new and extended platforms, the main line approaches were remodelled over a $^3/_4$ mile distance from the station, and also the Ranelagh Bridge locomotive yard facilities were improved.

1932 FACILITIES AT BRENTFORD DOCKS

The GWR's Brentford Dock, its principal waterside depot in London, was served by a short branch from the main line at Southall. By 1932 it was handling large and increasing quantities of coal, timber, grain, scrap iron, esparto grass and general goods, in particular there being a heavy tonnage of coal imported through Brentford. The dock was 15 acres in extent, with nearly 3,200ft of quays and accommodation for about 1000 wagons. The 900ft wharf along the frontage of the River Thames was constructed around 1920, to supplement the waterside facilities provided in the dock itself. Besides relieving the pressure of general business, the wharf was used by lighters too large to pass through the dock entrance.

The facilities available at Brentford Dock depot were improved in 1932 by the provision of two electric cranes on the riverside wharf. The new cranes were of the semi-portal level-luffing type. They spanned two sidings and were borne on a travelling leg on the riverside and an elevated gantry rail on the inner side. They could traverse practically the full length of the river frontage. The cranes could be worked at any jib radius between a maximum of 50ft and a minimum of 20ft, the maximum height of lift when working with a grab being 35ft from rail level. The gear also permitted loads to be dealt with at 35ft below rail level. The hoisting speed of the cranes with a full load was 200ft/min, while they luffed at 150ft/min. They could travel at 50ft/min. They were made by Messrs Cowans, Sheldon & Co. These cranes were equipped with grabs having a maximum coal lifting capacity of 25 cwts, made by Messrs J.Westwood & Co.

Three electric capstans of the hand-lever type, fitted with wire ropes, and capable of moving twelve 20-ton trucks at 100ft/min were provided to facilitate the movement of trucks under the cranes and along the river front. The sidings serving the river front were also improved.

1932 IMPROVEMENTS AT KINGSWEAR

The GWR's facilities at Kingswear on the River Dart consisted of a timber wharf and jetty, equipped with four steam cranes, fitted with buckets, and one hand crane. In 1932, these facilities were considerably improved. The jetty was demolished, and the wharf reconstructed in reinforced concrete for a length of 360ft, and advanced several feet into the river, affording a deeper

Plate 86 The GWR's riverside wharf at Brentford Docks, showing the two new electric traversing cranes and lighters alongside the wharf.

Plate 87 One of the new 3-ton electric cranes at Brentford Docks, showing the grab for unloading coal. The travelling leg on the riverside and the elevated gantry on the inner side can also be seen.

and more satisfactory berth. The steam cranes were replaced by two 3-ton electric cranes, equipped with grabs, to speed up the discharge of vessels using the wharf, at which large quantities of coal, etc were regularly imported, for conveyance by railway to inland destinations. The cranes worked on a 7ft gauge track, with a standard gauge siding between, and they could traverse the full length of the wharf. They could work at any jib radius between a maximum of 35ft and minimum of 15ft. The maximum height of lift when working with a grab was 20ft above rail level, while loads could also be dealt with 30ft below rail level.

The reconstruction of the wharf was undertaken by Industrial Construction Co Ltd, the new cranes were made and erected by The Clyde Crane & Engineering Co Ltd, and the grabs were supplied by Priestman.

1932 RECONSTRUCTION OF EIGN BRIDGE

The then eighty-year-old Eign bridge, carrying the GWR double line over the River Wye, about a mile south of Hereford, was rebuilt in 1932. The old bridge consisted of three spans of about 43ft 6in, 72ft 0in and 43ft 6in. The new structure, which was the same overall length, was built in two clear spans of 79ft 6in each, by the provision of a new pier in the centre of the river. The reconstruction was of interest on account of the method adopted in handling the new superstructure.

In reconstructing underbridges of similar dimensions it was usual to resort to single-line working at the site for a period of some weeks, and this necessitated laying-down of running junctions on either side of the bridge, and the provision of appropriate signalling arrangements. In the case of the Eign bridge, the existence of suitable siding accommodation in the vicinity allowed an alternative means. A siding at Rotherwas, although the property of

Plate 88 Discharging a cargo with one of the new electric cranes at the GWR's new wharf at Kingswear.

Plate 89 The Eign bridge near Hereford showing the old structure which had existed for eighty years being dismantled. The columns in the river which had to be pulled over can be seen.

the Government, was placed at the service of the engineer for about two months, and this place was utilised for assembling the whole of the new superstructure which would have to carry the down line. This consisted of two spans of 83ft 9in each, overall, weighing 86 tons. These spans were rivetted up, and bitumastic floor covering was laid complete, ready for the reception of ballast and permanent way. Then, it was arranged with the Traffic Department for a long week-end occupation of both lines at the site of the bridge. This commenced at 2300 on Saturday night, and the demolition of the old superstructure carrying the down line was pushed forward vigorously. At the same time, two 36-ton cranes were engaged at Rotherwas in loading up the two complete spans. One of them was loaded on the GWR 120-ton CROCODILE L, and the other on a borrowed LMSR 80-ton vehicle. These were exceptional 'out-of-gauge' loads, the maximum height above rail being 18ft 9in and the overall width 15ft 8in; but the only obstruction of the passage of the load from Rotherwas to the bridge site was the starting signal for Rotherwas box. This signal was therefore taken down and re-erected after the loads had passed.

By noon the following day the old superstructure carrying the down line had been removed and loaded up for transit, leaving only the old cast-iron columns in the river to be dealt with. These had to be got out of the way before the new superstructure could be placed in position. They were dealt with by tipping them over into the river bed, from where they were later recovered and broken up. The columns offered considerable resistance to overturning. Each of them required a pull of nearly 100 tons, by a steel hawser, one end of which was attached to the head of the cast-iron column and the other to a winding engine anchored in a neighbouring field. By 2200 on Sunday night the two new spans had been placed in position. The completion of the floor at the junction of these spans was then proceeded with, and four hours later at 0200 on Monday, the new ballast and permanent way had been laid, and the down line ready for restoration to traffic. During a similar week-end occupation of the two lines on the following Sunday, the remainder of the old bridge, carrying the up line, was removed and the new superstructure substituted.

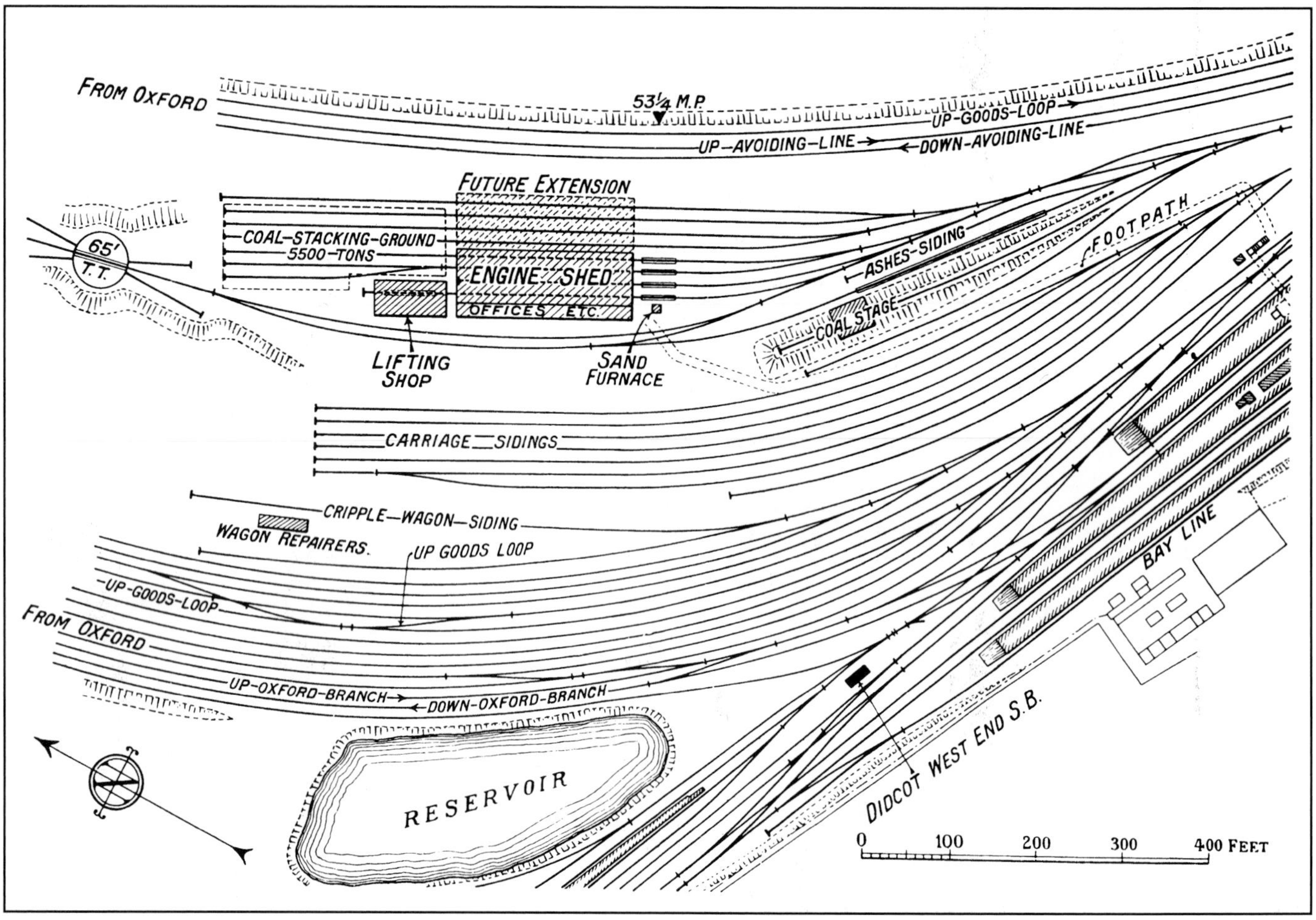

Map 12. The new locomotive depot at Didcot. Visible at the top right are the steps from the subway approach under the station. The future extension to the engine shed was never built.

Plate 90 The new Didcot engine shed, general view showing the water tank and coaling ramp on the left, and the shed itself on the right.

Plate 91 The new Great Western Railway Engine Shed at Didcot.

Plate 92 An interior view of the new four-road engine shed at Didcot, offices and stores on the left hand side behind the brick wall.

Plate 93 The engine lifting shop of the new shed, showing an engine undergoing repair.

1932 IMPROVED LOCOMOTIVE ACCOMMODATION AT DIDCOT

Originally there was a small broad-gauge locomotive shed at Didcot, opened in 1857. This was replaced by a three-road standard-gauge shed, of brick walls and a timber pitched slate-covered roof, with a continuous smoke vent running along the peak, sited alongside the station on the northern side.

The GWR used the Development (Loan Guarantees and Grants) Act of 1929 to bring improved locomotive accomodation to Didcot, which was sited further away from the station, this leaving the old site open for more freight sidings. The scheme included a

Plate 94 The engine shed stores at the new Didcot depot.

new four-road straight engine shed, 210ft by 67ft, designed to accommodate sixteen engines, with office and stores accommodation 210ft by 15ft alongside. Other features included a new lifting shop 84ft by 42ft complete with a 50-ton overhead engine hoist, together with a typical ramped approach to a coal stage 43ft by 36ft, with overhead water tank 44ft by 36ft with a capacity of 74,250 gallons serving water cranes in front of the shed, and a new boiler-washing apparatus and sand-drying plant.

1932 LONDON LORRY REPAIR SHOP

The rapid growth of the GWR fleet of road motor vehicles in London necessitated the organisation by the Road Transport Department of a comprehensive maintenance scheme. At this time, there were over 500 motor vehicles covering over 70,000 miles per week. For many years there had been a small repair shop at Alfred Road, Westbourne Park. In 1932, this was incorporated into a greatly expanded structure 230ft by 120ft, the building being steel-framed, lit by roof and side windows, and largely free of roof supports in the floor.

At one side of the repair shop, there were ten inspection pits approached by a short flight of steps at each end. Each pit was lit by two electric lamps, which could be swivelled to focus on any point in the pit area. Work benches were provided for the fitters. Underground ducts were provided to carry off exhaust fumes from the lorries. When it was required to run the engine of a lorry, its exhaust was connected by a flexible pipe to one of the many ducts, an electric

Plate 95 The Road Transport Department repair shop at Alfred Road, Paddington. The structure in the centre of the picture is the foreman's office (upper floor) and tool room (ground floor).

Plate 96 The Traeth Bach Viaduct at Penrhyndeudraeth in North Wales, as reconstructed.

Plate 97 A section of the Traeth Bach Viaduct, showing the continuous timber outside guard along the track, the fence using old signal rodding, and the public highway alongside.

fan started and the fumes were sent high into the air outside the shop.

The maintenance scheme was as follows. Every motor vehicle in service was brought to the repair shop once every six weeks for inspection, and every two years for a complete overhaul. The inspection was to ensure that the vehicles were in good running order and to carry out any necessary adjustments, and normally was completed in eight hours. For inspections, each lorry was marked with a letter A, B, C, D, E or F, corresponding to one of the six successive inspection weeks, and a number 1, 2, 3, 4 or 5 indicating a day of the week, Monday to Friday. By this means, everyone knew when any vehicle was due for its inspection. A record sheet was issued after every inspection, showing what work had been done on the vehicle and by whom. The overhaul enabled the repair and/or renewal of parts, as well as a general repainting, and normally took about a fortnight. Emergency work was done as and when required.

Repairs and repainting of horse-drawn vehicles were also carried out in this shop since it was rebuilt. A spray-painting plant was added a year or so later. This repair shop was open day and night, being responsible at night for dealing with emergency calls for the whole London area. Around 6,000 gallons of petrol were issued weekly. Work was carried out to substitute pneumatic for solid tyres in the first two years or so, by which time the conversion was practically complete. An air-compressing plant was installed for the inflation of lorry tyres, as well as pumping lubricating oil and operating a sand blast for cleaning sparking plugs (because of carbon deposits from the rudimentary type of petrol used in those days, sparking plugs had to be cleaned regularly). A range of machine tools was provided, driven by an electric motor through line shafting. Portable gantries were provided for lifting parts. Other equipment included a battery charging plant, sparking plug testing apparatus, oxy-acetylene welding plant, stores, tool room and offices.

1932 RECONSTRUCTION OF TRAETH BACH VIADUCT

Traeth Bach Viaduct, near Penrhyndeudraeth, on the Central Wales division, was completely reconstructed, with the removal and replacement of practically half of the piles in the frames carrying the superstructure. This viaduct, which was wholly of timber, was 435ft long, and consisted on 22 spans of 19ft each. The reconstruction work was carried out without interference to traffic, either rail or road, and wholly on week-days.

Traeth Bach Viaduct, locally known as Briwet bridge, was constructed in 1865. A ferry previously existed at this point, and a condition of transfer of the land to the railway company was that a roadway should be constructed on the viaduct and maintained by the railway company in perpetuity; the tolls, however, becoming the property of the land (and ferry) owners. These conditions remained when this work was carried out, and the repair work included the reconstruction of the superstructure of the road portion of the viaduct.

Plate 98 The old bridge, looking down the River Towy.

Plate 99 The new bridge, looking in the same general direction but a slightly different angle.

During the work, opportunity was taken to increase the strength of the structure to carry the GWR 'blue' classification of locomotives. Work commenced in May 1931, and no more than twelve men were employed upon it at any period. About 180 tons of timber in beams and decking were removed, and some 250 tons of new creosoted pitch pine were used in the reconstruction. The rails were carried on longitudinal timbers with a continuous timber outside viaduct guard. The level of the rails was raised 5in as a result of the reconstruction. Some 6000ft of old signal rodding were used to provide new fences. An occupation key-box and a telephone were installed by the Signal Department, rendering it possible to obtain possession of the line for short periods, as required, and without any delay.

1932 RECONSTRUCTION OF BRIDGE OVER THE RIVER TOWY

The original bridge over the River Towy at Carmarthen on the Aberystwyth line was built in 1858-60 for the Carmarthen and Cardigan Railway. This old bridge consisted of four spans of wrought-iron plate girders, supported on masonry abutments and timber pile piers, each pier consisting of two groups of six 12in by 12in piles cross-braced. Originally the floor was of timber, but this was replaced with steel cross girders around 1900 to meet the demands of heavier traffic. The ravages of time and the constantly increased axle loads of rolling stock made the construction of a new structure imperative.

The new structure was constructed parallel to, and on the up-stream side of, the original bridge, and was designed with provision for future doubling if desired. The new abutments were of mass concrete on piled foundations, and the piers were steel cylinders, sunk to a maximum depth of 27ft below the river bed, and filled with concrete. The superstructure was steel throughout, manufactured by the GWR's regular supplier, Fairfield Shipbuilding & Engineering Co Ltd of Chepstow. The new bridge had four spans of about 80ft. When the abutments were completed, the eight main girders (the heaviest weighing 32 tons) were despatched by special trains from the factory to the site, and off-loaded from the old bridge, by two steam cranes, into their respective positions in about nine hours.

Consequent upon the new alignment of the bridge, considerable alterations to the permanent way and connections at each end were necessary, and advantage was taken of this to remodel, improve and extend the facilities at the adjoining Carmarthen station, which was then rapidly developing as the largest railway centre in West Wales. Increased passenger and milk platform accommodation was provided, new carriage cleaning and other sidings were built, and extensive signalling alterations and improvements made.

1932 INSTALLATION OF COLOUR LIGHT SIGNALLING BETWEEN PADDINGTON AND SOUTHALL

Paddington station, before the installation of colour light signalling, required four mechanically-operated signal boxes, with a total of 214 working levers, divided as follows; Paddington Arrival 70, Paddington Departure 65, Bishop's Road 26 and Westbourne Bridge 53. After the installation of colour light signalling, it had three all-electric boxes with a total of 286 working levers, made up of Paddington Arrival (which incorporated the former Bishop's Road box) 143 levers, Paddington Departure 76 and Westbourne Bridge 67. Of course, the track layout had been altered and enlarged in the meanwhile, and Bishop's Road had become part of Paddington station.

On the four mainly passenger lines between Paddington and Southall, the existing semaphore signals were replaced by colour light signals. The type of signal used was that known as 'searchlight' which gave a powerful light easily picked up from the footplate. The indications given by the previously existing semaphores were reproduced light for light, so that the same indication was now given by day and by night, instead of, as formerly, semaphores by day and lights by night. The signals between Paddington and Southall therefore remained the same as those which had been there before and had always been regarded as satisfactory.

The searchlight signal, as illustrated, consisted of a multi-coloured spectacle somewhat similar to, but smaller than, the spectacle of an ordinary semaphore signal. This miniature spectacle moved in front of a concentrated filament lamp combined with a special optical mirror. Normally, a red or yellow light was projected through a clear lens in front of the spectacle, the light being changed to green when the spectacle was moved, through operation of an electrical control, when the signal lever was reversed.

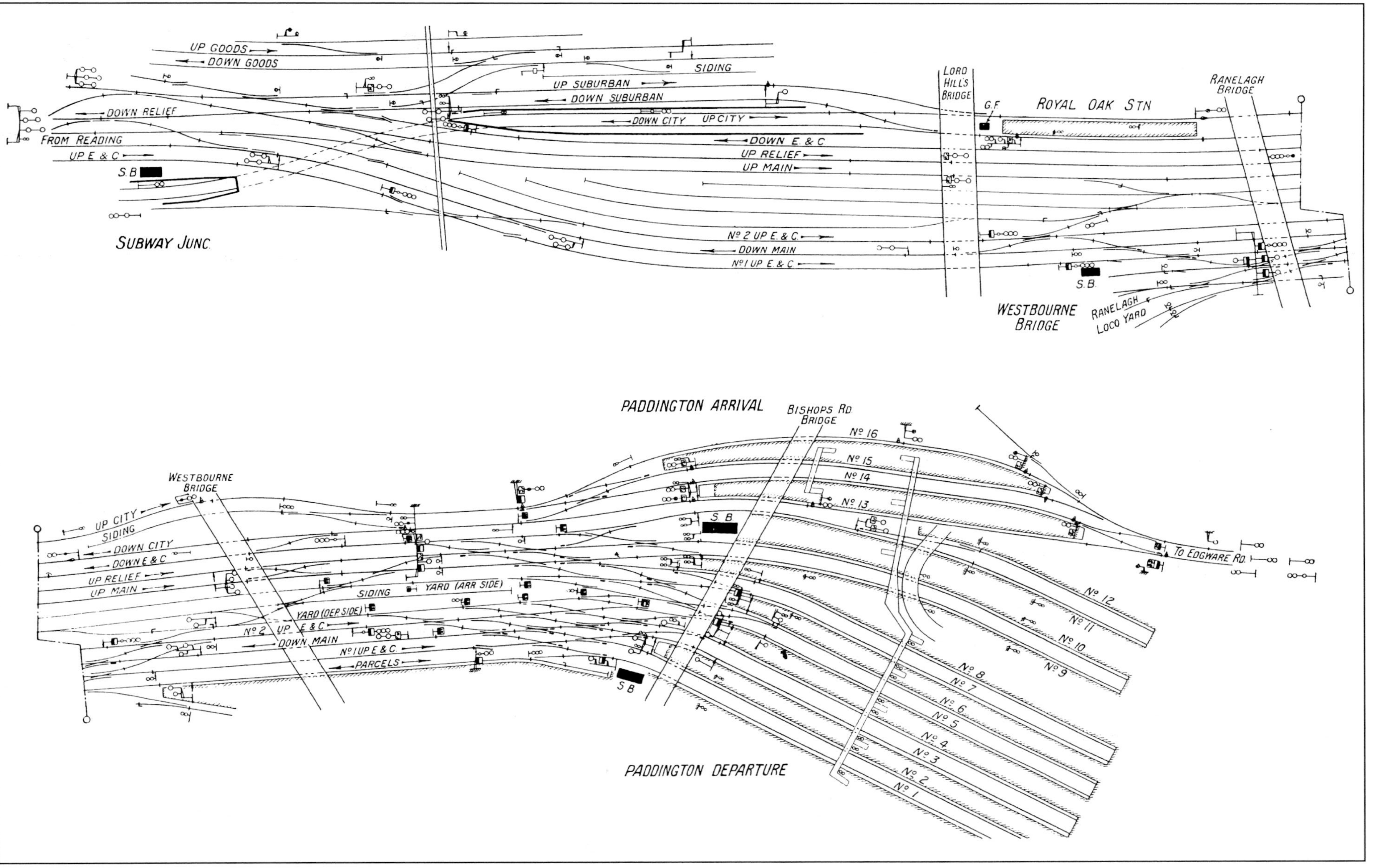

Map 13. Signal diagram of Paddington power signalling installed in 1933.

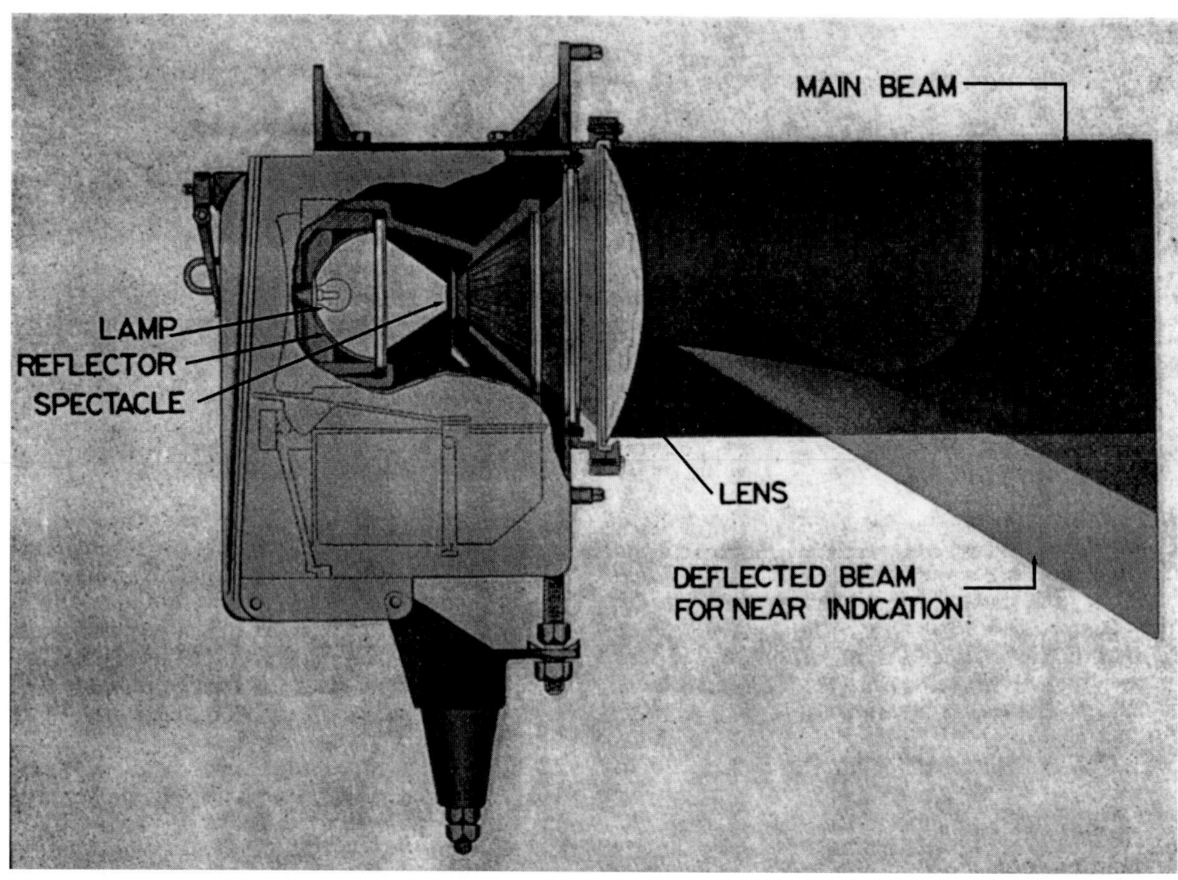

Plate 100 A diagram of the 'searchlight' signal of the type installed between Paddington and Southall.

The spectacle fell by gravity to show a red or yellow light when the lever was put back to 'normal'. Each signal was fitted with a large black circular disc to provide a suitable background for the light beam. In addition, the beam was protected from the sun by a hood projecting forward from the back disc.

Plate 101 Paddington Departure signal box and a route indicator.

There being no mechanical wires between the signal box and signals, the necessary detection of points was effected electrically. Repeaters were provided in the signal box to give a visual indication as to whether or not the lamps were lit, and to show the position of the spectacles, that is to say, red, yellow or green. These repeaters were also used to interlink the signals with the block, so that the relative home and distant signals could be 'proved' at danger at the moment 'line clear' was returned to the signal box in the rear. The distant signal showed a green light only when its relative home and starting signals were showing green lights. The automatic train control ramps provided at each distant signal were also incapable of being energised to give a 'clear' indication in the cab of the engine unless the distant signal showed a green light and the lever controlling the signal was 'reverse'.

The four lines were continuously track circuited, the tracks being used to replace the signals to 'danger' and to lock the levers controlling the signals. Starting signals were also locked in the

Plate 102 Interior of the new Paddington Arrival signal box.

Plate 103 Paddington up home starting signal gantry and cable gallery on the wall of the goods depot.

Plate 104 Signals and train stop at Royal Oak.

'normal' position until 'line clear' was received from the signal box in advance. A signal put to danger by the operation of the track circuit was incapable of again showing a green light until the controlling signal lever had been put back to 'normal' and pulled again.

As discussed, the locking frame in each of the three new boxes had its interlocking electrically actuated; that at Westbourne Bridge was the first on the GWR to be so treated. The signal levers were approach locked, and so an automatic time release was given by means of thermal relays. They could be restored at any time, but normal indication locks were provided to ensure the 'danger' aspect of the signal. The point levers were of the pull-through type, that is, they did not allow for the check locking that used to be thought necessary in power signalling. The signals detect each point in the route, whether it was a facing, trailing or trap point. Normal and reverse track locking and sectional release route locking were provided on all point levers. There were the usual repeaters for all signals and points, and lights showing when the electric locking was free were provided on all track-controlled signals and point levers. Calling-on and shunt signals were controlled by means of push buttons, interlocked with the corresponding stop point lever. The function of the push button was to release the track locking on the signal lever and to select the signal circuit when the lever was pulled.

Route indicators, mostly of the compartment type, were used. Two indicators of the 'music hall' type were fitted on the up main and relief inner home gantry signal, as there was a large number of platform destinations to indicate. All route indicating ground signals were made up in one case. The engine and carriage line signals were four-aspect, showing green for clear, yellow for caution, and red for stop, and an automatic calling-on signal was provided if the section ahead of the signal was occupied. The calling-on signal took the form of a small green light which showed when the lever was pulled with the track circuits ahead of the signal occupied, and a short approach track circuit occupied in addition. In the case of the automatic signals on the carriage roads, this small green light was exhibited automatically when the necessary conditions were fulfilled.

Plate 105 A signal gantry at Southall East Junction, carrying the up main and up relief home signals.

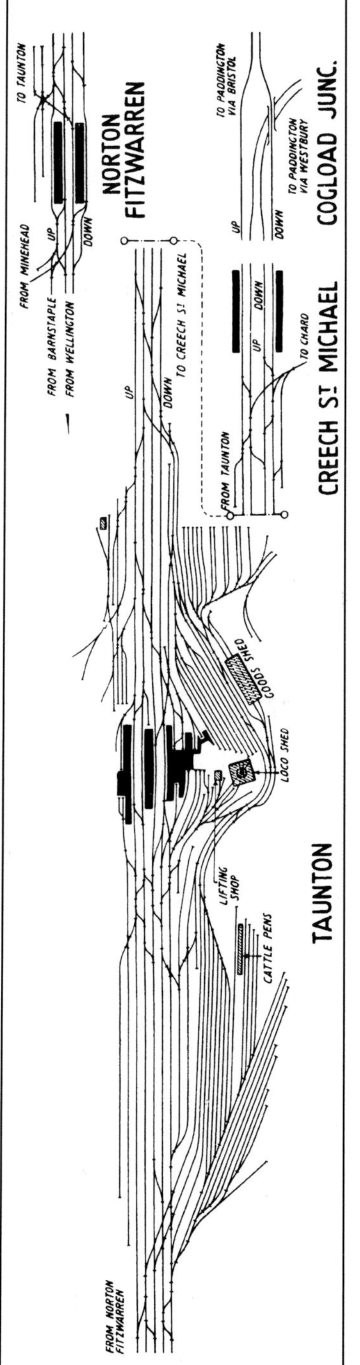

Map 14. Diagram of the quadrupling of the line between Cogload Junction and Norton Fitzwarren.

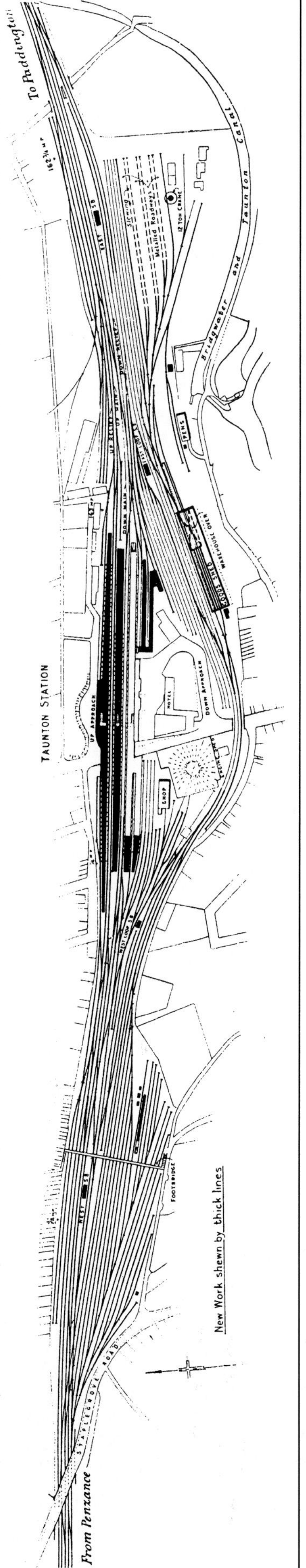

Map 15. Diagram of Taunton station and the lines in its vicinity, showing the new engine shed and goods shed. New work is shown by thick lines.

Calling-on, warning and shunt signals on the passenger roads took the form of an illuminated stencil representing a small semaphore arm with a 'C', 'W' or 'S' as required. These signals were normally not illuminated.

On the electrified Hammersmith and City lines train stops worked in conjunction with all stop signals which were the multiple lens type. Levers were provided in the locking frame for converting the controlled signals on the electrified section into automatic signals. The circuits for these signals were arranged for train stop proving.

The point machines were of DC type and were fed from a 120 volt 200 ampere-hour battery. On the arrival side of the station, owing to lack of space, a special gallery was built along the goods shed wall to carry the cables and apparatus cases. Duplicate power supplies were provided, and both AC and DC ring mains were provided in the yard to guard against cable failures.

The searchlight type colour lights installed between Paddington and Southall (and in other similar schemes carried out around this period on the GWR) differed from the searchlight type signals installed on other railways, inasmuch as what might be regarded as the distant-signal indication was retained and was not, as on other railways, combined in the aspects of the stop signal. There were, thus, upper and lower light units; the upper had two aspects of red and green, and the lower had two aspects of yellow or green. The advantage claimed by the GWR for this departure from the principles to be found elsewhere was that the indications given by the semaphore signals, and to which GWR train crews were accustomed, were retained.

1932 RECONSTRUCTION WORK AT TAUNTON

Another major scheme undertaken by the GWR in conjunction with the Development (Loan Guarantees and Grants) Act of 1929 was the reconstruction of Taunton passenger and goods stations, the enlargement and modernisation of the locomotive depot, and the quadrupling of the lines from Cogload Junction to Norton Fitzwarren. This work took over two years, but was completed in 1932.

Trains to and from the West, via Westbury and Bristol, all converged

Plate 106   Taunton West junction, showing the goods lines leading off to the right.

Plate 107   Norton Fitzwarren, as rebuilt to a four-line station with two island platforms.

Plate 108   The road side of Norton Fitzwarren station building.

at Cogload Junction and Norton Fitzwarren, while at Taunton, which was the junction station for Ilfracombe, Minehead and Chard, there was a very large exchange between local and through trains, for both passenger and merchandise traffic. The growing popularity of the West of England as a holiday resort naturally increased traffic on these lines.

The quadrupling of the line extended over seven miles and involved the building or reconstruction of sixteen bridges, the making of a large number of culverts, the excavation of 140,000 cubic yards of material to form embankments, and the erection of seven new signal boxes. The outstanding feaure was the provision of the flyover at Cogload Junction, which is described separately.

Taunton passenger station was almost completely rebuilt. The new station consisted of four main line and seven bay line platforms, the former varying from 1400ft to 1200ft in length. These alterations involved the widening and lengthening by 50ft of the bridge carrying the railway over Kingston Road. The 'all-over' roof of the old station was replaced by 'umbrella' type verandahs covering each platform. The footbridge was replaced by a subway 140ft long and 15ft wide, from which access was provided to all platforms by means of stairs and luggage lifts. A new booking hall was constructed on the approach road level at the north end of the subway, adjoining the up main platform, while on the down side, the booking hall and parcels office were enlarged. Adjoining a new block of station buildings on the up side, commodious refreshment and dining rooms were provided; a refreshment room was also installed on the island platform.

The goods station was enlarged to nearly double its previous capacity and equipped with modern mechanical appliances for handling merchandise. The two platforms in the new shed were connected by movable bridges, and the berthing space for road vehicles considerably augmented. A spacious new warehouse, 150ft by 60ft, was erected over the west end of the shed, which was equipped with electric lifts and hoists. A 12 ton crane was installed in the yard, together with improved cattle pens.

Linked to the line quadrupling between Cogload Junction and Norton Fitzwarren were various track

Plate 109 The new entrance hall and booking hall on the up side at Taunton, showing the widened approach with a fine vintage taxi.

improvements at Wellington, Sampford Peverell, Tiverton Junction, Cullompton and Stoke Canon on the line between Norton Fitzwarren and Exeter.

1932 MODERNISATION OF THE WOLVERHAMPTON LOCOMOTIVE WORKS

The GWR locomotive works at Stafford Road, Wolverhampton, were originally built in 1858. From time to time, they had been extended, with the result that the general layout of the plant, which had spread on each side of the main road, and at two different levels, had become inconvenient to operate. The GWR therefore took advantage of the financial assistance afforded by the Developments (Loan Guarantees and Grants) Act of 1929 to undertake a complete reorganisation of these works. This started in late 1929 and was completed in 1932, resulting in an excellent layout of workshops, fully equipped with the latest appliances.

The accompanying plan shows the new layout, but it also brings out the difficulties and restrictions of the particular site, intersected as it was by public highways, main railway routes of both the GWR and LMSR and adjoining property. At this works, no new building of locomotives was undertaken, the work being entirely that of repair. The locomotives dealt with were for the most part of the lightest types, but a number of King class locomotives were stationed at Wolverhampton for the London expresses, and the equipment was adequate for dealing with light or intermediate repairs on these large engines.

In the reconstruction, an entirely new building, incorporating erecting, machine and wheel shops, was built. This was of impressive size, being 450ft long and 196ft wide, arranged in three bays, two forming the erecting shop and the third the machine and wheel shop. Each bay of the erecting shop was equipped with two 50-ton overhead electric gantry cranes, and in the machine bay there were in addition two 6-ton overhead electric cranes. Outside, at the south end of the shop, there was a 33ft electric traverser and beyond this a 6-ton electric gantry crane of 75ft span, extending over the 'heavy' storage space. Next to this was the tank shop, 104ft by 35ft, which was fitted with a 7-ton overhead electric crane. Beyond this again was a light hand-operated traverser serving the wheel storage sidings.

At the north end, an engine weightbridge was provided, capable of weighing the heaviest locomotives, an examination house 70ft by 20ft with a 1-ton overhead hand crane, and a scrap yard served by a light hand traverser. On the east side there was a boiler house containing two Lancashire boilers with automatic stokers for heating the shops. The old high level erecting

Plate 110 Another view of the new station entrance at Taunton on the up side.

Plate 111 The new booking hall on the up side.

Plate 112 The main line platforms at the reconstructed passenger station at Taunton.

Plate 113 A general view of the reconstructed station at Taunton, as seen from the London end.

Plate 114 The new up side platform and buildings at Taunton station.

Plate 115 Work in progress at Stoke Canon converting the station into a four-line station, in connection with the Norton Fitzwarren to Newton Abbot line improvements.

and wheel shops were converted into modern boiler, boiler testing and tube repairing shops, with two 25-ton overhead electric cranes in the boiler shop and a 2-ton overhead hand crane in the tube repairing shop. The old boiler shop was used to extend the foundry, in which a 10-ton overhead electric crane was installed, and also to form new copper and tinsmiths' shops, which were formerly on the low level. The remaining portion was used for the millwrights' shop, in which pits and a traverser were installed for the repair of traveling cranes. Part of the old high level machine shop was converted into a carpenters' and pattern-makers' shop, while the remaining portion was used for the pneumatic and hydraulic power plants, electric power substation and general office stores.

Engines for repair, on arrival at Stafford Road, were put into the sidings until such time as they could be brought into the repair shops, where they were dealt with in accordance with the usual categories of light, intermediate or general repairs. The engines were sent from the various depots throughout the system to the works on receipt of an advice from Swindon, and all classes were dealt with, with the exception of the large express passenger engines. The engines came in at the south end of the shop, where the necessary stripping was carried out, and in the case of a general repair, where the boiler was removed from the frame and sent direct to the boiler shop located on the south side of the Victoria goods line, where a special track was laid for the purpose. The general layout plan shows also the large running sheds from which, due to the restrictions of space, there was a somewhat circuitous exit for locomotives to and from the main line.

1933 REPLACEMENT OF PONSANOOTH, RINGWELL AND CARNON VIADUCTS

The railway from Plymouth to Truro, which opened in 1859 and was extended to Falmouth in 1863, traversed many cross valleys of depth too great to be economically filled by embankments, and it was necessary to build structures capable of carrying the lines across the valleys. Excluding the Royal Albert Bridge at Saltash, for economy timber viaducts were used

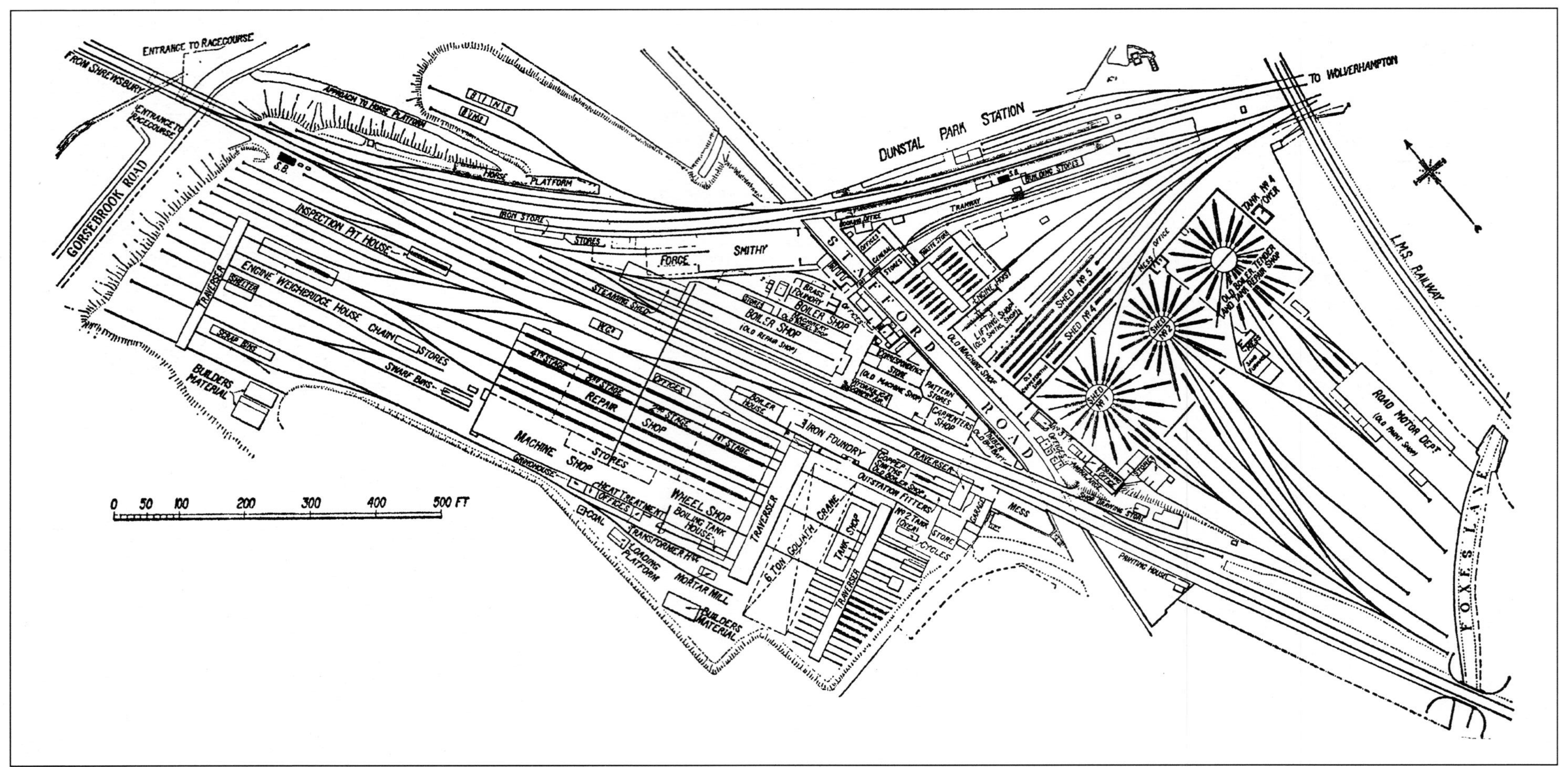

Map 16. Wolverhampton Works. Layout of shops and running sheds as modernized.

Plate 116 New locomotive repair shops under construction at Wolverhampton.

and forty-two timber viaducts were placed on the 65 miles of track between Plymouth and Falmouth and ten on the 26 miles between Truro and Penzance. These viaducts, although similar in general design, varied in detail, and could be divided into two classes. The first type had masonry piers where good foundations were to be had, built from 60 to 66ft centres apart and carried up to a level about 35ft below that of the rails. From the tops of these piers three sets of struts radiated fanwise, four struts in each set making twelve on each pier, the struts held together by horizontal and diagonal braces of timber. On the top of the struts rested the main carrying beams in three runs for the single line of railway. The top width of the viaduct varied from 15 to 16½ft, according to the construction of the parapets. The second type of structure depended on timber trusses to carry the decking, and these trusses were for the most part supported on timber piles which formed the piers. This type of construction was

Plate 117 The exterior of the newly-rebuilt GWR Wolverhampton Stafford Road Works.

Plate 118 Inside the locomotive repair works, 50-ton overhead gantry cranes moving an 0-6-0PT to another position.

adopted where the railway had to cross tidal creeks, and deposits of mud of depths up to 70ft existed. The usual span for this type of structure was 40ft, the height ranging from 40 to 100ft. Over the years, these timber viaducts were replaced by more durable structures, capable of carrying heavier axle-loads. Ponsanooth, Ringwell and Carnon timber viaducts were the last viaducts on the Falmouth Brach to be replaced, except Collegewood (dealt with separately).

Ponsanooth viaduct was the highest on the Falmouth branch and the fourth highest in Cornwall, and carried the line across the lower valley of the River Kennall. There were eight buttressed piers, incorporating so-called gothic openings which were then filled in, six spaced at 66ft centres and one at each end at 63ft together with an embankment pier at 43ft centres. The usual wooden superstructure was then placed on top of the piers. This viaduct thus had 11 spans and was 650ft long. Work was started in 1927 for a double-line masonry replacement, scaffolding being used for the first time in the building of the new piers (hitherto, men and materials were just lifted to the tops of the piers). The new structure was brought into use in 1930.

Ringwell viaduct was a relatively small structure built in 1861 with three visible masonry piers, of section 22ft by 6ft, at 66ft centres, with a landward fan at each end on additional piers that were buried in embankment slopes. The six spans gave a length of 370 ft, with height of 72ft. In 1932 it was decided to replace this viaduct by an embankment by tipping some 70,000 cubic yards of filling material, with the provision of a 6ft culvert. This method of replacement was economically possible because of the short length of the structure and the contour of the adjacent ground. This was opened to traffic in September 1933.

On a falling gradient of 1 in 68 within a short distance of leaving Ringwell viaduct, the line faced the crossing of a deep valley across Restronguet Creek, which was a part tidal inlet in which silt accumulated from mine workings higher up the valley. This was not an ideal foundation for a viaduct expected to be nearly 100ft high. After due consideration, Carnon viaduct was built on buttressed piers. At each location, a pair of cast iron cylinders were sunk, each 16ft in diameter, cast in segments and bolted together. They were weighted and sunk through the sand and silt until they reached bedrock. The sand was excavated and water pumped out. This enabled foundations to be built within each cylinder, 13ft wide and 8ft thick, up to the surface level. The cylinders were then withdrawn by hydraulic jacks and an arch turned to connect the two sections and form a base on which each pier was then constructed.

Plate 119 The new erecting shop of the GWR Stafford Road Works, Wolverhampton, showing the two bays used for locomotives in course of repair and reconstruction.

Plate 120 Centre bay of main locomotive repair works, showing progress of repairs, looking north.

Plate 121 The third bay of the main locomotive shop, comprising the machine and wheel shop. Modern for its time, but nowadays the unprotected line shafting with belt drives to the machine tools looks old-fashioned and dangerous.

This arrangement applied to the central five piers, the remaining piers being formed on conventional masonry foundations. From the tops of the piers, the usual wooden superstructure was built. This viaduct had twelve spans and was 766ft long. In 1932, it was decided to replace the wooden structure by a nine arch masonry replacement, which was built on the southern side of the original. This was opened for traffic in June 1933.

1933 SOUTH WALES DOCKS IMPROVEMENTS

By acquiring the South Wales docks, following upon the passage of the Railways Act of 1921, the GWR

Plate 122 Machine shop bay looking north.

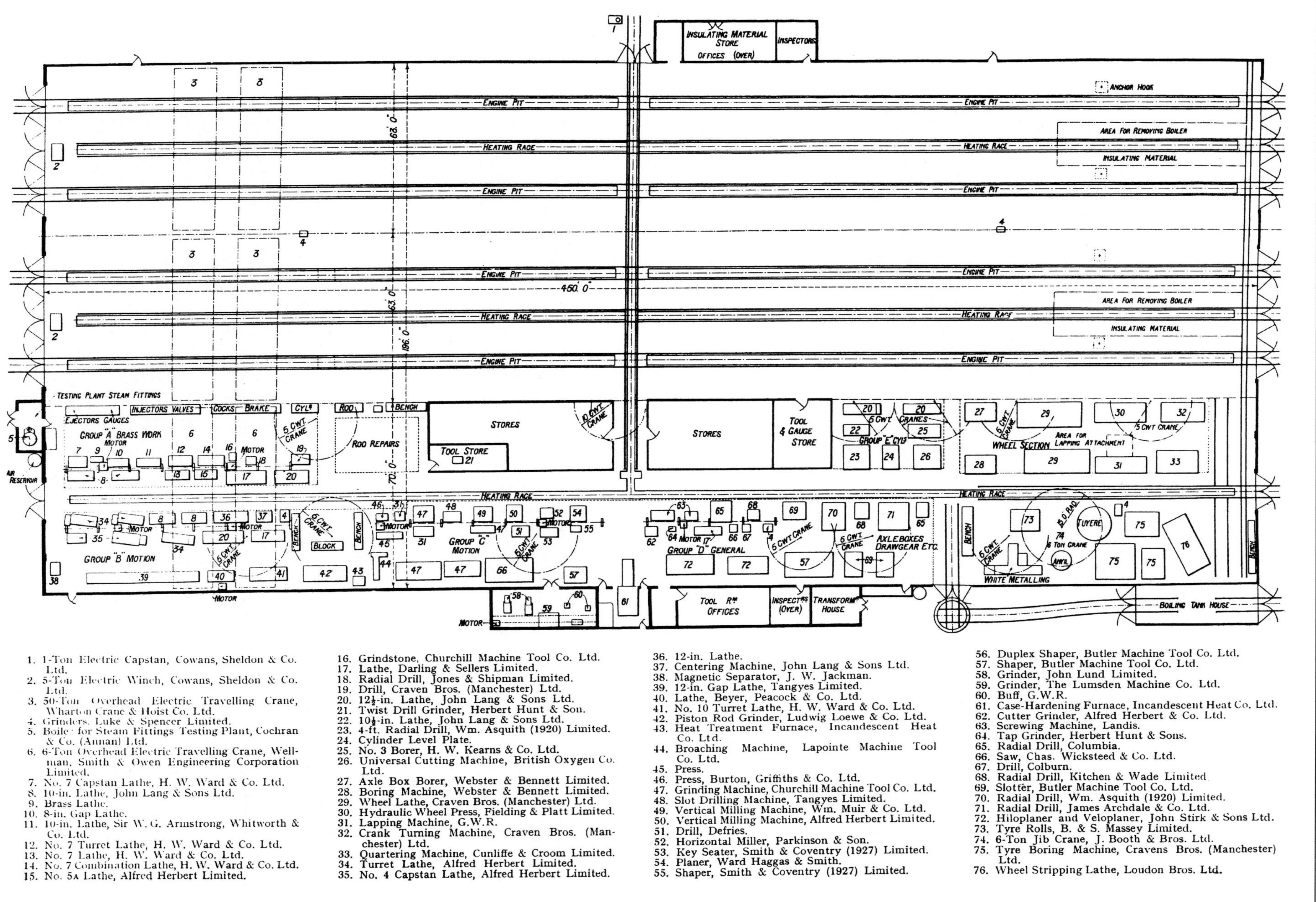

Map 17. General plan of new locomotive erecting and machine shops at Wolverhampton, showing the disposition of equipment.

Plate 123 Wolverhampton locomotive repair works 6-ton gantry crane over inspection yard.

Plate 124 The former Brunel timber viaduct at Ponsanooth in Cornwall.

Plate 125 The new masonry viaduct built at Ponsanooth to replace the old timber structure.

Plate 126 The Ringwell Brunel timber viaduct 370ft long, which was replaced by an embankment.

added a new feature of transport to their existing extensive railway undertaking. The yearly imports and exports at the principal South Wales ports of Cardiff, Swansea, Newport, Barry, Port Talbot and Penarth then normally reached about 35 million tons. These six ports handled the coal exports of the South Wales coalfields. Interspersed among the various collieries were hundreds of iron, steel and other works producing for the home and export markets, while in the background connected by rail routes with the South Wales ports were the manufacturing areas of the Midlands. Thus, the South Wales ports met the trading and other needs of a large and important part of industrial Great Britain.

In 1929, at the GWR AGM it was stated that the company would have to combat the consequences of the trade depression in those branches of industry upon which the GWR relied for so much of its traffic, namely coal, iron and steel. The South Wales ports suffered severely by this depression. The tonnage of the GWR's six principal ports in South Wales was

Plate 127 An aerial view of GWR Barry Docks showing the facilities existing there in 1928.

Plate 128 Aerial view of Cardiff Docks.

31½ millions in 1927, but this dropped to 29 millions in 1928. Taking both exports and imports together, the drop was nearly 3 million tons, with a loss of nearly £300,000, added to which was also a loss in railway revenue through traffic not passing. The bulk of these losses were represented by coal and coke shipments. Coal exports from South Wales in 1913 were 39 million tons, whereas by 1928 exports had dropped to 26½ million tons. Since 1923, no less than 117 coal mining pits had closed by 1928. These losses were due to domestic troubles in the coal industry, foreign competition and by coal being superseded by oil (for instance by the Royal Navy).

The GWR made determined attempts to use the various docks for traffic other than export coal, and some interesting developments took place. The equipment of the docks, throughout the coast from Newport to

Plate 129 An aerial view of Newport docks, looking north.

Plate 130 An aerial view of Port Talbot docks, looking south.

Swansea, had all been installed to deal almost exclusively with coal and indeed the traffic was so great and the congestion at times so severe that there would have been little chance of handling anything else. Of the South Wales docks, Swansea perhaps suffered the least, because there quickly developed a diversity of traffic through this port, as well as continued demand for export anthracite. Swansea benefitted as being a port for discharging of oil tankers, and the export of tin plate. In addition, many improvements were made at Swansea docks to facilitate trade, in particular in the years up to 1934.

The most distinctive feature of the hugh system of docks in South Wales, for which the GWR was responsible under the Railways Act of 1921, was the shipment of coal. In no other single district in the world had 38,899,474 tons of coal been shipped in one year, the stupendous figure to which the traffic attained at the South Wales docks in 1913. That was the record year, of course. While coal traffic never again reached such a figure, the GWR consistently followed a policy of reconstructing and improving the coal-shipping appliances, because by the early 1930s total shipments were still about 30 million tons a year.

The operations on shore were entirely under the control of the GWR at the ports of Barry, Cardiff, Newport, Penarth and Port Talbot, while at Swansea also the bulk of the coal was dealt with by the GWR's appliances, although at that port the LMSR had a few coal-shipping machines. At the smaller ports of Briton Ferry and Burry Port, the GWR controlled all the shipments.

The men who fed the coal trucks to the shipping appliances, and by means of these appliances loaded or 'tipped' the coal into the vessel were the "coal tippers". They were employees of the GWR. "Coal trimmers" worked on board the ships and were the employees of the shipowners. The work of the "trimmers" was to dispose of the coal in the holds so that the vessel should sail on an even keel, and it was to that end that they "trimmed" the coal. The tippers and the trimmers worked in two shifts, the first from 0700 to 1600 hours with a meal interval of an hour, and the second from 2030 to 0530 hours also with an hour's interval. On Saturdays, coal-shipping generally ceased at 1200 hours, only one shift being worked, but should it be possible for a vessel not completed by noon to finish loading by 1300, the extra hour was worked to enable the vessel to sail at the earliest moment after finishing, and so avoid detention in dock over the weekend.

The majority of the coal-shipping appliances at the ports were of the type called "hoists" or colloquially "tips". These appliances hoisted the loaded truck to a sufficient height above the quay level to enable it to be tipped towards the chute of the appliance. The height at which the chute was fixed above ground level was regulated by the height of the side of the vessel. However, at Port Talbot there were three conveyor-belt appliances. At these appliances the coal passed from the truck to a box or "hopper", and thence on to a moving belt which carried the coal to the chute. This type of appliance had certain advantages, but required a considerable area of suitable ground for its layout.

A gang of tippers consisted usually of four men, although at some appliances the number was five. Comprising a gang of four at an ordinary hoist would be the weighman, capstanman, cradleman and hoistman. The loaded wagons of coal were placed by the docks traffic-men into the roads feeding the hoist. There were two, three or at some of the newer hoists, even four, feeding roads for conducting the loaded wagons to each hoist. These feeding roads were "humped", that is the section nearest the hoist sloped downwards towards the weighing machine, at which point all the feeding roads converged. The locomotive bringing the coal forward for shipment propelled the "string" of wagons over the hump, towards the hoist. A sufficient number of brakes were put down to prevent the wagons from crashing into the hoist. Further locomotive

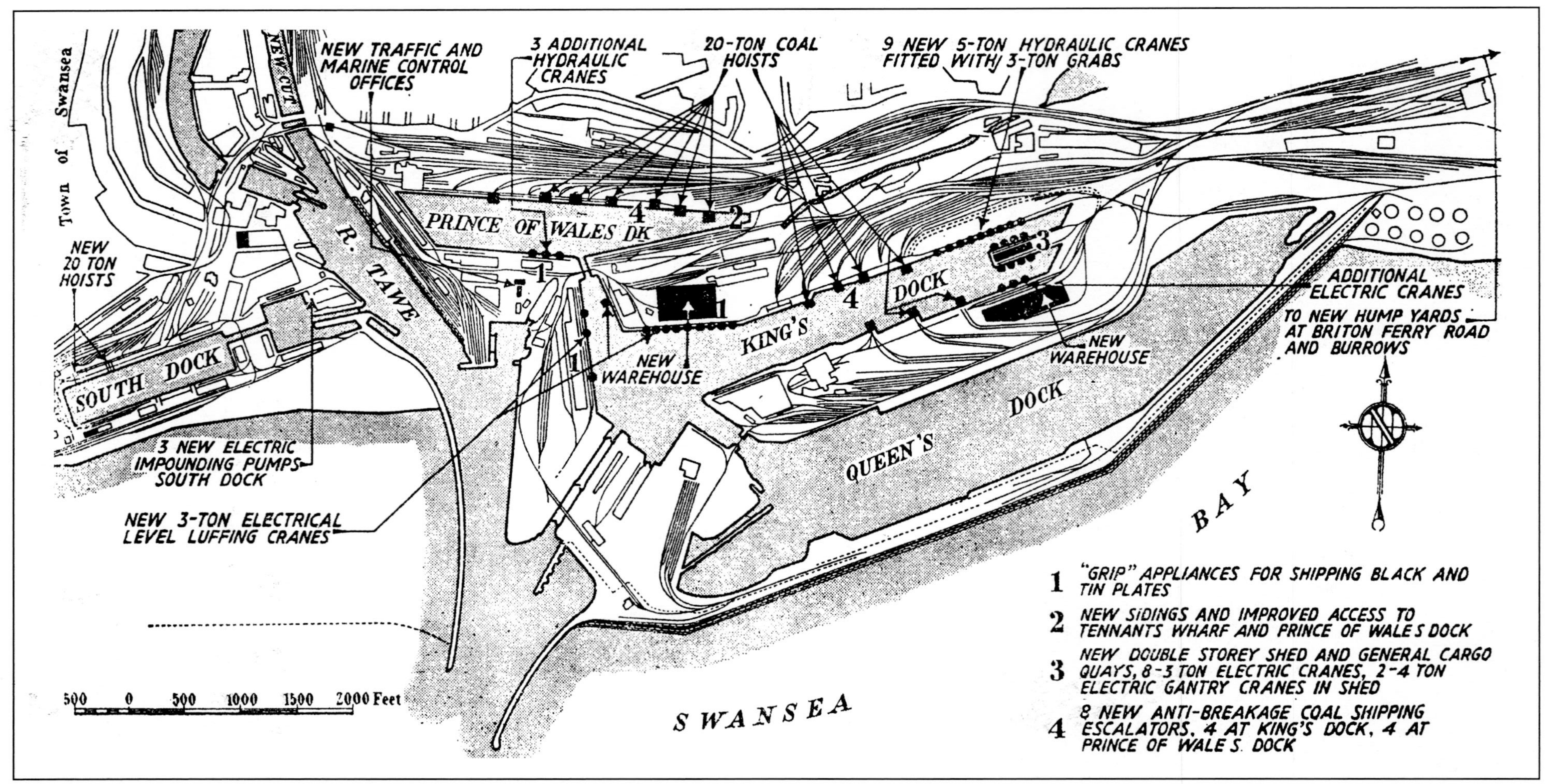

Map 18. Swansea docks showing the principal works completed in 1934.

Plate 131 The steamer "City of Christiana" at Newport Docks in 1928, taking a cargo of 3000 tons of steel rail sleepers for East Africa. About 1800 tons were from Guest, Keen & Nettlefolds of Dowlais and the remainder from The Ebbw Vale Coal, Iron and Steel Co of Ebbw Vale. The dock cranes can be seen, as well as some GKN wagons and one LNWR.

assistance was then only required when the wagons at the back of the run needed to be pushed over the hump. On some long roads there might be as many as 20 or 30 wagons to be shipped before such assistance was required.

The weighman walked alongside the wagons noting the numbers and the type of coal, according to the labels, making up his official record, variously termed "tipping invoice", "tip note" or "tip weigh slip". He had to make a separate slip for each type of coal. Having taken these details, and checked that the chute was in position and everything ready to start loading, he proceeded to bring down the coal. A few of the wagons were uncoupled, the brakes being released gradually so as to bring the leading wagons on towards the weighing machine. This work was usually done by the weighman, although he might be assisted to some extent by the capstanman. Before uncoupling wagons, he would check that sufficient brakes were put down on the wagons left in the road to prevent them from following down the slope.

In selecting the road from which the weighman took the next wagon, he had to have regard to any "mixing" instructions, the mixing of coal at shipment being a very important requirement of South Wales shippers. When the wagon had been brought to a stand on the weighing machine, the weighman recorded the gross weight. The official record provided for gross, tare and nett weights, but as the empty wagon was re-weighed after shipment, the weighman had to wait meantime until the new tare was obtained, before he could fill in the latter two columns. The gross weight having been ascertained, the weighman was finished, for the time being, with this wagon. The capstanman then took charge of it, attached his chain or rope, and by means of the hydraulic capstan, hauled the wagon the short distance from the weighing machine to a turntable just on the shore side of the hoist. This turntable was necessary to give the truck a direct run into the rails leading on to the hoist cradle. Sometimes, also, the wagon, if it happened to have one end-door only, and that end was to shoreward, had to be turned completely round, so as to present the end-door towards the ship. The turntable was operated by the capstanman, who ran the wagon into the hoist and on to the cradle thereof, with the help of his capstan and chain or rope.

The cradleman received the wagon on the cradle, which was roughly the equivalent of an ordinary lift floor without sides or roof. He then applied a "scotch" to prevent the wagon from running back. The operation of the movements of the cradle, and of all the machinery of the hoist itself, was under the control of the hoistman, who worked in the top-house, his cabin at the top of the structure, from the situation of which he was sometimes called the "topman" or "tophouseman". The cradleman, having safely scotched the wagon on the cradle, signalled the hoistman, and the latter raised the cradle, the cradleman travelling up on it at the side of the wagon, to the point where the "heel" of the chute was fixed. The end door of a coal wagon, as most people know, was hung by a steel bar, across the top, and fastened near the bottom, in some cases by two pins (one of either side of the wagon), and in other cases by a bar attached to the door which engaged with suitable catches on the ends of the sides of the wagon. It was the cradleman's duty now to unfasten the wagon door, either by knocking out the pins, or by disengaging the bar.

The wagon, having arrived at the heel of the chute, the cradle (or that portion of the cradle on which the wagon stood), was tilted, so that the back end of the wagon was raised and the weight of the coal swung open the end-door, the coal poured through on to the chute of the hoist and thence down into the hold of the ship. The duty of the GWR ended at the moment

Plate 132 Loading up pitwood at Barry Docks for despatch to the South Wales collieries.

Plate 133 Unloading a large cargo of pit props from SS "Bisley" at Swansea Docks in 1929.

when the coal had been tipped into the chute. The reception of the coal on board from out of the chute, the position at which the point of the chute was to be placed, and all other matters relating to the receiving of the coal on board ship, were entirely the responsibilities of the shipowner, and under the control of the coal trimmers.

If, as sometimes happened, the coal was not dislodged freely from the wagons, owing to its being wet and coagulated, and consequently did not "run" when the wagon was tipped, the cradleman had to disturb the contents by poking with a long bar. In some extreme cases, such as when shipping "washed duff" coal, a wagon might have to be brought down to the ground level, and the coal dug out with shovels by the coal tippers, before it could be loosened sufficiently to be discharged over the chute.

The contents of the wagon having been tipped, the wagon itself being prevented from falling into the chute by horns on the cradle which engaged the wheels of the wagon, the cradle was brought level again, and the empty wagon lowered. On some appliances the empty wagon was brought down to ground level; in other cases "high level" or overhead gantries were provided, which enabled the empty wagon to be run away while the empty cradle descended to ground level to receive the next loaded wagon. Whether the empty wagon ran away overhead, or on ground level, it was weighed, separate machines being provided at the majority of the appliances for this purpose, and with the new tare in his possession the weighman was now able to complete the record of the nett weight of coal shipped.

Though the operations take some time to describe, when the ship was receiving the coal freely, the cycle from

Plate 134 Some 4000 tons of raw sugar in sacks in the Cardiff Docks transit shed in 1929.

Plate 135 A view at Penarth Docks, showing the coal-tipping appliances in operation. Note the fine array of wooden wagons in the liveries of GLM, Albion, GKN and Cambrian.

Plate 136 A loaded wagon of coal being weighed before shipment.

the weighing of the full wagon to the discharge of the empty wagon from the appliance was very quickly performed. The speed of shipment entirely depended upon the rate at which the ship could receive the coal. Frequently, however, there was a run of loading without interruption. Then, the usual time occupied in the complete operation was about one to two minutes per wagon. As many as fifty-one 12-ton wagons have been shipped in an hour at one appliance, representing over 600 tons, while thirty-eight 20-ton wagons have been shipped in the same time, representing 750 tons of coal, both instances occurring during ordinary working.

The tipping weight slip was a document of far-reaching importance. The fact that the coal was weighed at the ship's side immediately before loading gave the utmost accuracy in the total weight carried by the vessel. All the coal shipped was bought and sold on the weights recorded at the coaling appliances, the GWR's figures being accepted by the buyers and sellers, and also by the shipowners and charterers in calculating the freight. The GWR, therefore, stood in the position of an independent authority between all parties, and a high standard of accuracy in the weighing was always maintained. Besides the actual weights, the weighman recorded various incidental particulars in regard to the times of commencing and finishing work, any delays to the work, and other useful information.

The coal tippers were paid on a tonnage basis for the shipment of coal, with certain incidental payments in respect of "mixing", waiting time, "digging out" and so on. Their wages were pooled, so that each man received an equal share, and they also had the benefit of a minimum wage. The coal trimmers, working on the ship, really controlled the rate at which the coal was loaded, because it was impossible to tip faster than the rate at which they could deal with the incoming coal. They actually controlled the letting out of the coal from the point of the chute, wing doors being provided near the point of each chute, and the opening of these doors was controlled by the trimmers, who usually had at least one man on deck to give orders as to where the point of the chute should be directed, and also to control the flow of the coal. Of course, it frequently happened that the chute was left open for considerable periods while

Plate 137 A loaded wagon, having been received on the cradle by the cradleman, starts its upward journey.

Plate 138 Coal being tipped into the chute of a hoist from a 20-ton wagon. Two men, indicated by the arrow, may just be seen on the cradle. Note the wing doors at the end of the chute. Probably they were shut for the photograph, so that the coal was stationary in the chute and could be seen clearly.

the cargo was being "run up" in the hold of the ship, and then each wagon-load went freely over and directly into the hold. When the free loading had to be pulled up for trimming work to be done, the wing doors were closed, so as to allow the coal to dribble from the chute when required, or perhaps the coal tippers might be called upon to cease tipping for the time being. The coal trimmers were also paid on a tonnage basis, and pooled their earnings.

When shipping coal, to prevent breakage it was the practice to ship sufficient coal, by means of an anti-breakage box, to form a 'cushion' on which the remainder of the coal could fall from the hoist chute with the minimum amount of breakage. This method did obviate breakage to a large extent when the coal was shipped by hydraulic hoists, but although several types of boxes were used, the method had its limitations both in regard to speed of operation, and also as to the amount of breakage it prevented.

The GWR recognised the need for an improved method further to lessen breakage, and at the same time to ship the coal more expeditiously. With these objects in view, a new anti-breakage device was inaugurated at one of the modern 20-ton hoists at Swansea. This device consisted of a vertical casing of rectangular section, all sides being enclosed except the one at

Plate 139 Shipment of coal by means of a belt-conveyor appliance at Port Talbot.

Plate 140 Front view of the coal anti-breakage appliance at Swansea Docks.

Plate 141 Side view of the anti-breakage appliance when attached to the shute of the hoist. Note the trays on the right-hand side returning to the top hanging down in a vertical position.

which the coal entered, and this was provided with a series of telescopic doors, the uppermost of which was attached to the coal chute. The interior of the casing was occupied by a number of steel plate trays, 4ft 0¾in by 2ft 8in, attached to a pair of endless chains which passed over sprocket wheels at the extreme ends of the casing. These trays received the coal from the chute and lowered it gently to the bottom of the ship's hold, the speed of lowering being controlled by an automatic centrifugal brake operated off the top sprocket wheel shaft. After the coal was released from a tray, the tray continued in a vertical position on the belt outside the vertical casing until it reached the top, when it immediately fell into a position ready to receive more coal. The whole apparatus was suspended from a crane on the coal hoist, which adjusted the height so that the drop of coal was the least possible. The overall length of the anti-breaker device was about 31ft, while the overall weight, full of coal, was about 7½ tons.

Duff coal has already been mentioned briefly. For some years there had been an increase in the quantity of small or "duff" coal sent down from the washeries at the South Wales collieries for shipment at the GWR's docks. This coal usually consisted of the fine residue remaining

Plate 142 Three-quarter view of the coal anti-breakage appliance at Swansea Docks. While the background is distractive with a distant coal hoist showing above the appliance, this photograph shows more clearly the inside of the coal chute and the trays hanging down on their return to the top.

Plate 143 A coal tipper trying to dislodge stuck duff coal by hand by prodding it forward from above.

Plate 144 Two coal tippers trying to make the stuck duff coal run by hand by pulling it forward from below.

after the coarser sizes of coal had been sorted out by washing operations at the collieries. It was generally termed "washed duff" although frequently wagons of "dry duff" were presented for shipment. This fine coal had very adhesive qualities; it held together in the wagons in a massed form, and would not run out from the end door when the wagon was tilted towards the chute at the usual angle for shipping coal, at about 45 degrees.

Washed duff, being in a more or less wet condition, was rather more difficult to get from the wagons than dry duff, although it was surprising to what a degree the latter would hold together. Incredible as it may seem, a wagon of duff coal could be tilted right up so that the end door swung fully open, and practically the whole 12 tons or so would remain in a fixed mass in the vehicle. For this reason, some means had to be employed to dislodge the coal to allow it to fall on to the shipping appliance chute. Usually the coal tippers removed the duff coal by means of scrapers. These implements were long poles, with a kind of "spade" or "hoe" at the end, which the men thrust into the coal so as to get it to run. Very often, however, the men would have to go into the wagons and dig away the duff with ordinary shovels. There are occasions when almost any coal, beside duff, would present some difficulty in clearing from the wagons. That is after heavy rain, or during frost following wet weather, when the contents of wagons congealed.

The difficulties of effecting shipment of coal which would not run freely from the wagons naturally led to a slower rate of shipment. At times it took almost an hour to clear one wagon, so that the average speed of working of the coal-shipping machines was detrimentally affected. The GWR therefore introduced a number of machines specially designed to expedite clearance of wagons containing coal which did not run freely. The machine chosen was the "Norfolk" digger, so named because it was the invention of Mr T.L. Norfolk, engineer-in-chief to the Mersey Docks and Harbour Board. The appliance consisted of a kind of straight spade, the blade of which was just the width of the inside of a coal wagon, and was so operated mechanically that it could dig into the wagon transversely at any point between the ends of the wagon.

To avoid damage to the bottom of the wagon, the spade was fitted with a telescopic spring lip, which incidentally facilitated the brushing out of the wagon. In the operation of discharging a wagon, the spade, with its wedged-shaped blade, was pressed downwards through the contents of the wagon, in a series of vertical slices, commencing near the open door, so that as the wedge was driven downwards, the detached portion of the coal gravitated into the chute and was delivered into the vessel. The thickness of each cut, and the quantity of coal displaced, varied with the degree of consolidation of the coal.

The appliance was operated by hydraulic motors and spur-wheel gear, the whole being self-contained and mounted on a movable carriage, travelling in guides attached to the front members of the hoist, so that the machine might be adjusted to suit the varying heights of the coal chute, and

Plate 145 A Norfolk digger about to take a cut into a wagon of stuck duff coal.

Plate 146 Another photograph of the Norfolk digger a minute or two later, showing the wagon of duff coal at a steeper angle and the wagon almost emptied by the actions of the digger.

when not required could be housed clear of shipping and moving parts of the hoist.

The Norfolk digger cleared the contents of a 12-ton wagon in two to three minutes, and was therefore a great improvement upon the former manual method of dealing with consolidated small coal or duff. Initially, the GWR arranged for one of these appliances to be supplied to each of the Barry, Cardiff, Newport and Port Talbot docks.

Advantage was taken of the Development (Loan Guarantees and Grants) Act of 1929 to improve these docks, in three main categories:

(a) Provision of new coal shipping appliances
(b) Provision of new general cargo cranes
(c) Improved general facilities and equipment, such as storage sidings and dock lines.

Regarding the coal shipping business, the main consideration was that the new appliances were capable of tipping the modern 20 ton wagons then being promoted by the GWR, as well as the smaller 10 and 12 ton wagons still extensively used. There already existed

Plate 147 New coal hoists constructed by Vickers-Armstrong Ltd for the GWR Barry Docks.

Plate 148 New 20-ton traverser coal hoists at Queen Alexandra Dock, Cardiff.

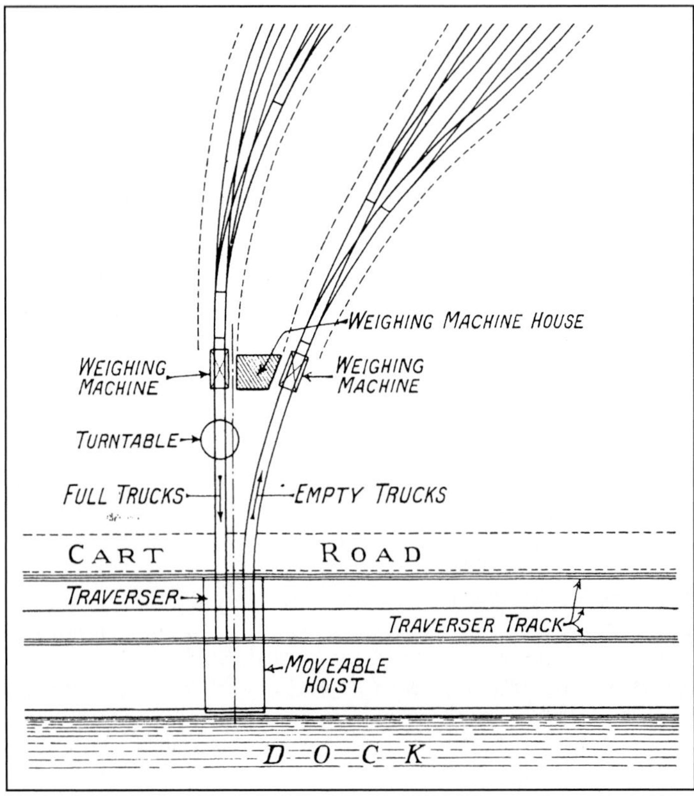

Fig 9. Arrangement of traverser hoists and feed roads at Queen Alexandra Dock, Cardiff.

Plate 149 One of the largest of the new coal handling plants installed at Roath Dock, Cardiff, by Spencer (Melksham) Ltd. It was equipped with 48in troughed bands. The wagon tipper could empty a 20-ton wagon in 72 seconds.

54 hoists capable of dealing with the higher capacity wagons, together with 65 lesser hoists. Under the 1929 Act, 25 new large capacity hoists were installed, making a total of 144 coal-shipping appliances at the six docks. These new hoists were equipped with telescopic nose-pieces (enabling the finer adjustment of the shute) and anti-breakage machines, which successfully minimised the breakage coal during the tipping operation. Their height of lift was ample for bunkering all classes of vessels, including the largest types of general cargo liners. The opportunity was taken of improving the hoist feed roads as much as possible.

The most extensive scheme of modernisation was at Barry Docks where sixteen new coaling hoists were provided. At No 1 Dock, hoists Nos 1,2,3,4,5,6,8 & 19 were replaced by modern hoists, as were No 22 and No 24 at No 2 Dock. The existing hoists at Barry were of the well type, the supporting tip towers being hollow to accommodate the hydraulic rams which lifted the hoist cradle. In the new type of hoist erected by Messrs Vickers-Armstrongs, the cradle was lifted by overhead suspended cables and tackle. This variation in design, combined with the increased width of hoist at the base, necessitated considerable alterations in the foundations. The new hoists were about 90ft high from the quay level of the dock, with a maximum lift of 60ft and, including the height of the tower under the hoist, stood at a height of about 135ft above the bottom of the dock.

The increased height and width of the new hoists, and consequent greater effect of wind pressure, necessitated the cutting down of part of the masonry towers forming the foundations of the existing hoists to a depth of about 11ft, and the provision of foundation bolts 10ft 6in long and of 2in diameter, with suitably built-up steel frames. In addition, the towers had to be widened at the top from 30ft to 37ft 6in to accommodate the bases of the new hoists. To avoid the necessity for pile driving or sinking of caissons, this additional width was obtained by building out from the sides of the masonry tower reinforced concrete corbels from a depth of 12ft below the coping, steel cantilevers 14ft long being erected at the sides of the towers to support the shute nose machinery, the anti-breakage box, and gangways. About 850 tons of concrete and old rail reinforcement were required in each hoist foundation, the outer shuttering for which was erected from floating rafts. The programme allowed 1½ months for the demolition of an existing hoist, 2½ months for foundation work and 6 months for the erection of the new hoist, gantry alterations being carried out concurrently. Only four hoists were out of commission simultaneously.

The adoption of 20-ton capacity wagons required the provision of 16ft diameter turntables and 35-ton capacity full and empty wagon weighbridges at Barry. To obtain sufficient clearance between the full and empty wagon roads, on account of the increased dimensions, a partial reconstruction of the approach viaducts was necessary; also owing to the increased weights the viaducts were strengthened.

At Swansea, six new coal hoists were installed; two fixed hoists at South Dock, three fixed hoists at Prince of Wales Dock and a movable hoist with traverser at King's Dock. No 8 hoist, which was located on the jetty at the extreme eastern end of the Prince of Wales Dock coaling quay was placed parallel with the dock-side line of the jetty, which latter did not run parallel with the coaling quay. As the old hoist was built exactly square with the general quay line, the new arrangement, by projecting the shute squarely into the ship, was an improvement. The movable hoist for King's Dock was placed westward of the existing No 1 hoist on the Tennant Lay-bye. This berth was 570ft long and afforded a useful addition to the loading facilities. Another improvement at King's Dock was the renewal and bringing back into use the old traverser at No 3 hoist, greatly facilitating the working on the north side of the dock, and enabling two shipping appliances to be worked into one vessel at the same time.

Plate 150 Three new 3-ton hydraulic cranes brought into commission at the GWR Roath Dock in Cardiff in 1928. They are unloading pit props for use in the South Wales coal mines.

At Port Talbot, two new fixed jetty hoists were erected, and in the case of one of them, the opportunity was taken of practically doubling the capacity of one of the feed roads.

At Cardiff, on the south side of Queen Alexandra Dock, three movable hoists, with electric traversers, replaced old coal hoists and coaling cranes, and completed the similar equipment (nine appliances of this type) of the 2,400ft of quay there devoted to coal loading. These traverser hoists moved on a track alongside the edge of the quay, with another track behind them on which ran wagon traversers having tracks to take two wagons, one full and one empty. With a movement of the traverser of only 12ft the full wagon could be passed to the cradle of the hoist and shipment proceed while the traverser was moving to a set of feed roads for the empty wagon to be turned off at the same time as another full wagon was being received. The general arrangement of the traversers and the feed roads is shown in the diagram. Each coal shipping point on the quay was provided with a mechanically operated turntable, 16ft in diameter, on which the new standard 20-ton wagons, because they had a door at one end only, could be turned if necessary. The turntable gear was hydraulic, and each turntable was provided with a tilting arrangement giving the loaded wagon sufficient impetus to send it on to the traverser. The wagon traversers also had a tilting arrangement on each track, so that the full and empty wagons could be quickly moved to and from the hoists and shipping points.

Modern weighing machines capable of weighing up to 35 tons were placed at the ends of the full feed roads and adjacent to the turntable. The feed roads were regraded so that wagons

Plate 151 One of the new 20-ton wagon coal hoists under construction at Barry Docks.

could move freely on them, the loaded wagons gravitating to the weighing machines, where they were stopped for weighing. The rails on the machine itself were graded at 1 in 64, which was sufficient to move the trucks on to the turntable. A similar arrangement applied in the reverse direction to the empty trucks which passed over re-taring weigh-bridges. Nearly all the sets of full roads consisted of four sidings and the empty groups of three or four. This enabled different kinds of coal to be mixed at the time of shipment and the empty wagons to be sorted on their return. The traversers were operated by electricity and had a travelling speed of 375 ft/min. The hoists were mainly worked by hydraulic power at a pressure of 750 to 800 lb/sq.in, but the motive power for travelling was electricity, the speed being 30 ft/min.

On the west side of Bute East Dock at Cardiff, a new fixed hoist was built, while two other new fixed hoists were constructed on the east side of Roath Basin, the northernmost erected on a jetty and the southernmost flush with the quay.

At Newport, No 6 fixed hoist on the west side of the North Dock was replaced by a traverser hoist similar in principle to, but different in certain respects from, those just described at Queen Alexandra Dock at Cardiff. At the Newport hoist the full wagon left the feed roads and, after passing over a weigh-bridge and turntable, ran on to a low-level traverser and was conveyed, parallel to the quay, to the hoist, which it entered a little above quay level. The wagon was then raised in the hoist, tipped and lowered to a point about 18ft above quay level where it left the hoist and ran on to a second traverser, travelling on a gantry immediately above the full-wagon or low-level traverser. The empty wagon was conveyed back to a point immediately above that at which it entered, where it left the high-level traverser and passed over a bridge and a re-taring weigh-bridge into the empty wagon roads. The movement of the hoist and the operation of the traverser was effected by steel hauling ropes, hydraulically operated from the north end of the hoist and traverser tracks. The hoists could be moved at a rate of 20 ft/min and the traversers at 100ft in

Plate 152 New 20-ton wagon hoist at North Dock, Newport.

20 seconds, start to stop. The lifting power of the hoist proper was 32 tons at 180 ft/min, the cradle being suspended and raised by hydraulic cylinders mounted on the hoist structure to a maximum height of 60ft above the quay level. The hoist travelled on bridge rails, the front one of which was fixed on the coping of the quay wall and the back one on reinforced concrete piles. These piles, 18in in diameter, were driven to a depth of 50ft below the quay level. Similar reinforced pile and beam foundations were constructed for the low-level trasverser track and the steel gantry carrying the high-level traverser track.

Turning to the general cargo cranes, 35 were purchased under the 1929 Act, 24 electrically operated and 11 hydraulically operated. The main considerations were the ability to operate alongside ships, suitable capacity having regard to the class of traffic and general utility in the shape of level luffing and speed of lifting, lowering and slewing. The new appliances went up to a height of 70ft and the crane hook could be lowered to 40ft below quay level.

At Newport, five new 3-ton travelling electric cranes were installed on the South Quay of South Dock, making for that wharf, which was about 3,600 ft long, a total equipment of 30 electric and hydraulic cranes of varying capacities up to 10 tons. On the north side of the Queen Alexandra Dock at Cardiff, twelve new cranes of 3-ton capacity were installed, as well as one on the north side of Roath Dock. These were all electric cranes and replaced old steam and hydraulic machines. The quayside crane equipment on the north side of Penarth Dock was augmented by three new hydraulic luffing cranes of 3-ton lifting capacity. At Barry the 3,500ft general cargo quay on the south side of No 2 Dock was fitted with an additional six new 3-ton hydraulic traversing cranes,

Plate 153 One of the GWR's modern coal-shipping hoists. Loaded wagons ran into the cradle at ground level, and empty ones were sent away on the high level.

making a total for this particular wharf of 29 cranes of capacities ranging up to 10 tons. At Port Talbot, two new movable hydraulic cranes, each of 3-ton capacity, were installed, one on what was known as Steel Works Wharf and the other on the reconstructed Talbot Wharf. At Swansea, six 3-ton electric cranes were provided. Four were positioned at the eastern end of No 3 quay of King's Dock, and with a further six electric cranes also of 3-ton capacity, equipped the 1,100ft of the general cargo quay. The other two cranes were erected at King's Dock, one at 'C' Shed wharf and the other at 'A/B' Shed wharf.

General improvements carried out under the 1929 Act at the South Wales Docks were as follows. At Cardiff, electric pumping plant supplied in lieu of steam plant. At Penarth, the installation of an economiser at the power station. At Barry, electrification of the hydraulic plant, involving the supply of eight sets of electrically-driven hydraulic turbine pressure pumps and two sets of electrically-driven centrifugal pumps. Supply and erection of high-tension and low-tension electrical equipment and laying of high-tension cables. Arrangements in connection with the supply of electricity. Port Talbot, supply and erection of horizontal compound condensing hydraulic pumping engine. Swansea South Dock, power house installation of engines and pumps from the power station at Cardiff. Western power station extra hydraulic pumping engine. Provision of two new hydraulic mains from eastern and western power houses at Prince of Wales Dock and the transfer of accumulators from Cardiff. Impounding pumps at South Dock basin. Three new electrically-driven pumps each of 15,000 gallons per minute capacity were installed in place of two centrifugal pumps to maintain the requisite level of water in the South Dock and Basin. Work in renewing electric cables and improvement in distributing arrangements involving the erection of new transformer at South Dock, enlargement of King's Dock sub-station and the provision of screening at North Dock sub-station.

At Swansea, also, additional warehouse accommodation of 23,940 sq ft was effected by joining up the 'A' and 'B' sheds at King's Dock. Further improvements were made by setting back the roadway at No 4 quay, King's Dock, to provide a greater depth of quay for working purposes and by filling in the old Prince of Wales Dock lock and the construction of a dock wall across the inner entrance. This work yielded improved rail and road access in the vicinity, as well as providing an extra quay. Additional sidings were put in at Tennant's Wharf, Prince of Wales Dock, involving lifting the quay wall, filling across from Tennant Canal, extension of siding accommodation and provision of direct access between the eastern end of the quay and the main running line leading to King's Dock junction.

1933 SOUTH WALES MARSHALLING YARDS

Under the 1929 Act, the GWR was given the opportunity to remodel two

Plate 154 New 3-ton electric cranes at South Quay, Newport Docks.

important freight-marshalling yards in South Wales, Rogerstone and Severn Tunnel Junction, on up-to-date lines, as well as the coal-sorting and storage yard serving Swansea Docks. In connection with the last mentioned, a comprehensive scheme was carried out to divert the passenger traffic from the old Rhondda and Swansea Bay Railway to the almost parallel GWR lines, as between Briton Ferry and Swansea (Riverside), so as to release them for coal traffic exclusively, and to effect economies by abandoning parts not so required.

Rogerstone yard was situated at the lower end of the South Wales Western Valleys and all traffic from these and the Penar and Sirhowy branches destined for Newport, Cardiff, Penarth and Barry Docks, as well as all places on the main line, passed through this bottle-neck. Prior to the remodelling of the yard the sidings were inadequate, resulting in delays to trains waiting to be dealt with and late starts to the trains leaving this depot, and this in its turn caused wastage of power. The reconstruction scheme involved complete remodelling of the arrangements and the introduction of a hump yard.

The new yard at the north end provided for 18 double-ended sidings to accommodate 1,120 wagons and two reception sidings each to accommodate a 75-wagon train. The hump yard was situated between the reception sidings and the marshalling sidings. It was approached by 234ft rising at a gradient of 1 in 63, to a summit level of 10ft, and fell beyond for 150ft at 1 in 30. From the base of this gradient the sidings dropped at 1 in 224 throughout. The siding points connected with the hump were worked by an electro-pueumatic ground frame.

At the south end the sidings, to which four new ones for marshalling inland traffic were added, were flat-shunted, so that operations could be in progress simultaneously at both ends of the yard. Before the hump was introduced it was necessary to marshall down trains (in the Welsh valleys 'up' and 'down' referred to the gradient up the valley and down to the coast) from the various valleys, so that wagons for the docks were already in separate sections on arrival at Rogerstone. This work, having to be performed at the various colliery and works sidings, nearly all of which were situated on heavy gradients, together with the intensive passenger train service operated, caused serious delays to traffic. The provision of the hump enabled traffic to be sent from the collieries in whatever order was most convenient.

On arrival, trains were placed in one of the reception sidings and the engine was immediately released and sent to shed or to take up further duties. The wagon examiners then passed along the train and marked any wagons needing repairs. The hump engine was placed at

Page 155 Three new 3-ton hydraulic cranes at Penarth Dock.

the rear of the train and, on the instructions of the head shunter, began slowly pushing the train forward over the hump. The head shunter marked on the front of each batch of wagons the number of the siding into which it was to be gravitated, and the pointsman in the hump ground frame operated the points according to the shunter's chalk marks. Shunters in the sidings controlled the speed of the wagon by hand-placed slipper brakes or by pinning down the side brakes. So that the work could be carried on at night the track sidings were electrically flood-lit. The hump was open for two consecutive turns of duty, namely from 1200 to 2000, and 2000 to 0400 hours, which periods coincided with the clearance of traffic from the collieries. Such trains as might arrive at other times were dealt with at the south end of the yard. The average time occupied in dealing with each train over the hump was about 13 minutes, and the average number of cuts per train was 14.

Severn Tunnel Junction was situated at the west end of the Severn Tunnel, where the South Wales main line which passed through the tunnel and the main line from Gloucester converged, so that all traffic from the west and south of England, Bristol, Swindon, London, Gloucester, Banbury (and a large proportion of the traffic from the Birmingham and Worcester areas) to and from South Wales passed through these yards. Prior to 1931 the marshalling yard at Severn Tunnel Junction dealt with traffic between the Cardiff and Newport districts for the south and west of England and London, and from the Swansea district for the south and west of England only. London district traffic from the west of Bridgend was dealt with at Stoke Gifford, at the east end of the Severn Tunnel. Under the new scheme all the work at both depots was concentrated at Severn Tunnel Junction, and this gave more economical working and better transit, but also better loadings, improved timekeeping, and a reduction in the occupation of the tunnel. The old yard had accommodation for 1,405 wagons. As remodelled the accommodation was increased to 2,652 wagons.

Owing to the situation of the railway on an embankment and the nature of the adjoining ground, it was not possible to concentrate the whole traffic in one yard with a hump, but despite this, efficient

Plate 156 Reconstruction in ferro-concrete of the old timber wharf on the east side of the North Dock at Newport.

working was made possible by the rearrangement and enlargement of the depot. Up trains terminating at Severn Tunnel Junction were received into one of three reception lines on the south side of the up yard. The trains were then drawn into the shunting neck and split up into the sorting sidings at the west end. Out-going trains having to attach or detach wagons were dealt with at the east end of the yard, so that the operations at each end could proceed simultaneously.

A double-ended yard on the down side was considered to be too costly and, therefore, both incoming and out-going trains were dealt with from the west end of the 19 sidings, which were, however, divided into three groups so that three engines could proceed with their sorting work simultaneously. The yard was provided with gas flood-lighting.

At Swansea, before the amalgamation, the Rhondda and Swansea Bay Railway paralleled the GWR main line from Briton Ferry to Court Sart, and again from Dynevor Junction to its terminus at the Riverside station in Swansea. One of the beneficial features of the 1921 Railways Act was that it enabled uneconomical parallel lines to be turned to good account either by the separation of different classes of traffic or by the abandonment of redundant works. In this particular case a scheme was devised and under the 1929 Act was realised for diverting the passenger traffic of the R&SB line on to GWR metals, where they provided a suitable alternative route, and using part of the former exclusively for mineral traffic from the two systems. In addition, it was possible to abandon certain sections and stations of the R&SB owing to the diversion of the passenger trains.

Under this scheme the marshalling sidings at Burrows, between Briton Ferry Road and the docks at Swansea, were enlarged and remodelled, and these, together with the old R&SB double track between these points, were handed over for the exclusive use of the Docks Department for its traffic. The abandonment of the Swansea end of the line and the diversion of the passenger trains further contributed to the more efficient working because formerly passenger trains to the Riverside station had to cross the lines leading down to the docks, thus causing interruption to the even flow of coal traffic.

The principal features of the scheme can be gathered from the diagram, the R&SB passenger traffic was diverted by the GWR main line through Neath to Swansea High Street, and a shuttle service of railcars connected Briton Ferry to the GWR Vale of Neath

Plate 157 The new transit shed on the Mole, King's Dock, Swansea.

Plate 158 A range of the GWR's modern movable coal hoists at Bute Docks in Cardiff.

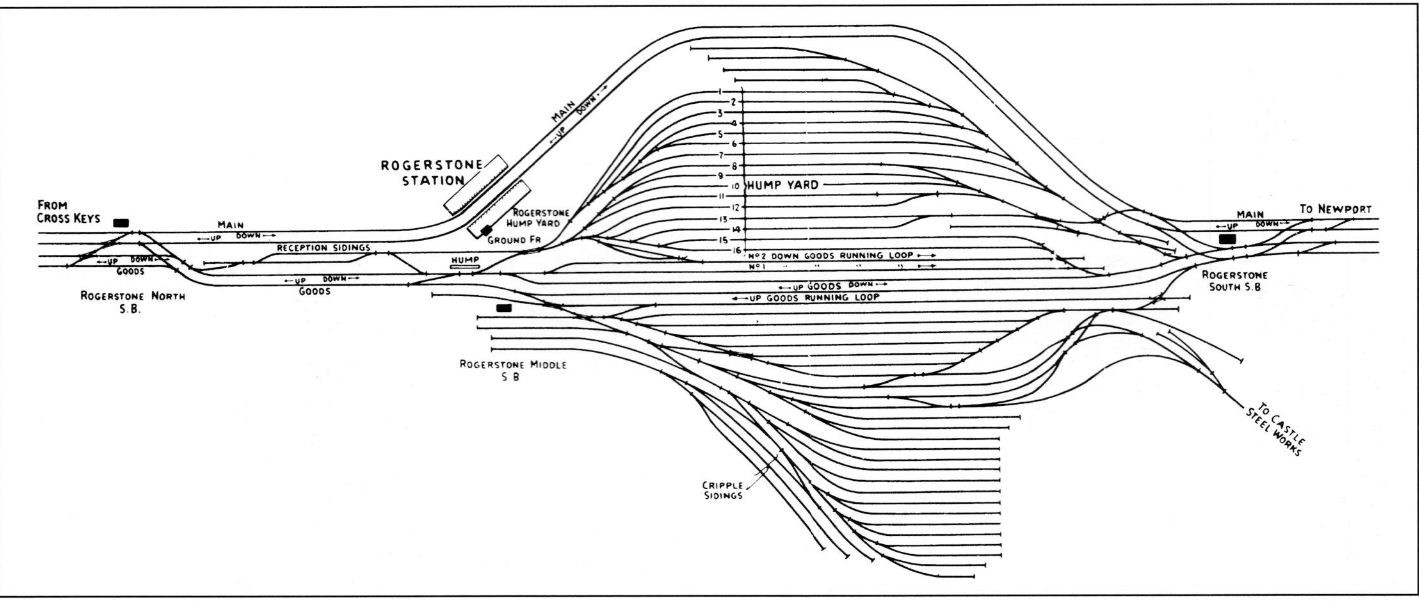

Map 19. The new 'hump' marshalling yards at Rogerstone.

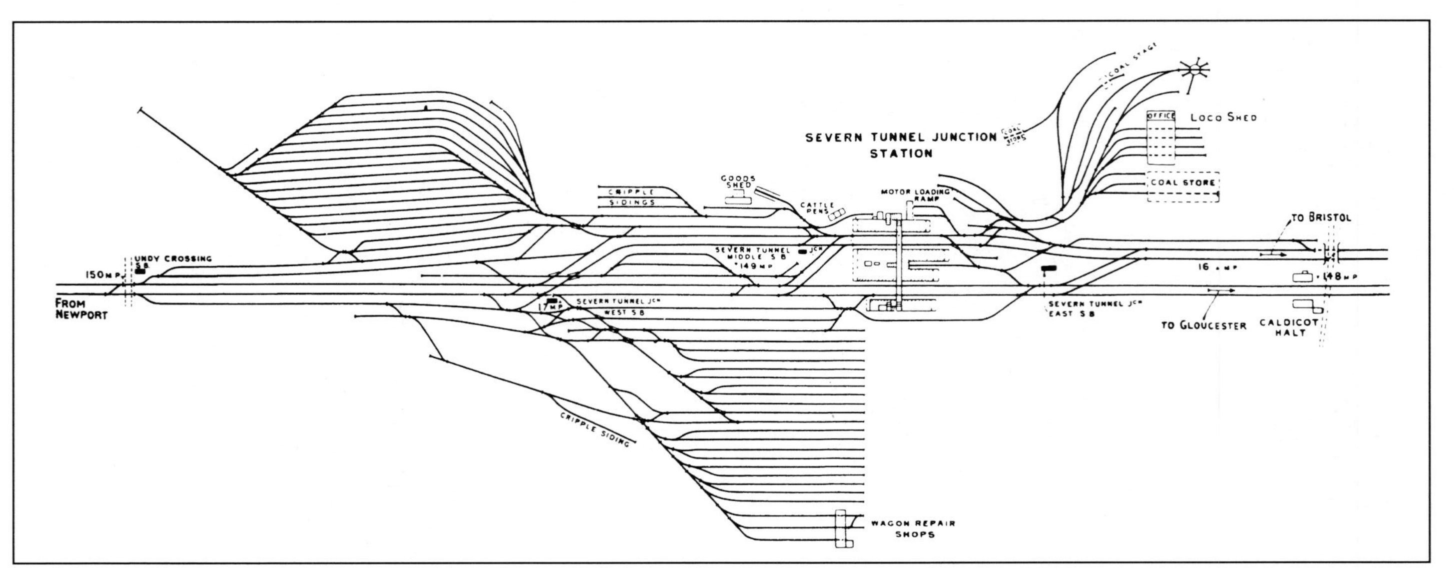

Map 20. The new marshalling yard at Severn Tunnel Junction.

Plate 159 The new up or Bristol yard at the west end of Severn Tunnel Junction.

terminus at Swansea East Dock. The Neath Canalside passenger traffic was moved to the GWR main line and the branch was used only for goods traffic. Down mineral traffic was diverted at Dynevor North Junction on to the former R&SB line, which was singled thence to Jersey Marine Junction South, at which point a new double line junction was laid in. At this double junction all goods and mineral trains, both of GWR and R&SB origin, were diverted on to the former R&SB lines, with the exception of trains already sorted for shipment, which went to the former reception sidings.

At the former Jersey Marine passenger station now abandoned, the extensive Burrows riddling and storage sidings began with a nest of reception sidings leading to a new hump yard. Over this hump the coal trains were sorted according to the various descriptions and qualities of coal, ready for shipment. After the various classes of coal were sorted in the riddling sidings, unless they were required for immediate shipment, they were taken forward and put in to the storage sidings ready for when they were wanted. As the trains were formed in the riddling sidings, they were moved forward in to the various storage sidings there to await the time when they were required to go forward as complete trains for shipment. Under the new scheme there were four complete nests of storage sidings, as well as a nest of outship sidings to hold traffic for shipment that had for any reason to be returned temporarily from the docks. From Jersey Marine there was then no signalling on the docks lines, a feature which was considered to facilitate the handling of traffic. Empties and general cargo inwards traffic from the docks ran to the existing up hump sorting sidings, which were enlarged, on the north side of the Vale of Neath line. The accommodation at Burrows sidings was increased by 1,782 wagons, or about 60%. It might be noted that the working of Burrows sidings was by the Docks Department, unlike other marshalling yards which were handled by the Traffic Department.

In connection with the new hump yard provided at Burrows Yard an additional signal box was required, and it was decided to use a box which was taken out of use at Jersey Marine station. The box was mounted on two 12in by 6in timbers, 20ft long, placed on the wheels of a platelayers' trolley, and pulled by hand for the distance of about one mile. The work of disconnecting was started at 0645 and the box was placed in its new permanent position at 1500 the same day.

1933 NEW LOCOMOTIVE RUNNING DEPOTS

The 1929 Act provided the means to build some new running depots and to improve some existing depots, as follows.

The reconstruction of Bristol Temple Meads station, described elsewhere, provided the opportunity to remodel the locomotive running sheds and shops adjacent to Bath Road. The old engine sheds were built in the time of the Bristol and Exeter Railway and were therefore designed for broad gauge locomotives. One of the sheds was of the turntable two-unit type 330ft long by 154ft wide, equipped with two 45ft turntables, from each of which radiated 24 roads. The other shed was straight, 209ft long by 95ft wide, with six roads, each with an engine pit 190ft long. The erecting, machine and smith's shops, and the Locomotive Superintendent's office, together with the stores, were between the two sheds, and in the locomotive yard near the straight shed was a coal stage with one single and two double tips, on the top of which was a 42,400 gallon water tank. There were a 65ft turntable and a 55ft turntable in the yard.

In the new layout a straight road shed of what is now the standard type, 212ft long by 157ft wide, with ten

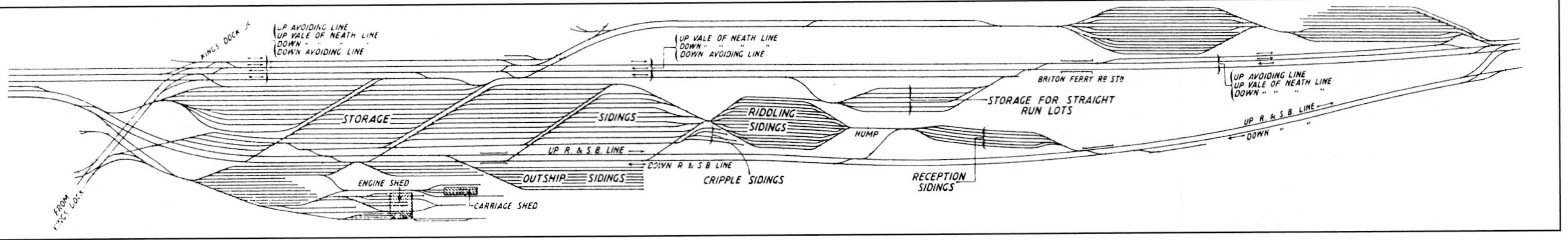

Map 21. Layout of the new Burrows sorting sidings at Swansea.

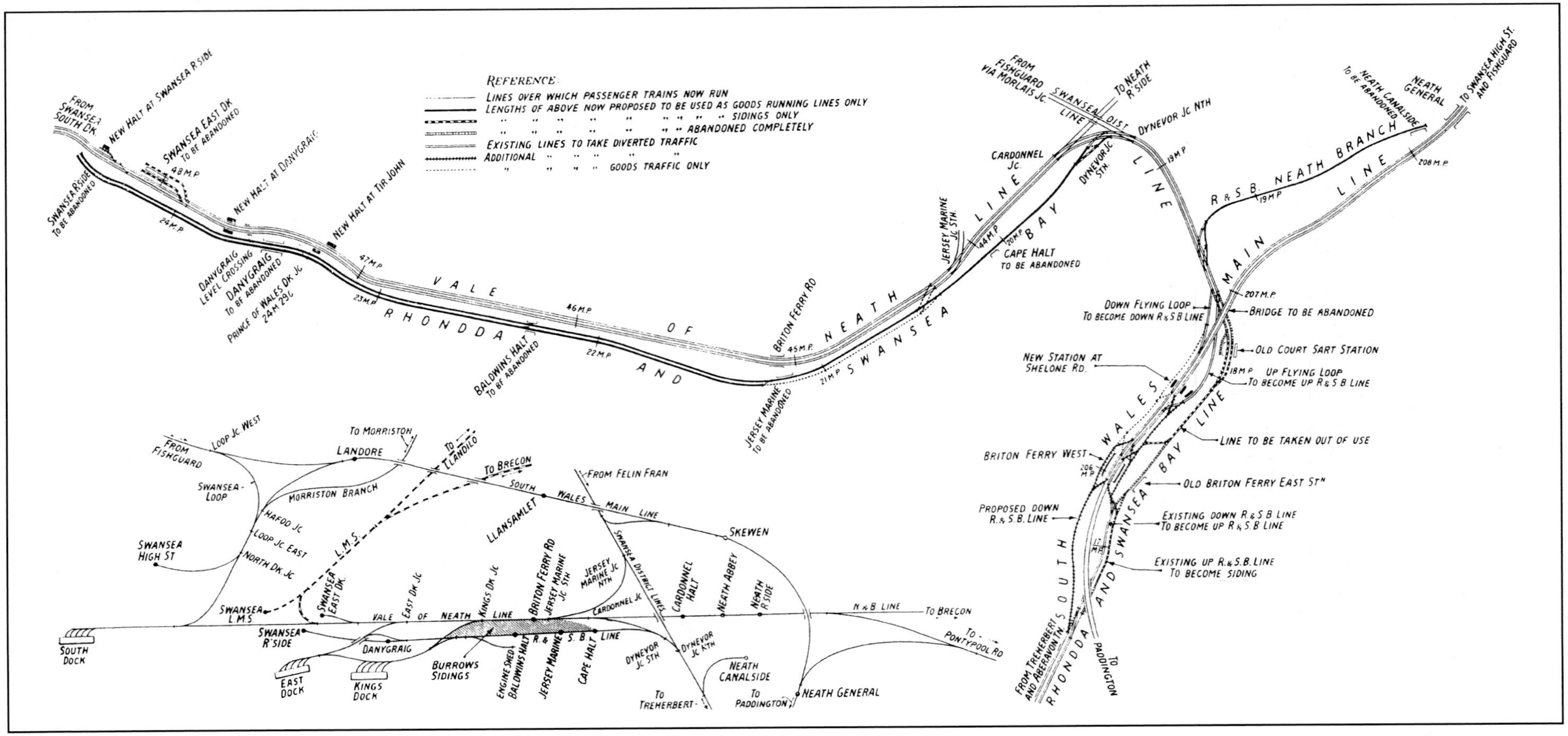

Map 22. Re-arrangement of passenger and goods working between Briton Ferry and Swansea. The table of references applies only to the detailed map and not to the key plan inset below it.

Plate 160 The signal box in the process of being moved by man-power for about one mile from Jersey Marine station to Burrows Yard.

roads, was provided. The engine pits of these roads were 196ft long and in addition there were ten pits outside the sheds each 40ft long. The usual mess room and office accommodation adjoined the shed, as well as a boiler house containing two boilers for boiler washing and heating the buildings. Two sand dryers were placed just outside the shed. On the side of the old straight engine shed a new lifting shop 145ft long by 70ft wide was erected, and in this was a 50-ton electrically-driven overhead crane, machine tools, smiths' hearth, carpenters' and smiths' shops, repair pits, etc. Between the lifting shop and the engine shed was placed a new coal stage, 103ft long by 27ft wide, with three tips, on top of which was a 131,500 gallon water tank. Two 65ft turntables werre situated in the locomotive yard.

At Plymouth, owing to the closing down of Millbay engine shed, the accommodation at Laira shed was too heavily taxed. The old shed was therefore extended, and alongside was constructed a new four-track shed 210ft long by 67ft wide, a size adopted generally as a standard for the smaller modern locomotive depots provided by the GWR. A store 60ft

Plate 161 The new engine shed at Pantyffynnon.

Plate 162 The old 'A' shed at the GWR's Swindon Locomotive Works in November 1929.

Plate 163 The reconstructed 'A' shed, set back and faced in stone to match the other buildings, in November 1930.

Plate 164 Work in progress on the new Carriage Shed at Swindon Works.

Plate 165 The new carriage shop at the GWR's Locomotive Works at Swindon in 1930.

Plate 166 New 10-ton and 3-ton 'Goliath' travelling overhead cranes with 73ft span, in the concentration yard at Swindon Works. These were built by S.H.Heywood & Co Ltd of Reddish near Stockport.

by 30ft was also built. The building was steel-framed with brick panels up to the underside of the steel window sashes. Between these and above them, corrugated asbestos sheeting was fixed and the roof was boarded and covered with asbestos. Skylights covered the clerestory above each roof bay for its full length, the clerestory having side louvre ventilators. There were asbestos-sheeted smoke troughs, with uptakes at intervals, above each of the four roads, which accommodated 12 large express engines, and each of which was provided with an engine pit 196ft long inside the shed and a 40ft pit beyond outside.

As the site of the shed was formerly an old refuse pit formed on what was originally a creek of the Laira estuary, the foundations had to be piled. A total of 196 reinforced concrete piles 14in by 14in were driven, varying in length from 26ft to 32ft, and on these reinforced concrete beams were moulded to form part of the walls of the engine pits. The coal stage was also extended on pile foundations and the locomotive sidings remodelled.

In connection with the big Cardiff General station reconstruction scheme, described elsewhere, the locomotive depot at Canton had several improvements made to it, including new coaling and watering facilities and a new Mundt 65ft turntable. In this

Plate 167 The new repair shop at Cathays, Cardiff, for wagons in the South Wales area.

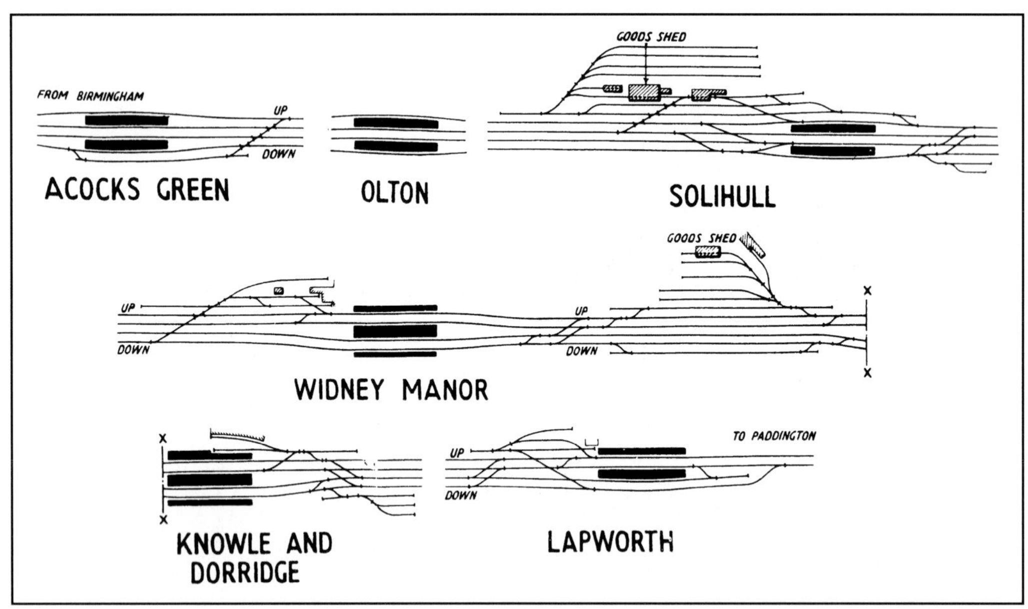

Map 23. Quadrupled track on the Hatton to Birmingham line between Acocks Green and Lapworth.

Plate 168 Work in progress of widening the span of the Chessett's Wood Bridge in connection with quadrupling the Birmingham main line.

Plate 169 New girder bridge over Warwick Road at Olton.

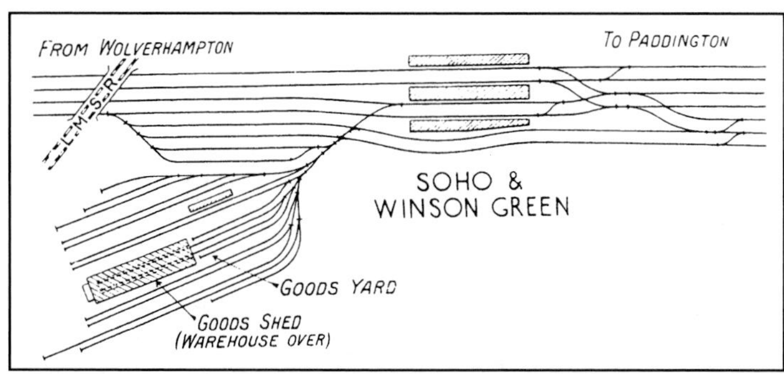

Map 24. Plan of the new warehouse and depot at Soho and Winson Green.

design, part of the weight is taken by the ends of the table, the main girders of which were so shallow and flexible that the unloaded end of the table would not rise when a locomotive ran on or rested on one end. Hence no balancing of the locomotive was necessary, and a revolution could be started as soon as all the wheels had passed on. Rotation was performed by a winch gear at one end of the table. There were ball bearings both at the central pillar and the race wheels. This type of table was claimed to give reduced maintenance costs. At Cardiff East Dock a new 210ft by 126ft engine shed, together with improved coaling and watering facilities were constructed.

New engine sheds were completed at Landore, Pantyffynnon, Radyr and Treherbert. These so-called Loan Act sheds were typical of the economical structures built at trading and industrial estates for machine shop works and light factory engineering at this time. The roof was composed of metal sheeting on timber boards, with a raised glazed central louvred ridge. The timber purlins were fixed to mild steel trusses, which sat on steel beams supported on stanchions. There was a separate pitched roof like this for each pair of running roads. The walls were brick lower half and asbestos sheeting with industrial windows for the upper

Plate 170 The new four-storied warehouse erected by the GWR at Soho & Winson Green in Birmingham in 1933. Probably by chance, the photographer has caught a time when the bulk of the wagons in front of the warehouse were carrying sheeted-over sawn timber, and one can but query if this was a traffic that needed warehousing under cover? Be as that may, it is interesting to see that the over-hanging loads were not given separate runner wagons for the overhang, but each wagon's load overhung the next wagon, a neat and economical arrangement.

Plate 171 A view of the ground floor of the new warehouse, forming a convenient transit shed.

half. The offices, stores and mess rooms, which ran alongside the side of the shed, were divided from the running shed by a full height brick wall. The roof to these lean-to offices was made of asbestos slates with boards on timber rafters. The offices and stores were separated by internal brick walls and full length glazing ran along the roof where it joined the eaves to the main shed roof. In the running shed, the smoke vent troughs had stacks spread out to vent at each third bay. Shed doors were timber with a glazed strip running full width over the top. The floor in the shed was concrete, but the offices and stores had wood block floors. Didcot, described elsewhere, was one such shed which may still be seen.

At Landore, a new 210ft by 67ft shed was built adjacent to the existing shed, including the usual stores and a workshop with a 50-ton hoist. A new coal stage with a water tank of 45,000 gallons capacity over it, a sand-drying plant and a 65ft turntable were also provided.

The shed at Pantyffynnon was constructed to house engines which previously had to run light from Llanelly to work coal trains from the Pantyffynnon district to the docks. Thus, although it was officially only a subshed to Llanelly, it came to possess its own allocation of locomotives. The Pantyffynnon shed was opened in March 1931. The building was 210ft long by 67ft wide. It was of the straight-road type, with four roads and was designed to hold 20 engines. The layout included a new 65ft turntable, and modern coal stage with elevated road, carrying a water tank 32ft by 30ft, with a capacity of 45,000 gallons. A boiler-washing plant was installed, and a new pump house and pumps.

The building at Radyr replaced a small Taff Vale sub-shed which had become inadequate for requirements, accommodating only 6 engines. The new steel-framed building opened in 1931 and was a standard straight road depot 210ft long by 67ft wide, erected on a 2ft thick reinforced concrete raft, with four roads accommodating 24 locomotives. There was a new coal stage also built on a concrete raft. A 65ft Mundt turntable on a concrete raft was substituted for the earlier one about two years later.

At Treherbert, the new shed replaced the existing Taff Vale depot which stood on an adjoining site and which took only 8 engines. The new

Plate 172 The third floor interior of the new warehouse at Soho and Winson Green.

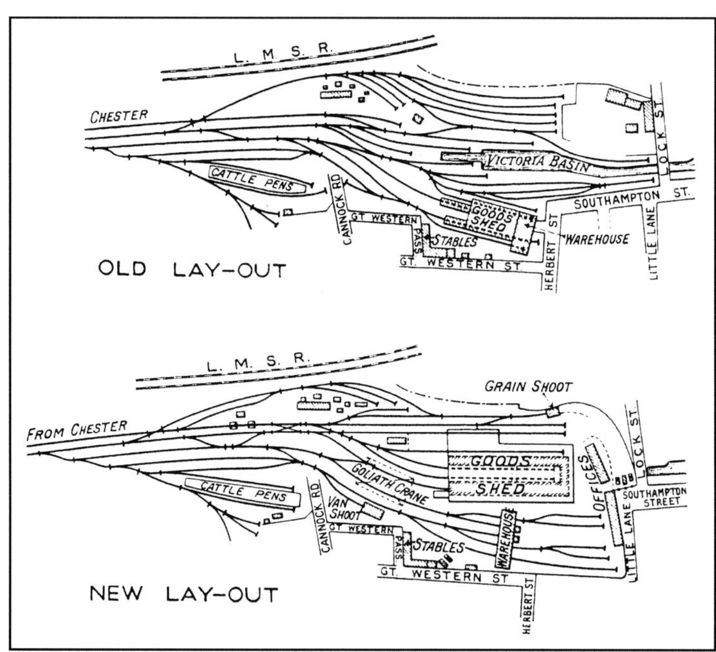

Map 25. The old layout at Wolverhampton (Herbert Street) is shown on top, and the new layout below.

depot was like that at Radyr, the new steel-framed building being a straight road depot 210ft long by 67ft wide built on a reinforced concrete raft but accommodated slightly fewer engines with a nominal capacity of 20. There was also a new coal stage and turntable.

The locomotive depot at Port Talbot (Duffryn Yard) needed to be improved consequent upon the closing of the shed at Aberavon, and the concentration of Rhondda and Swansea Bay engines at the shed at Duffryn Yard, as it tended to be called at this time. The existing lifting shop was enlarged. New offices and boiler house were provided, the boiler house having metal corrugated walls and roof. In addition, a new coaling stage brick built with a pitched slate covered roof and a ramp approach was added. The turntable was moved to a more convenient site at the rear of the shed. The watering appliances were rearranged for better access.

At Merthyr, the shed was extended by 45ft, to give accommodation for 12 engines. A 55ft turntable was installed on a site adjacent to the offices at the rear of the shed, replacing a smaller turntable located in front of the shed. A new covered coaling plant was installed before the new turntable. Engine pits were added and the yard layout improved.

At Severn Tunnel Junction, an extra bay was added to the locomotive shed, making it into six covered roads; also the conventional coal stage was extended by providing a corrugated steel-framed shed so that coaling could be handled either side of the ramp.

About ½ mile south of Kidderminster, on the Loop Line, a new locomotive yard and engine shed were provided, replacing a single road shed adjacent to the station. The new shed had a steel frame with corrugated iron sheeting and, enclosing two roads, measured 200ft by 30ft. Office, mess room and workshop acomodation was provided. There was an elevated coaling stage, and a 22,500 gallon water tank as well as a sand-drying plant.

At Taunton shed, a new lifting shop was provided.

1933 IMPROVED ROLLING STOCK CONSTRUCTION AND REPAIR FACILITIES

The 1929 Act gave the opportunity to carry out improvements to the GWR's facilities for constructing and repairing rolling stock. Caerphilly Works had already been

Plate 173 The new goods shed at Herbert Street, Wolverhampton.

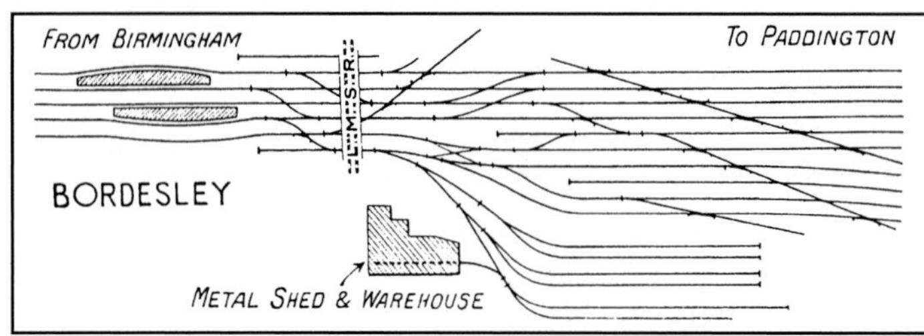

Map 26. Plan of the new shed and warehouse at Small Health, near Bordesley.

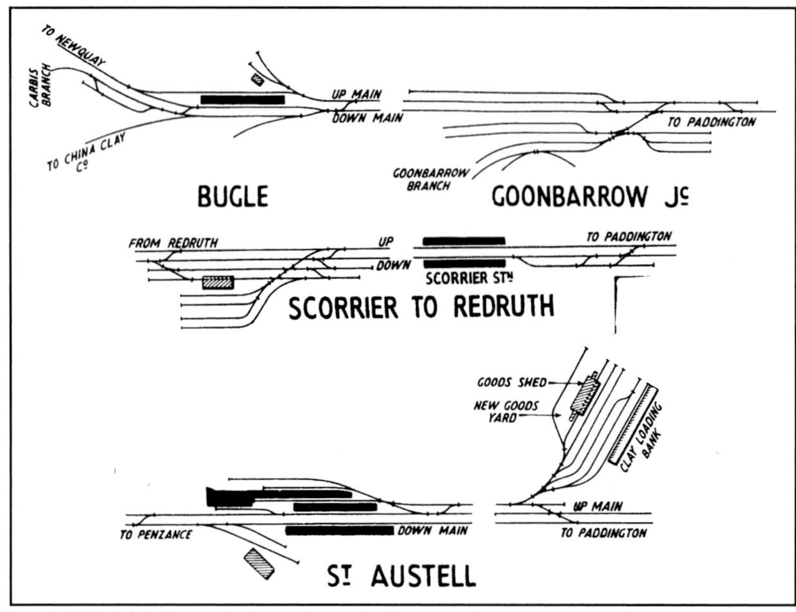

Map 27. Track improvements in Cornwall.

dealt with before these provisions came into force (see elsewhere), but major improvements were carried out under the Act at Wolverhampton (see elsewhere). There were smaller improvements at Swindon and Cardiff.

At Swindon, a new carriage shop was completed and brought into use. It enabled the maintenance of carriage stock, a large proportion of which surprisingly before had to be repaired on sidings in the open, to be brought under cover. The new shop made possible the systematic repainting and reconditioning of carriages, improving their appearance and effecting an economy through the better preservation of the body work by a more frequent repainting; also by more frequent attention to, and adjustment of, the running gear, it effected a saving in wear and tear. The rebuilding of the old 'A' engine shed at Swindon, a wooden structure built in 1846, was completed by the erection of a stone building in the same style as, and set back so as to be in continuation of, the other buildings adjacent to the main line.

Also at Swindon, the old spring shop was doubled in size and four additional triple-chamber gas-fired furnaces, one 25ft by 2ft 9in coil spring furnace, as well as the machine makers' machines formerly housed in the wagon works, were installed. The locomotive repairing shed 'B' was extended over the site of the 80-year old 'A' shed which served originally as a broad-gauge engine shed, and which was demolished, partly to make room for the new up relief line (in connection with the Didcot to Swindon line improvements discussed elsewhere) and partly because of the demand for the development of 'B' shed. The engine traversers of 'B' shed were extended to serve the twenty new or remodelled pits of about 48ft length, and the tracks for the overhead cranes were extended to allow operation in the extension, in which a new stores was built. The demolition of the old building displaced a plant for the recovery of oil from machine-shop turnings, for which a new house was built with an improved layout to facilitate the arrival and despatch of the turnings and the handling of the recovered oil. It was on a site close to the machine shop which it served.

For the repair of carriages and wagons in South Wales, a new works was built at Cathays in Cardiff, where there was erected a well lit and heated shop 420ft long and 144ft wide, with three equal bays, with two lean-to buildings along one side containing a general store and a timber store. The machine shop was formerly one of the Engineers Department shops, and the former timber drying shed was converted into a boiler house for heating both the repair works and the adjoining Engineers Department shops.

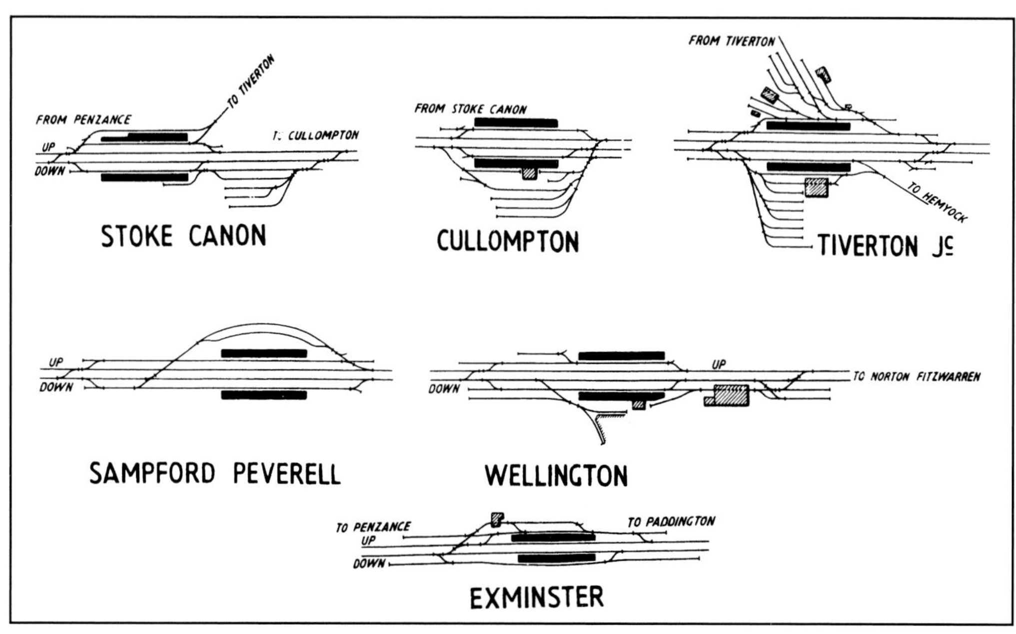

Map 28. Improvements to line capacity at the stations between Wellington and Stoke Canon.

1933 QUADRUPLING THE BIRMINGHAM MAIN LINE

Before the First World War, the GWR had a scheme for providing four running lines out from Birmingham (Snow Hill) as far as Rowington Junction, where a branch to Henley-in-Arden left the main line. The construction of the direct line between Tyseley and Henley-in-Arden, as well as changed conditions resulting from the war, however, caused the widening works to be carried out only as far as Olton, five miles from Snow Hill. The development of traffic, past and prospective, made it desirable to continue the quadrupling as soon as a favourable opportunity occurred, and when the Government facilities under the 1929 Act became available, the work was put in hand. This work gave four lines all the way from Birmingham to Lapworth, a distance of $12\frac{3}{4}$ miles. The abandonment of the Rowington Junction to Henley-in-Arden branch, owing to the removal of the rails for war purposes and the diversion of the local traffic to the roads, made the extension of the two additional lines beyond Lapworth unnecessary.

The work involved about 450,000 cubic yards of cutting and embankment as well as the construction of 33 bridges and five stations. Steam and petrol-driven excavators were used, and all the excavation material was shifted by Decauville narrow-gauge railway. Between the main and relief lines high-speed junctions with switch diamonds were laid at Lapworth, Knowle and Solihull. No curves had a radius smaller than one mile, except at one spot in the relief line at Knowle and another at Olton, where the radius was 4000ft. The permanent way was the usual standard 95 lb/yd bull-headed rail in 60ft lengths resting in cast-iron chairs weighing 46lb each on creosoted Oregon pine sleepers. A 12in layer of clinker ashes was laid throughout on the formation, and above this top ballast of crushed stone was used. The formation in cutting was drained by stoneware pipes, varying in size from 6in to 12in diameter and laid along both sides at the toe of the batter. A 6in pipe was laid in the 6ft way through the stations between the platforms. All the pipes were open-jointed with catchpits at suitable intervals.

The principal bridge on the work was a large steel underbridge at Warwick Road, Olton, Owing to the road being widened from 36ft to 60ft, it was necessary to have five girders of 152ft span.

Plate 174 Cullompton, a typical enlarged four-line two-platform station.

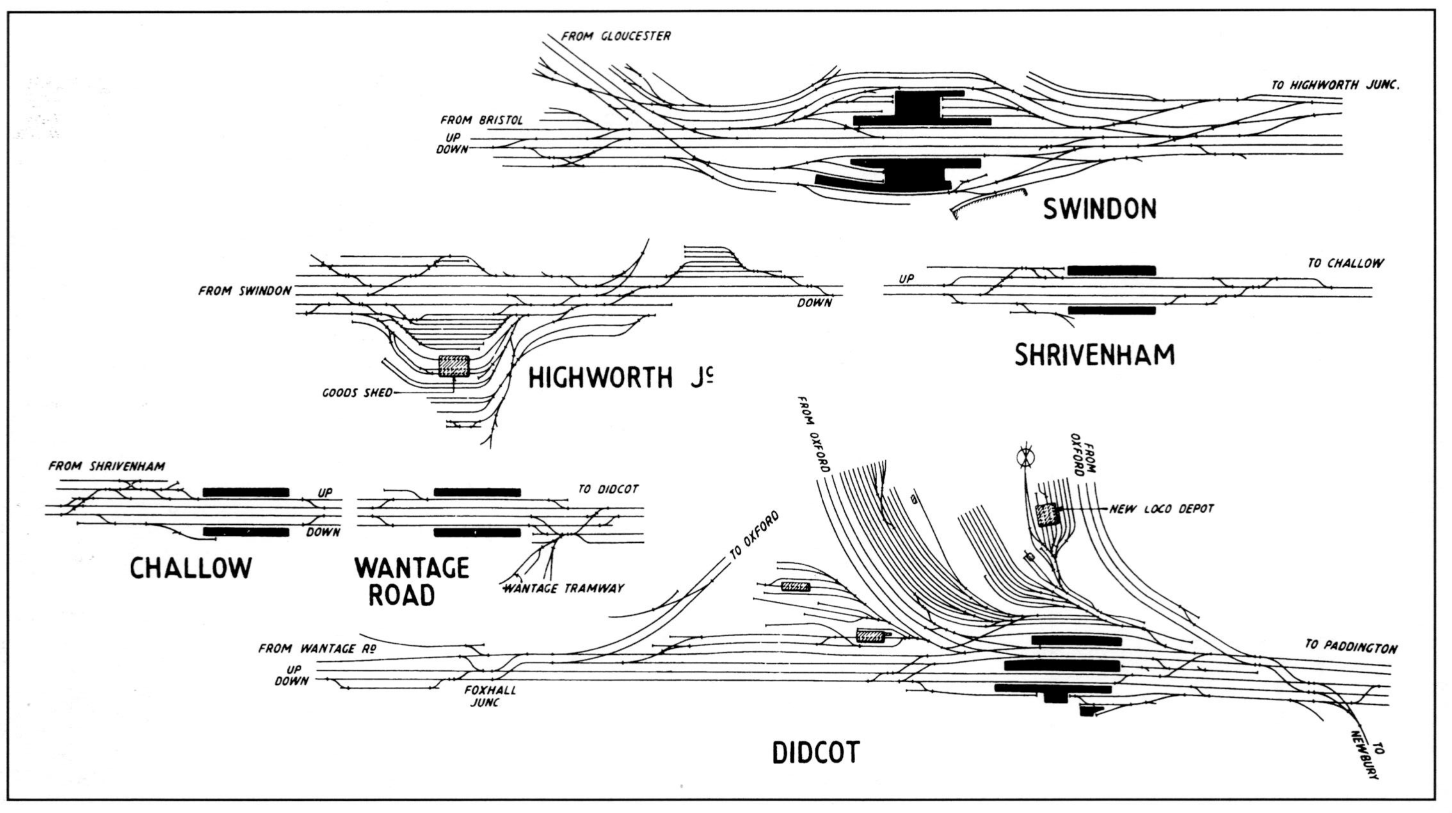

Map 29. Improvements to station layouts between Swindon and Didcot.

Plate 175 General view looking east of the reconstructed Didcot station, showing the new Didcot engine shed on the left, the old broad gauge narrow gauge transfer shed right foreground, and the new passenger station centre mid-distance. Photograph taken from the roof of the provender store large building.

Plate 176 The reconstructed Didcot station, showing the straightened lines through the station. The modern engine shed is on the right. The tall building on the horizon is the provender store.

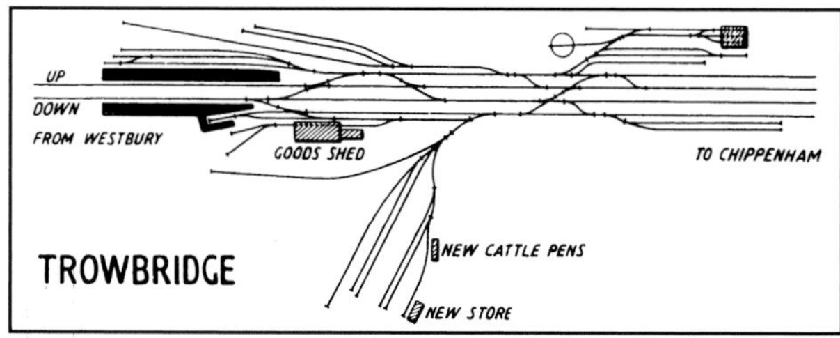

Map 30. Improvements at Trowbridge

These were of the open lattice type with parallel booms 175ft long overall and 20ft high, and each weighed about 160 tons. The floor was of steel plate and cross girders and rail bearers, and the whole bridge contained nearly 1,000 tons of steel. Cross bracing was provided between the tops of the girders. The abutments were of mass concrete reinforced in places with old steel rails. There were ten brick-arch bridges on the work, and the whole of the masonry was in lime mortar, with the exception of one or two arches in cement mortar. The face brickwork in all cases was of Staffordshire brindle brick.

The five stations situated on the widened length were all entirely rebuilt or extensively remodelled. At Olton and Solihull the old stations were demolished, and new station buildings were built below the level of the line and were connected to the two island platforms by subways. At Widney Manor, Knowle and Dorridge, and Lapworth, the station offices were at rail level, and the platforms, on which the usual waiting rooms etc were provided, were connected by footbridges. All the platforms were covered with umbralla roofing, covered with corrugated steel sheeting. Provision was made for the Knowle racehorse traffic by a loading platform for 14 horse-boxes, as part of the up main platform. Carriage sidings were laid out on the down side of the line. At Knowle a new goods yard was provided about $1/4$ mile on the Birmingham side of the passenger station. The goods shed was 120ft by 40ft and was steel-framed covered with corrugated steel sheeting. A 1 ton travelling crane was provided for its entire length. At Solihull also a new goods yard was laid out with a similar goods shed. Ample cattle pens, roads and stacking space were provided at both Solihull and at Knowle.

All lines were track-circuited throughout, and between Acocks Green and Solihull semi-automatic signalling was installed. There were new signal boxes at Solihull and Olton, and where facing points were beyond the Ministry of Transport limitation of limit distance for manually-worked points, they were electrically operated.

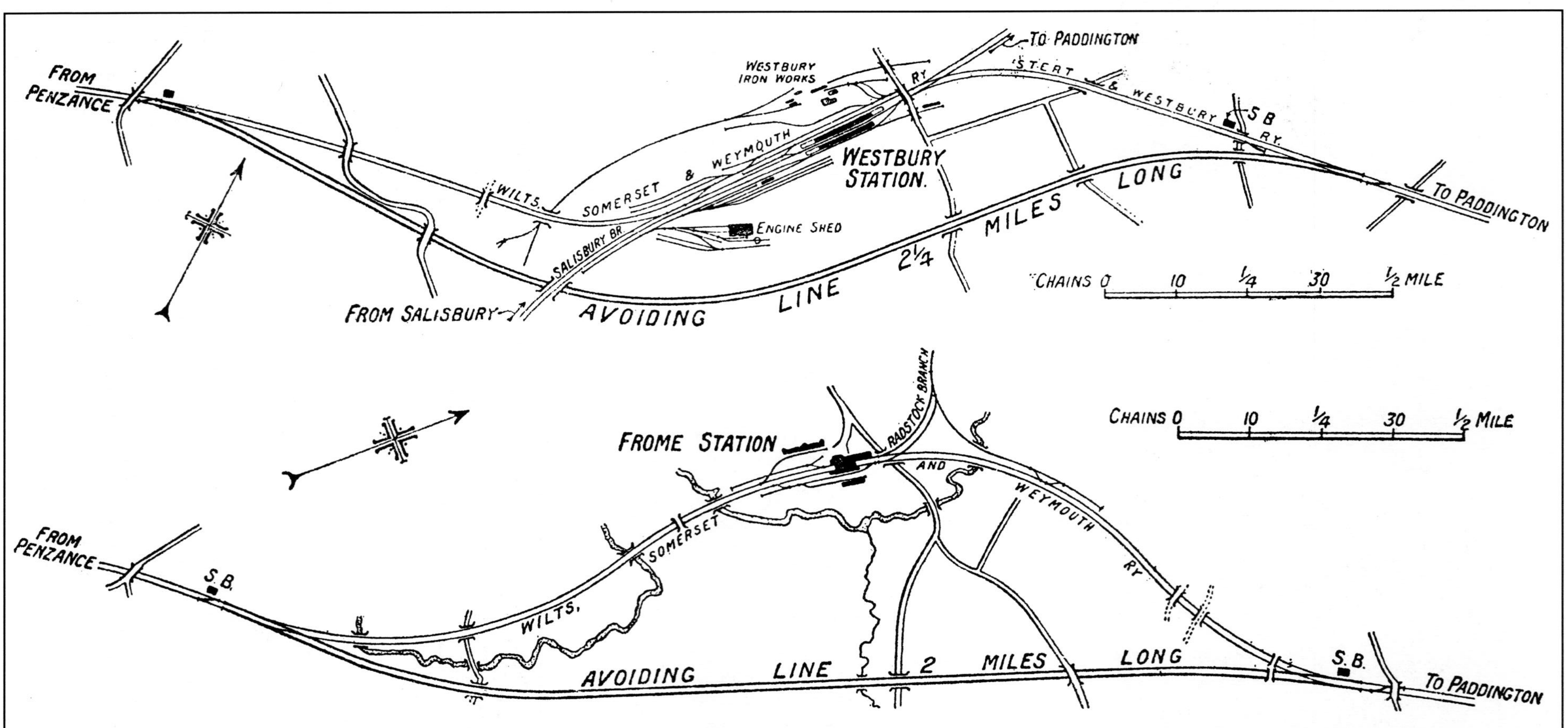

Map 31. Plans of the Westbury and Frome avoiding lines as originally announced. As constructed the signal box at the London end of the Westbury cut off was built adjacent to the actual junction and not as shown.

Plate 177 The site of Fairwood Junction to be on the Westbury avoiding line, showing the route of the new cut-off.

Plate 178 The Frome avoiding line under construction.

Plate 179 Building the Frome cut-off line, a view looking westwards at the site of Clink Road Junction.

1933 NEW GOODS TRAFFIC FACILITIES IN THE BIRMINGHAM AREA

In connection with the policy of speeding up goods traffic, and of catering for the modern traders' conditions, which call for increased storage accommodation, a number of goods sheds and warehouses were provided under the 1929 Act, several of which were in the Birmingham area (others are discussed elsewhere).

A new goods warehouse was erected by the GWR at Soho & Winson Green. Difficulty was experienced with soft soil, and to obtain a suitable foundation, it was necessary to resort to piling, some 400 piles being driven to an average depth of 15ft. The warehouse was built entirely of reinforced concrete, except for the external wall panels, which were of brick for sake of appearance. It was 300ft long and 75ft wide, and had three floors above the ground or platform level. These upper floors provided about 65,000 sq ft of fireproof storage space, which was a valuable addition to the district facilities. All the floors were served by four 3-ton electric lifts.

The ground floor formed a transit shed, with two platforms inside the shed, served by rail tracks accommodating 28 wagons in all. Access to these platforms was obtained by road vehicles by a number of loading bays, which were protected by cantilever roofs running the whole length of the warehouse. Office, mess room and other accommodation was provided for the warehouse staff and the men engaged in the yard. Additional siding accommodation was provided in the yard for 290 wagons, most of them in position to be served by road vehicles. To provide the sidings, about 175,000 cubic yards of earth were removed. New roadways were constructed with a total area of nearly 90,000 sq ft, over 55,000 sq ft of which were of concrete, the remainder being paved with granite sets laid on 9in of concrete.

At Wolverhampton (Herbert Street), the old yard was remodelled. The grain warehouse was extended and a new goods shed, offices and mess rooms, cattle pens, truck and cart weighbridges were constructed, and the old Victoria canal basin filled in. The goods shed was a steel-framed building, sheeted with corrugated galvanised steel, 530ft long by 73ft wide and was on the site of the old canal basin. Four platforms, two of which were approachable by road vehi-

Plate 180 Clink Road Junction on the new Frome avoiding line.

cles, extended the whole length of the shed in which there was accommodation for 75 wagons. The warehouse extension was of brick and steel construction, 60ft long by20ft wide, with four floors. The goods shed was equipped with mobile cranes, and the warehouse was served by 30cwt electric hoists. Of the sixteen new cattle pens, eight were covered. The cart weightbridge at the entrance to the yard was of 20-ton capacity. The remodelled yard had accommodation for 480 wagons.

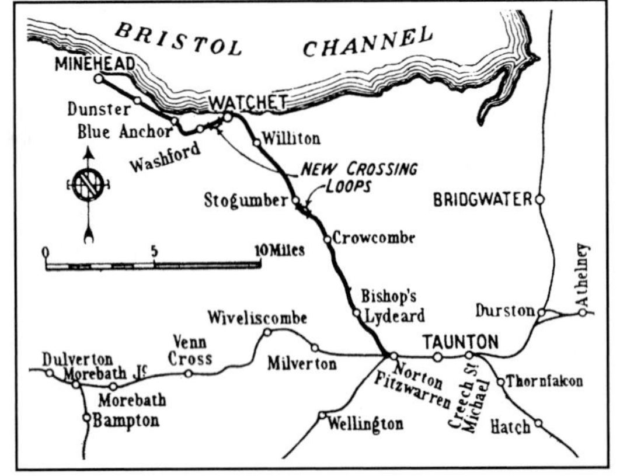

Map 32. Diagram showing the additional crossing loops provided on the Minehead branch.

At Small Heath, adjoining Bordesley station, one mile south of the GWR Snow Hill passenger station at Birmingham, a new warehouse of reinforced concrete frame and brick panelling was erected. At ground level, the building was 295ft long and there were four floors above, each 190ft long and varying in width from 85ft to 67ft. Office accommodation was provided for the staff. Inside the shed a siding for 15 wagons was laid alongside the platform, which was equipped with a 30cwt electric runway. Two 30cwt electric lifts and four 1-ton hoists provided communication from the platforms to all floors. In the goods yard additional siding accommodation for 60 wagons was arranged.

At Hockley, one mile north of Snow Hill, the old warehouse accommodation was extended in the form of a steel

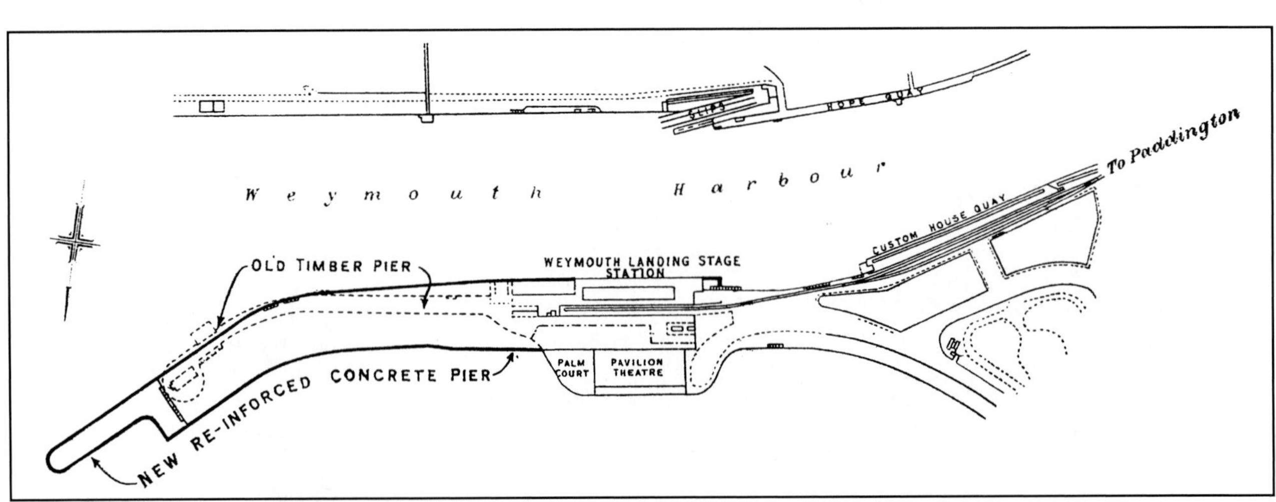

Map 33. Diagram giving outlines of the old and new piers at Weymouth.

Plate 181 The reconstruction of Weymouth Pier in progress, showing four of the new electric cranes, and the Great Western Railway Company's vessel, 'St Julien', at one of the additional steamer berths.

Plate 182 Reconstruction of the Weymouth landing stage and extension of the baggage shed in progress.

Plate 183 View from the north side of the new Weymouth pier, showing the two platforms and double track of railway.

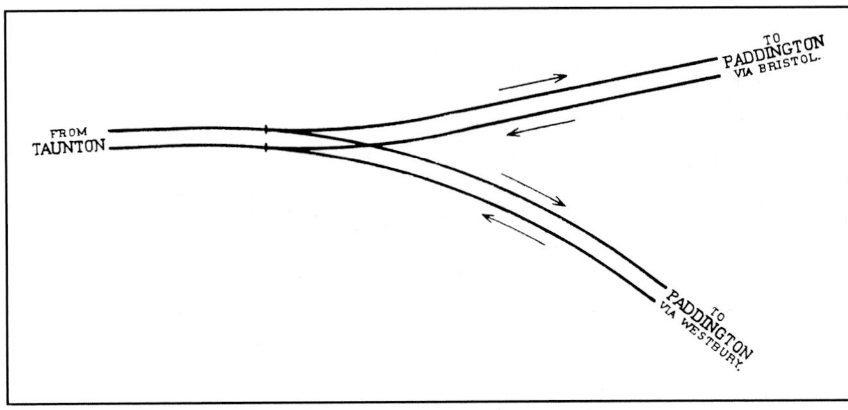

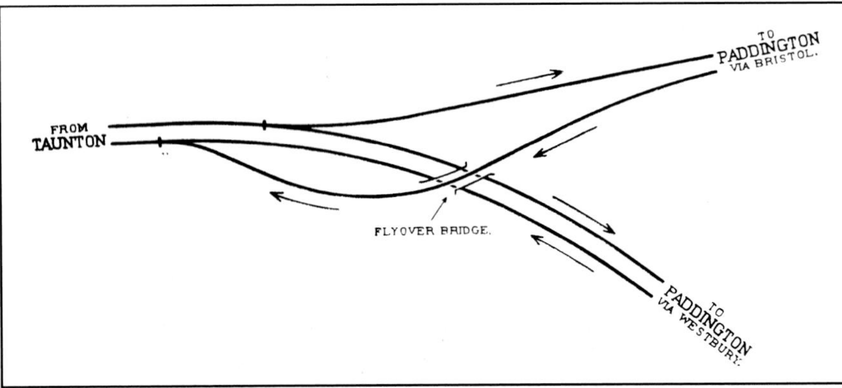

Map 34. The upper diagram shows the junction at Cogload before the construction of the fly-over bridge, the lower diagram shows the new lay-out with the fly-over bridge carrying the Bristol to Taunton line over the Taunton to Westbury lines.

framed structure with brick panelling, 92ft long by 117ft wide, consisting of three floors. It was equipped with a 30cwt lift and a 1-ton hoist serving all floors, as well as a spiral shute from the upper floors to platform level.

1933 DOUBLING OF LINES AND OTHER IMPROVEMENTS IN CORNWALL

Under the Act of 1929, the GWR doubled some lines in Cornwall. The line between Scorrier and Redruth, a length of $1\frac{3}{4}$ miles, the only single main line section between Paddington and Penzance (except that portion over the Saltash Bridge) was doubled in 1930. This additional track was laid on steel sleepers. As well as the doubling, a new shunting spur was put in at Redruth to hold 34 wagons, and a dead-end siding from this spur to hold 25 wagons. At Wheal Busy the former down refuge siding was converted into a loop to hold 35 wagons, an engine and a brake van. It was connected with the up main line at the east end and the down main line at the west end. Two bridges, four level crossings and a footbridge were enlarged.

The working of traffic on the branch to Newquay, which still remained single line for most of its length except for crossing places, was facilitated by doubling about $\frac{3}{4}$ mile of line in the neighbourhood of Bugle. At Goonbarrow Junction, about $\frac{1}{2}$ mile south of Bugle, one of the numerous branches in Cornwall for giving access to china clay and other works leaves the Newquay line, and at the other side of Bugle station two more of these branches diverge. This short section was doubled to ease the working of both passenger and freight traffic. The single line passenger platform at Bugle was converted into an island platform and its length increased to 400ft. On the platform new station buildings were erected and new access provided by a staircase from the main road overbridge, which was reconstructed and widened. The goods yard was remodelled and a new goods office built.

At St Austell, a site was acquired about $\frac{1}{4}$ mile on the London side of St Austell station, upon which a new goods yard was laid out. It contained a china clay loading bank built with concrete-arch facewalls and a 30ft wide roadway and accomodated 33 trucks alongside. There was total siding accommodation in the yard for 220 wagons, and two mileage roadways, each 30ft wide, on one of which there was a 6 ton hand crane to facilitate direct loading between road and rail vehicles. A new brick goods shed 200ft long by 40ft wide with a 25ft wide platform, occupied a position in the north-west portion of the yard, with office accommodation for the staff near the main entrance to the yard, which was approached by a new road. There was also an external uncovered platform 80ft long by 8ft wide. A 20 ton cart weighbridge was installed near the main entrance and a 35 ton truck weighbridge in the clay loading bank. An independent loop line 900ft long was laid in on the up side of the main line and connected with the sidings forming the up yard at St Austell passenger station. In connection with all this work, a public road bridge was reconstructed and lengthened, a footbridge lengthened and a new bridge built.

Plate 184 Building the fly-over at Cogload Junction. A view looking towards Taunton, showing the direct line from Castle Cary converging from the left.

1933 NORTON FITZWARREN TO NEWTON ABBOT LINE IMPROVEMENTS

The bulk of the traffic through Taunton continued along the main

Plate 185 Work in progress at the nearly completed Cogload Junction flyover.

Plate 186 The new steel fly-over bridge at Cogload, with the down Bristol line crossing the London direct lines at an acute angle.

Plate 187 The bodily removal of the Cogload junction signal box, to a new site.

line through Exeter to the West, and to facilitate the working of the express trains in conjunction with the slower stopping trains and goods trains, under the 1929 Act, six intermediate stations between Norton Fitzwarren and Newton Abbott were converted to four-line stations and at the same time were improved in other ways. These stations were Wellington, Sampford Peverell, Tiverton Junction, Cullompton, Stoke Canon and Exminster.

Besides the provision of extra up and down running lines, there were other improvements such as the building of new and longer platforms, new station buildings and other accommodation. At Wellington, where the new platforms were 700ft long, the goods shed was enlarged and a new goods office built in addition. At Sampford Peverell, the

Plate 188 The interior of cylinder for disinfecting passenger coaches and other vehicles at Swindon.

former halt was replaced by a new station with platforms 480ft long and new cattle pens provided. Tiverton Junction station was entirely rebuilt with 650ft platforms and a new goods shed equipped with overhead runways. The old locomotive shed was demolished and replaced by a new one with a new coal stage. The public road beneath the line was rebuilt with a bigger span and a greater width to carry the six lines above it. The Exe Valley and Culme Valley branches connected with the main line here. At Cullompton, Stoke Canon and Exminster new 720ft platforms and station buildings were provided and the accommodation increased. At Stoke Canon an independent branch-line platform 500ft long was provided for the Exe Valley trains. Except at Exminster, where there were two island platforms which gave four platform faces, only two main-line platforms were provided, the up and down

Plate 189 A coach being propelled into the disinfecting cylinder built at Swindon. Note the apparatus by which the door is rolled aside.

Plate 190 Disinfection in progress. In this picture the cylinder is sealed by the air-tight door.

through lines being between the up and down platform loops.

1933 DIDCOT TO SWINDON LINE IMPROVEMENTS

Prior to the early 1930s, the quadrupled tracks from Paddington ended at Didcot East Junction, the relief lines (the northern slow lines) merging into the Didcot Avoiding line. However, the opportunity was taken of the 1929 Act to continue the quadrupled lines through to Foxhall Junction and to make other improvements to the line to Swindon.

At Didcot, where the old main lines were somewhat curved through the station, the layout was improved. The two up lines and the two down lines which ran adjacent to each other were rearranged to alternate in accordance with the arrangement of the lines between Paddington and Didcot. The up local platform, an old wooden structure 220ft long, was replaced by a new island platform 810ft long, which served the Oxford branch and the up relief line. The new up line was on the position of the old down relief line and was straightened. The platforms serving the down relief, the up main and down main lines were lengthened to 1040ft each, and the old 8ft subway was widened between it and the platforms.

The junction and cross-overs at the east end of the station were realigned with switch diamonds to allow a speed of 40 mph. In October 1932, the old Didcot East signal box was replaced by a new building on the up side of the up relief line, made of concrete blocks in a steel frame under a hip gable roof. This new box was to work the enlarged and improved layout. The quadrupled tracks were extended from Didcot East Junction through the station to merge with the up and down main lines at Foxhall Junction, and the Newbury branch was connected with the main, relief and avoiding lines by a series of double junctions, this improvement being brought into use in December 1932. At the west end and at Foxhall Junction, where the relief lines commenced, 20 mph direct junctions were laid in and the down goods loop taken $\frac{1}{2}$ mile further west. At Didcot West End, the existing signal box was replaced by a larger one in September 1932. Between Didcot East Junction and Didcot West End, trains could run in either direction over any of the four main lines. Foxhall Junction signal box was replaced by a larger box in October 1931. An up goods running loop from Steventon and Milton Crossing already existed, but in October 1931, on the south side of the down main, a new down goods loop was installed. As described elsewhere, a new locomotive shed was built at Didcot.

The $3\frac{1}{2}$ miles of running lines between Wantage Road and Challow were increased to four, and both stations were given two platform roads and two through roads. At Wantage Road, the existing signal box was replaced by a larger one set back to give space for the extra tracks, to control the eastern end of the newly quadrupled layout from there to Challow. Shrivenham was similarly converted to a four-line station, and an additional running line provided for the $3\frac{1}{4}$ miles between Didcot and Steventon. The platforms at each of these three stations were increased to 600ft length, and new buildings, approach roads and horse and milk platforms built. The overbridges carrying public roads at these stations were reconstructed to span four lines

At Swindon a new marshalling yard was laid out on the up side of the line between Highworth Junction and Stratton Green bridge. It contained six new sidings giving additional accommodation totalling 4,750ft together with a new up goods loop 2,500 ft long. On the down side of the line new goods accommodation was provided giving a complete new layout for marshalling over 400 wagons. In addition there was a mileage accommodation for 240 vehicles and stabling room for 60 crippled wagons. A new goods shed with warehouse

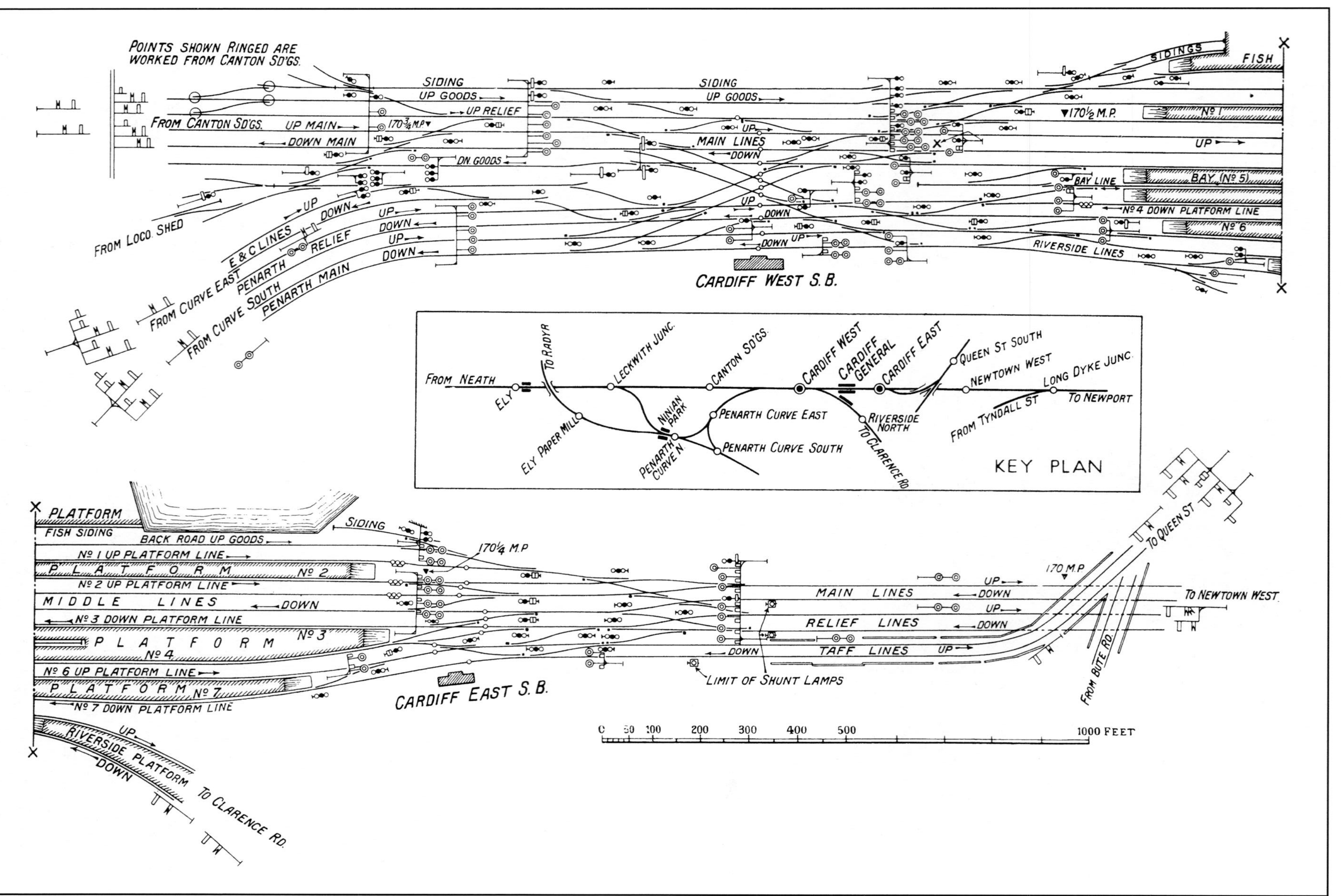

Map 35. Signalling diagram and key plan of the new power signalling installation at Cardiff GWR in 1933.

Plate 191 The new electrically-operated West Signal Box at Cardiff which replaced the former manually-operated West and Penarth Junction boxes.

Plate 192 The interior of the new Cardiff West signal box, showing the control desk with the Westinghouse type miniature lever frame with electric locking.

Plate 193 The new Cardiff East signal box showing its modern functional design.

accommodation, new offices, mess rooms, etc was built, and the lines through the goods shed accommodated 75 wagons. The new goods shed was a steel-framed structure 500ft long and 85ft wide, 400ft of which was covered with protective metal sheeting and 100ft was in brickwork, with an overhead warehouse having a floor space of 8000 sq ft. There were two platforms in the goods shed each 500ft long by 25ft wide and connected by a lifting bridge. A lift was provided to give communication between the platforms and the overhead warehouse.

Plate 194 The interior of the new Cardiff East signal box, showing the control desk with the Westinghouse type miniature lever frame.

Plate 195 The relay room on the first floor of the new Cardiff East signal box.

At the other end of Swindon station a new direct connection from the up main line to the up Gloucester platform was provided, and a new up goods loop between Rodbourne Lane and the west end of the station, involving the widening of Rodbourne Lane bridge, was also laid in, together with a new shunting spur on the down side and a considerable rearrangement of the locomotive works siding consequent upon this work.

1933 IMPROVEMENTS AT TROWBRIDGE

The 1929 Act was used to make improvements to both the passenger and goods station at Trowbridge. The up and down platforms of the former

Plate 196 General view of the railway lines adjacent to the new Cardiff East signal box.

Plate 197 The gantry carrying the up home signals at Cardiff East. Old and new signal boxes are on the right.

Plate 198 The signal bridge carrying the down home signals at Cardiff East.

were extended by 545ft and 650ft respectively, with a consequent rearrangement of the permanent way connections. In the goods yard, a new steel-framed corrugated-iron sheeted warehouse 80ft long by 20ft wide was built and the goods shed and office accommodation altered and improved. Additional mileage accommodation for 36 wagons and new cattle pens were provided. A new 30ft roadway was constructed to give improved access to the coal yard. In connection with these alterations, the bridge carrying the railway over

Plate 199 The GWR's bucket dredger "David Davies". The endless chain of buckets which brought up the mud can be seen.

Plate 200 One of the GWR's grab dredgers "Basingstoke" at work.

Plate 201 A dumb hopper barge, that is one having no motive power, used to carry the mud to the dumping grounds.

Stallard Street was reconstructed and widened.

1933 WESTBURY & FROME AVOIDING LINES

One of the first tasks to be undertaken under the Developments (Loan Guarantees & Grants) Act of 1929 was the construction of the Westbury and Frome avoiding lines. The original announcement of the work stated that the purpose of these straighter alignements was to provide better running of the West of England express trains. In the course of eliminating 30mph speed restrictions, it was not only time that would be saved. Slowing down, and re-accelerating, heavy trains involved an increase in coal consumption, as well as extra wear and tear in the machinery. On the other hand, in 1929, except for the summer service there were only three down and four up expresses running through Westbury without stopping, although no West of England

Plate 202 Close-up view of one of the grabs used in dredging. The chains in the centre were used to open and shut the jaws.

expresses then called at Frome. On the face of it these avoiding lines might have seemed expensive works for the advantages to be gained, though in the case of Westbury the benefits extended to more than the West of England trains. The station was quite a railway cross-roads in Wessex, and as the tracks existed in 1929 West of England expresses followed the least favourable alignement of any route passing through.

The West of England main line was perhaps the least busy route through Westbury. By far the heaviest flow of traffic was that between Bristol, Bath and Salisbury, including the constant succession of coal trains from South Wales to stations on the Southern Railway. The diversion of the high-priority non-stopping express passenger trains, clear of the station and of the busy junctions at the north and south end, avoided the holding up of heavy coal trains to give clearance to through expresses, and additionally improved the working of the passenger service between Bristol, Southampton and Portsmouth. The four junctions were laid out to permit unlimited speed over the new lines, while the re-alignement shortened the distance from Paddington to Castle Gary and beyond by 0.2 miles. Travelling in the down direction the Westbury avoiding line was entered at Heywood Road Junction, and the old line rejoined at Fairwood Junction just before Westbury water troughs were reached. As will be seen from the plan the Westbury avoiding line included some curvature; but the Frome line, entered at Clink Road Junction, was practically straight. It ended at Blatchbridge Junction.

The contract for the work was placed with Messrs Logan and Hemingway of Doncaster in 1930, it being estimated that the total cost of providing $4\frac{1}{4}$ miles of additional double track railway for the two avoiding lines would be about £220,000. They were brought into service in March 1933.

The distance by the old route was 15.2 miles and by the new 15.0 miles. Typical running times before and after, in both the down and up directions, were as follows: down before 18 minutes 25 seconds, after 15m 15s; up before 17m 55s and after 14m 50s. In round figures there was a saving of about 3 minutes in each direction with average speeds increased from $49\frac{1}{2}$ to $59\frac{1}{2}$ mph in the down direction, and from 51 to 61 mph in the up. This was a worthwhile improvement in the running of through express trains alone, quite apart from the improved operation of cross-country trains made possible at Westbury.

Plate 203 The bucket dredger "Foremost 49" added to the GWR's dredging fleet in 1934, and initially used at Cardiff.

1933 IMPROVEMENTS ON THE MINEHEAD BRANCH

A scheme of improvements was carried out by the GWR on the Minehead branch to enable accelerations of five to fifteen minutes to be made in journey times of trains between Paddington and Minehead, and also to improve the working of trains by eliminating delays experienced during the summer months.

On the $22\frac{1}{2}$ miles of the single track line between North Fitzwarren and Minehead, there were four crossing places where trains may pass each other, namely at Bishops Lydeard, Crowcombe, Williton and Blue

Plate 204 A well-timed exposure by the photographer catches the moment of the explosion.

Anchor. The scheme provided for the construction of two further crossing places, one at Leigh Bridge (between Crowcombe and Williton) and the other at Kentsford (between Williton and Blue Anchor), which divided the two longest sections on the branch. The crossing loops, 750ft long, were constructed to enable trains to pass through them at 40 mph, with new signal boxes being provided at each new loop. Next year, apparatus was provided on the engines and the loops to enable the single-line tokens to be exchanged automatically. The line between Minehead and Dunster was doubled and at Minehead station, the existing platform covering was extended by 200ft.

1933 PIER & HARBOUR IMPROVEMENTS AT WEYMOUTH

The need for improved accommodation at Weymouth for the Channel Islands and French traffic had been apparent for a number of years. There were heavy seasonal imports of flowers, new potatoes and tomatoes from Jersey and Guernsey, and broccoli and other vegetables from France. The nature of this traffic called for speed in discharge from vessels and dispatch by rail. Some idea of the increase in traffic can be gained from the fact that the harbour dues paid by the GWR to Weymouth Corporation increased from £4,099 in 1922 to £8,541 in 1928, when French broccoli from Roscoff was first imported to Weymouth, and in the years 1929-31 the dues exceeded £10,000 per year. Cargo vessels arriving at Weymouth were berthed at the so-called cargo stage, use being made also of the passenger stage when not in use for passengers. The continued expansion of traffic was increasing congestion and working difficulties.

Following negotiations between the GWR and Weymouth Corporation, a scheme for improvements, costing over £120,000, was agreed involving main harbour works to be financed by the Corporation backed by the GWR; permanent way, cranes, capstans etc to be paid for by the GWR; and widening the quay road, pier extension, dredging and public amenities to be paid for by the Corporation.

The improvements effected included the construction of a new pier, with a general width of 100ft, following much the same line as taken by the old structure, which was only 30ft wide. As shown on the accompanying diagram, the portion of the new pier 100 ft wide, ended about the position of the extreme end, or round head, of the old pier, but continued further seawards, 40ft in width, for a distance of about 260ft. The total length of the new pier was nearly a quarter of a mile. The work was carried out entirely in reinforced concrete of two types: a solid potion, in which filling was held by retaining walls built on piles, and an open portion built entirely on piles under which a half-tide bank was constructed to prevent silt from the bay entering the harbour.

The new pier was designed to accommodate one passenger, three cargo and two pleasure steamers simultaneously; berths for the latter, at the extreme end, were on either side of the extension, access to these was provided down the public promenade portion on the north side. Additional cranes were supplied, making a total of six electric cranes (one fixed and five travelling), capable of dealing with loads ranging from 30 cwt to 5 tons, with a maximum radius of 60ft, together with electric capstans. The additional berths and cranes, together with an extended double line of track in place of the former single line, greatly facilitated handling cargo traffic.

There were also improved arrangements for dealing with the passenger traffic, which had also increased in recent years, especially in the peak months of July, August and September. The platform accommodation, which

Plate 205 This picture shows the effectiveness of the explosion, with rubble lying on the track ready to be cleared away.

Plate 206 Aerial view of Paddington passenger and goods stations, and vicinity, with the canal and main streets marked.

formerly was adequate for only four coaches, was enlarged to accept 36 coaches. The baggage shed, directly opposite the passenger boat berth, was extended and renovated. It included facilities for Customs examination. A new refreshment room was provided. Other buildings were erected, including mess rooms and offices for the Customs and other staff.

1933 FLY-OVER JUNCTION AT COGLOAD

To cope with the increasing density of traffic on the main lines of the GWR between London and Taunton, via Bristol and via Westbury, it was decided to construct a fly-over bridge at Cogload Junction. By the construction of this bridge, the up and down lines via Westbury in the direction of Taunton had the down Bristol line on one side and the up Bristol line on the other side, thus taking the place of the double-line junctions which formerly existed. Furthermore, the new fly-over arrangement enabled a signal box and a complicated system of local signalling to be dispensed with. Readers will hardly need any explanation of how the introduction of a fly-over crossing avoids the constant interruption to traffic caused by the previous double junction arrangement.

To carry the down Bristol line, it was necessary to form embankment approaches to the fly-over bridge, of considerable length, with an easy gradient on the Bristol side but a somewhat steeper gradient on the Taunton side. The new bridge was built entirely of steel, with main girders of the Warren type, and vertical suspenders to alternate cross girders. The girders were 185ft and 161ft in length, weighing 88 tons and 70 tons respectively, the abutments being out of parallel due to the large skew angle of the crossing. The floor of the bridge consisted of cross girders at 11ft 9in centres, carrying rail bearers placed directly under the rails, and over the whole floor there was rivetted a steel deck on which was laid a standard ballasted cross-sleeper road. The total amount of steel-work in the span was 227 tons.

The construction of this fly-over junction formed part of an extensive scheme for the improvement of nearby working facilities, which included quadrupling the lines between Cogload Junction and Norton Fitzwarren, a distance of $7^1/_2$ miles, so enabling Westbury trains to run either side of the island platform at Taunton.

1933 DISINFECTING PLANT FOR RAILWAY ROLLING STOCK

At the Swindon Works a plant was built for disinfecting, killing vermin and destroying bacteria in coaches and other vehicles, particularly those used for the conveyance of flour and grain. The plant consisted of a steel cylinder 85ft long and 16ft 6in diameter, in which was fitted a railway track, upon which the vehicles to be treated were run in, without any dismantling. The cylinder was then sealed by an air-tight door being swung into position. The temperature in the cylinder was raised to 120 degrees Fahr (50 degrees Cent) by

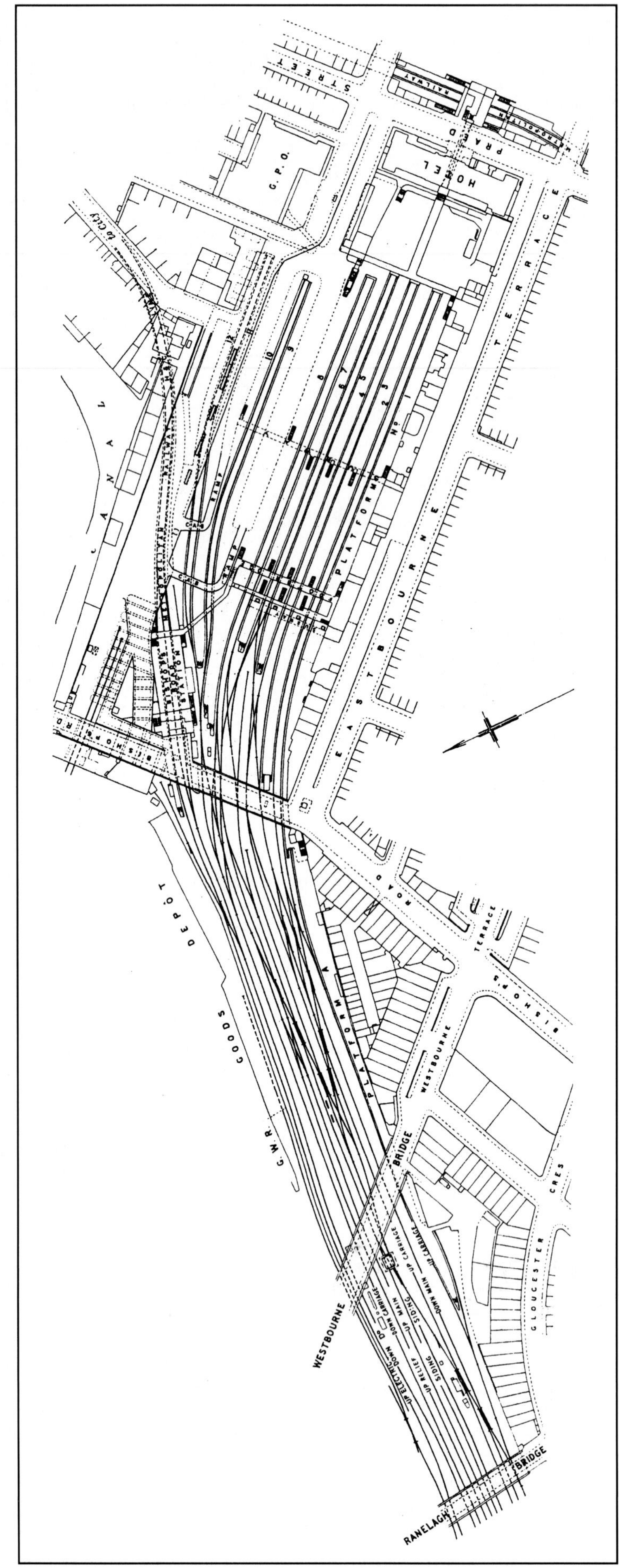

Map 36. Paddington station layout of approach lines and platforms in 1929, before the new extensions and improvements were started.

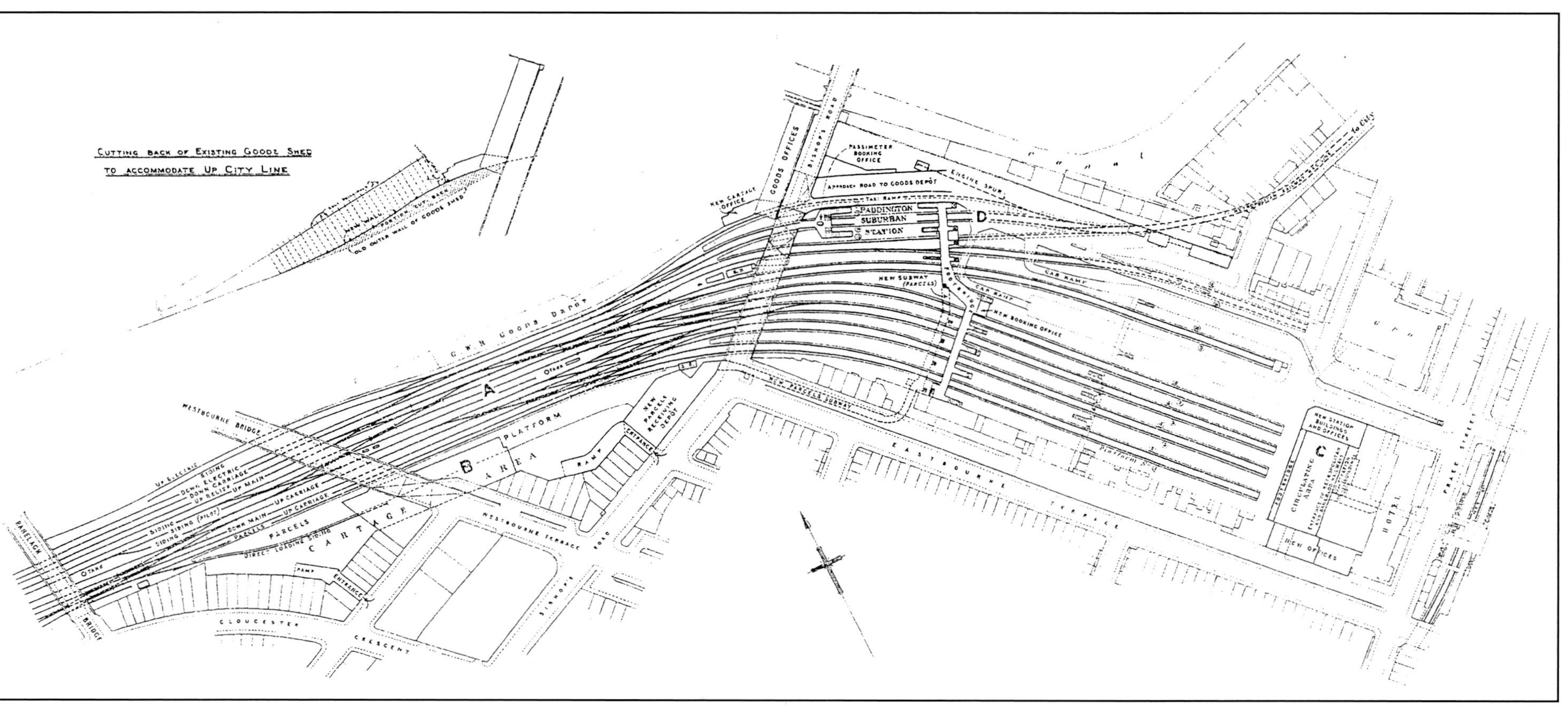

Map 37. Paddington Station new layout of approach lines and platforms, showing the new parcels arrangements, Bishop's Road station enlargement and new circulating area, 1933.

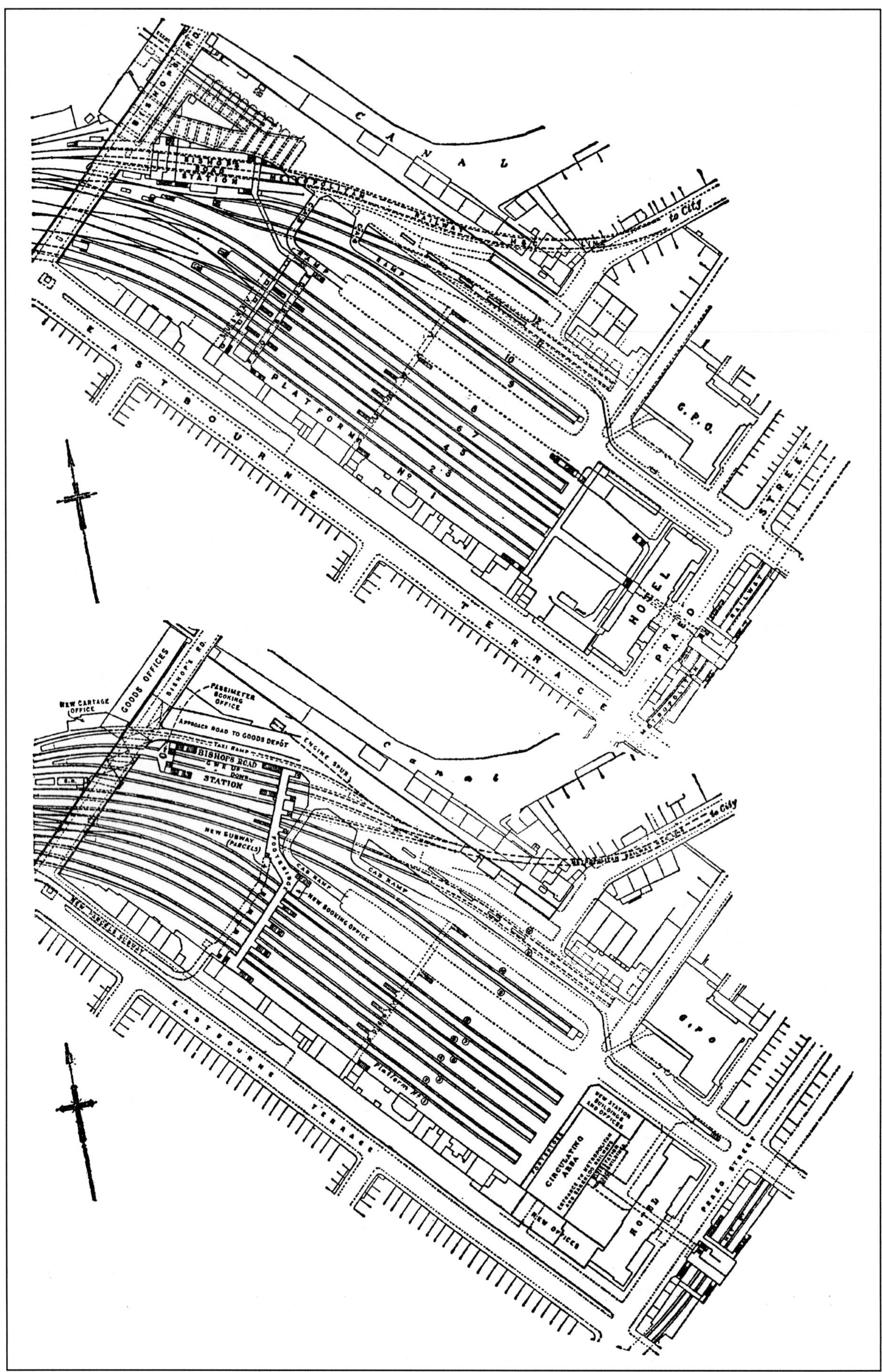

Map 38. Plans of Paddington Station before (above) and after (below) modernisation

Plate 207 The new GWR offices at Paddington, an imposing eight-storied building situated on the arrival side of Paddington passenger station.

steam-heating pipes, which completely encircled the vehicle under treatment, and the air was withdrawn from the cylinder by a pump, until a vacuum of 28in of mercury was reached. This temperature and vacuum were maintained for six hours, ensuring complete destruction of vermin.

In cases where vehicles had been exposed to infectious diseases, the above-mentioned temperature and vacuum were produced, and formalin was then introduced into the cylinder from a small tank connected by a pipe to an evaporating chamber on the steam-heating pipe line, where it became formaldehyde gas, and was drawn through perforated tubes into the cylinder. The gas penetrated to every part of the vehicle, thoroughly disinfecting everything, including such articles as cushions, bolsters and rugs.

1933 POWER SIGNALLING AT CARDIFF GENERAL STATION

At the time, one of the largest and most up-to-date signalling installations in the country was installed by the GWR at Cardiff, consequent upon the rebuilding of the station. Within the station area itself, electric power signalling, comprising colour light signals, electrically operated points and complete track circuiting, was installed, the whole being controlled from two new signal boxes, the East with 153 levers and the West with 339 levers. The latter displaced the old West and Penarth Junction signal boxes.

As will be described in more detail later in this book, the station was rebuilt to provide three down platforms (numbered 3, 4 & 7), three up platforms

Plate 208 The seven-storied extension of the Great Western Railway Company's offices at the eastern end of Paddington Station on the departure side.

(numbered 1,2 & 6), and a bay at the west end for arrival and departure of trains in the Swansea direction. In addition there were up and down middle lines and an up goods line for through traffic. The Riverside station, adjoining on the south side, retained its identity but was rebuilt as an island platform accommodating the up and down lines from Clarence Road.

Approaching from the east end, access from the down main line was given to Nos 3 & 4 platforms and to the down middle line; from the down relief line, access was given to Nos 3, 4 & 7 platforms and the down middle line; and from the down Taff Vale lines to Nos 4 & 7 platforms. Departures to the up main line could be made from Nos 1 & 2 platforms and the up good line; to the up relief line from Nos 1, 2 & 6 platforms and the up good line; and to the up Taff Vale line from Nos 4 & 6 platforms. On the north side there was a short dead-end siding for locomotives. Designing the layout for giving these facilities and fixing the signalling apparatus was difficult owing to the presence of restrictions on space imposed by the five underbridges in the area.

Plate 209 View in the other direction of the seven-storied extension of the GWR offices at the eastern departure side of Paddington station, showing the hotel on the right.

The design of the new East and West signal boxes marked a departure from previous GWR practice, and was at the time classified as industrial architecture incorporated with a touch of modernism. Both boxes were of similar construction, steel framed with red brick filling, and faced externally with multi-coloured sand-faced bricks. The ground floor contained a room into which was led the main power supply, with switchboard, transformers, battery room, central-heating apparatus and lineman's accommodation. The first floor housed the relay racks and cable runs, with a walkway below the interior of the interlocking frame giving access to the internal wiring and apparatus of the frame. The top floor was the operating room, with the interlocking frame, block telegraph, telephones, etc. On this floor, a bay window gave each box an unobstructed view of the whole of the area under its control. The interior walls of this room were faced with glazed buff tiling to the height of the window sill, the remainder of the wall being plastered and painted a light cream colour. The floors throughout were of patent fire-resisting type.

The interlocking frames were operated by miniature levers 4in long, spaced 2½in apart, with electric interlocking. Separate locks were provided for the interlocking, a second lock came into operation for track-circuit or other controls. The signal levers had three positions; normal, reverse and normal checklock. In the normal position the signals were at danger or, in the case of distant signals, at caution, with the locks of the electric interlocking de-energised. Provided that the track ahead was unoccupied and all points concerned in their correct position (bolted in the case of facing points), the lever could be reversed and the signal changed to clear.

All running signals were directly controlled by the track circuits over which they led and were automatically replaced to danger by the passage of the train, as well as constantly detected through all facing points in the route. In addition, they were provided with approach locking and automatic time releasing, preventing any attempt to alter the route once the signal for that route had been lowered, until a predetermined interval of time had elapsed. By this provision of route-locking, the route ahead was held; but to obtain the maximum traffic facilities sectional release locking was incorporated to enable a fresh route to be set in rear of the previous movement as early as possible. Signals could be placed at danger at any time, but the lever could not be replaced beyond the normal checklock position unless the signal was displaying the correct aspect.

The point levers had two positions only, normal and reverse, there being no check-locking. A stencil indicator behind the point lever was illuminated when the requisite track and detection controls were correct. The aspects displayed by the signals and the positions of the points were displayed by illuminated indicators on a board of the frame immediately behind the levers. In the case of signals, the indication was given by small glass roundels displaying the same indication as the signals themselves, while for the points the positions were indicated by an illuminated letter N or R according to whether the points were lying in the normal or reverse positions. Two small roundels were illuminated as each track-circuited section was occupied. Two of these diagrams were provided at the 339 lever West box because it would normally be operated by two signalmen.

Block working between the two boxes was retained, also with the signal boxes on either side. The block

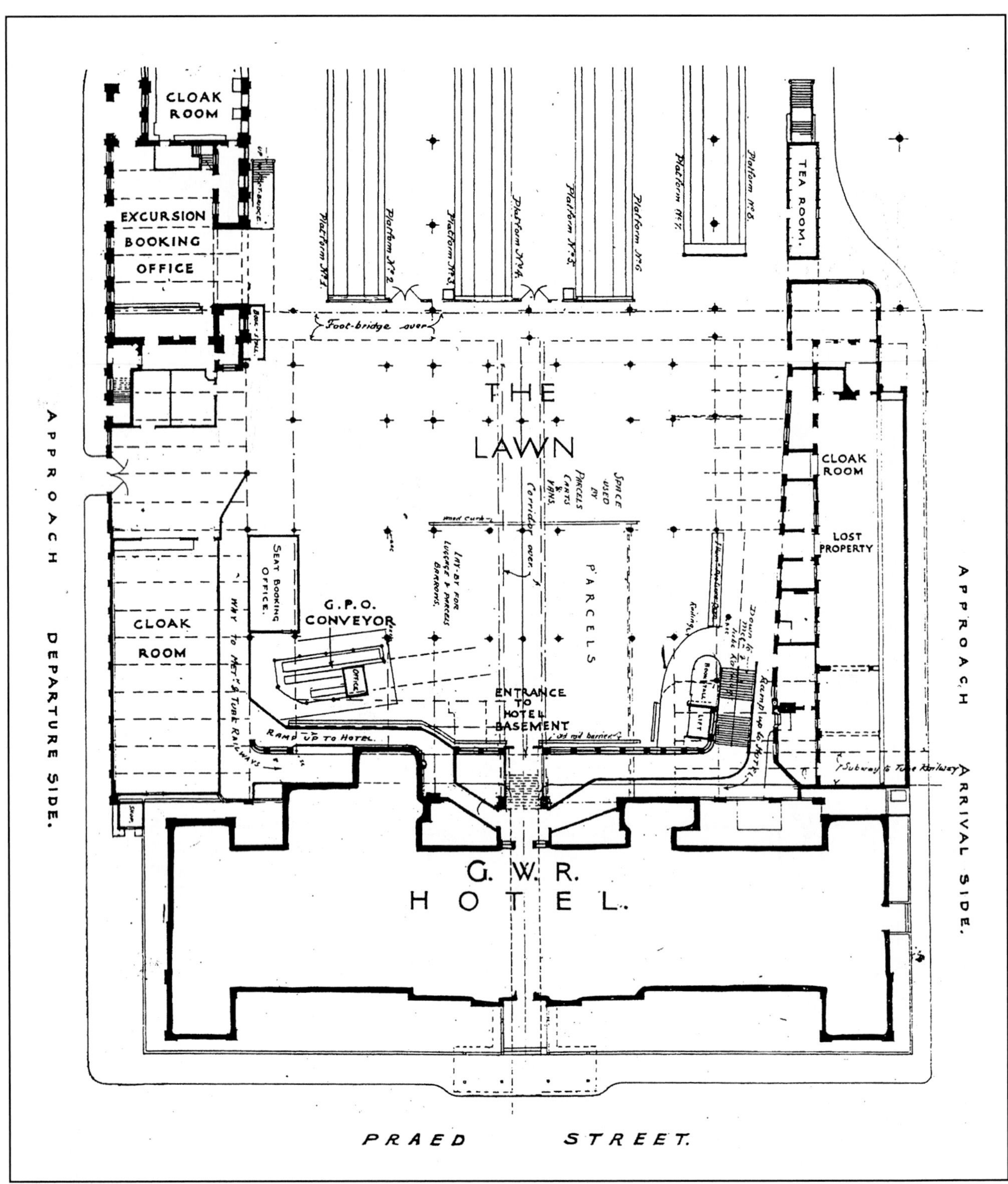

Map 39. Plan of the Lawn as it was before the alternations.

instruments were incorporated in the indication boards of the interlocking frames, while all box-to-box telephones were mounted on the front of these boards. The whole design gave the signalmen easy operation of the levers, block telegraph and telephones, as well as a clear unobstructed lookout through the windows.

For the main lines, signals of the searchlight type were employed, displaying two aspects, green and red for stop signals, and green and yellow for distant signals. These signals projected a high intensity beam, the light from a 12 volt 12 watt lamp being projected from a high efficiency glass reflector through roundels of coloured heat-resistant glass, the change in position of which altered the indication displayed. The indication given by these signals was visible over more than 6000ft even in bright sunlight. The point machines, of which there were around 140, were operated by direct current at 120 volts, taken from trickle-charged batteries. They were fixed, with

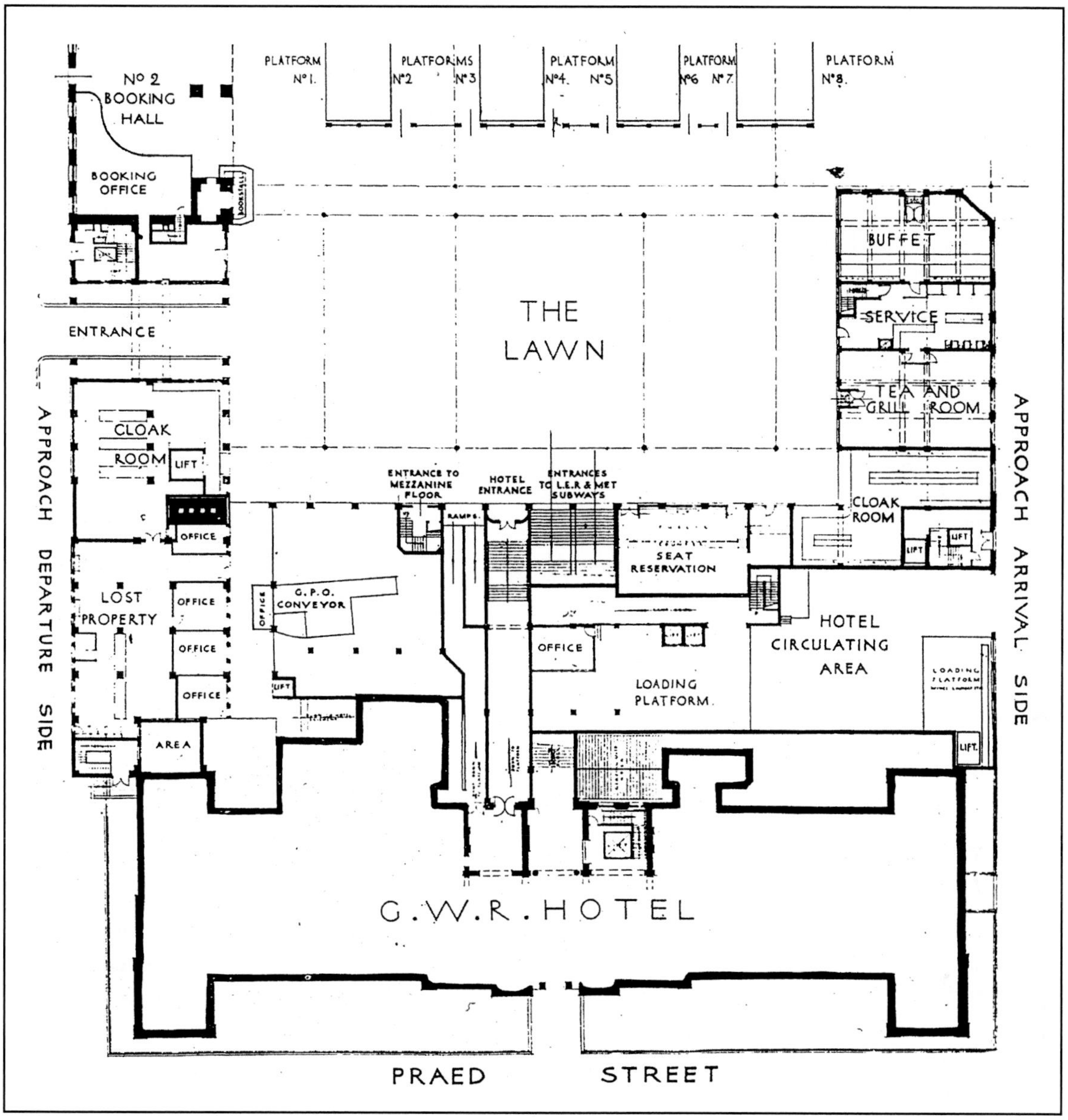

PLATFORM N°1. PLATFORMS N°2 N°3 PLATFORM N°4. N°5 PLATFORM N°6 N°7 PLATFORM N°8.

N° 2 BOOKING HALL

BOOKING OFFICE

BOOKSTALL

ENTRANCE

THE LAWN

BUFFET

SERVICE

TEA AND GRILL ROOM

CLOAK ROOM

LIFT

OFFICE

LOST PROPERTY

OFFICE

OFFICE

OFFICE

AREA

APPROACH DEPARTURE SIDE

APPROACH ARRIVAL SIDE

ENTRANCE TO MEZZANINE FLOOR

RAMPS

HOTEL ENTRANCE

ENTRANCES TO L.E.R. & MET SUBWAYS

SEAT RESERVATION

CLOAK ROOM

LIFT

LIFT

G.P.O. CONVEYOR

OFFICE

LIFT

OFFICE

LOADING PLATFORM.

HOTEL CIRCULATING AREA

LOADING PLATFORM

LIFT.

G.W.R. HOTEL

PRAED STREET

Map 40. Plan of the Lawn after the alternations, illustrating the clearance made to the Lawn to form the new concourse. The buffer stops were moved back, and gates and railings placed across this end of the Lawn. The new entrance to the subways of the Bakerloo and Metropolitan Railways is shown, as well as the hotel circulating area off the arrival side approach side approach road, and the new corridor and entrance to the hotel from the Lawn.

Plate 210 The old 'Lawn' at Paddington station, a rather dismal looking area much improved by the rebuilding.

few exceptions, in the six-foot way on extensions of the sleepers adjacent to the points, and combined in one mechanism the electric motor, facing point bolt, detection, cut-out contacts and circuit device. All cable in the main runs was of paper-insulated lead-sheathed type, terminated in connection boxes at various locations round the yard. The cables were run in wooden trunking supported by brackets from the walls or from concrete posts. Opposite each of the signal boxes, cables crossed below the rails in special cast-iron conduits laid in concrete.

Plate 211 This view shows the famous 'Lawn' at Paddington during rebuilding in February 1933. The parcels traffic was banished to platform A. Work was under way on the provision of new refreshment rooms (bottom right) and new offices. The exposed ironwork grill ends of Brunel's arched roofs can be seen. This work transformed the 'Lawn' into a spacious circulating area, roofed in steel and glass, and served by refreshment rooms, seat reservation and lost property offices.

1934 DREDGING THE SOUTH WALES DOCKS AND APPROACH CHANNELS

The waters of the Bristol Channel carry in suspension a lot of solid matter. The main proportion of this material is probably brought down day after day from inland, by the ebb tide of the River Severn, while some consists of sea sand. Towards the eastern end of the Channel, where the Severn runs into it, the water is always more or less brown in colour, on account of the earth matter contained in it. As the western, or Atlantic end of the Channel is approached, the waters become perceptibly clearer, and such material as is in suspension consists mainly of sea-sand.

The heavy proportion of mud and sand contained in the waters of the Bristol Channel largely arises through the effect of the considerable difference in the level of water between low and high tides. At the inner end of the Channel there is a rise and fall on ordinary spring tides of over 40ft.

Plate 212 The Ticket Office was extensively modernised as part of the improvements made at Paddington. This photograph was taken in May 1936 and shows the clean lines of the No 2 Booking Hall. The spaces between the ticket windows were filled with GWR posters.

Plate 213 A corner of the new Lawn circulating area.

At high water there may be 46ft depth on the entrance sill of one of the docks, this is reduced to a foot or two at low water. Thus, there is an immense volume of water passing up and down the Channel each tide. Vast quantities of mud are continually being churned up by the moving mass of water. The material in suspension is to a large extend deposited on the sides of the bed of the Channel at low water of each tide, and this was the aspect of the subject affecting the GWR's principal docks, which were situated on the north side of the Bristol Channel, running from east to west, Newport, Cardiff, Penarth, Barry, Port Talbot and Swansea.

To clear away the mud or silt which accumulated in the channels leading to the docks, and in the docks themselves, it was necessary to carry out continuous dredging operations so that an adequate depth of water might be maintained. The magnitude of the operations may be gathered from the fact that about five million cubic yards of material had to be dredged yearly at the South Wales ports. The work was carried out under the supervision of the Engineering Department in collaboration with the dock managers to ensure that the operations involved the least interruption to traffic. To ascertain the extent of dredging required, periodical "soundings" were taken and plans were made indicating the depth of mud to be dredged away.

The GWR maintained a fleet of dredgers and mud carriers (or hopper barges, as they were usually called). The more usual operation was by a "bucket" dredger. Buckets, fixed at intervals on an endless chain, which worked around a kind of ladder, scooped up the mud from pre-arranged depths below the surface of the water, whilst the dredger moved slowly forward, the ladder being adjusted to suit the rise and fall of the tide. As the buckets reached the top of the "ladder", a mechanism was operated automatically by which they discharged their contents to shutes on either side, down which the material slipped into barges or into the dredger's own hoppers. The material was then taken some miles down the Bristol Channel, to the dumping or spoil ground, which was situated where the material would be carried seaward by the natural action of the tide. The locations of dumping grounds were fixed with the sanction of the Board of Trade, and were suitably buoyed.

When the doors at the bottom of the hopper were opened to discharge, the water did not rush in and sink the vessel because the barges were kept afloat by buoyancy chambers. These doors were mud-tight, but not watertight, and normally the level of the water in the hopper was the same as that outside. As the solid material was loaded, the water was displaced and flowed away over the coamings round the top of the hold and through holes in the sides of the barge at deck level, called scuppers. When the dredged material was discharged, the hopper doors permitted the re-entry of water, and the hopper filled again to the level outside.

It was not possible for the large bucket dredgers to work close to the quay walls or in corners of docks, and therefore, a smaller type of vessel, termed a "grab" dredger, fitted with cranes and grabs, was used. The grab, which was suspended by a chain, comprised two jaws. It was lowered into the water in an open position and the act of withdrawal operated gear which brought the jaws together, enclosing the material into which they had sunk by their own weight. When the grab was raised, the crane was

Plate 214 The transformation of the Lawn is shown in this August 1935 photograph, now a pleasant circulating area for passengers. The removal of the parcels traffic to the new depot allowed the cast iron columns and short-span roof to be removed and replaced by a new three-bay roof. The lighting was improved. A new entrance was made for the GWR Royal Hotel, and the entrance to the Bakerloo and Metropolitan Underground stations upgraded.

slewed round over the hold, the gear operated to open the jaws, and the load was deposited either in a hopper receptacle on the dredger itself, or into a hopper barge alongside.

The dredging depth of the bucket dredger varied from 40 to 50ft, and their lifting capacity, under normal conditions, was anything up to 750 cubic yards per hour. In the case of steam hopper barges (that is, with their own motive power), the carrying capacity of the more modern type of craft was about 900 cubic yards; the figure in the case of the "dumb" hopper barges (non-steam that is with no motive power of their own) being considerably less.

The GWR's fleet consisted in 1933 of six bucket dredgers, six grab dredgers, twelve steam self-propelled hopper barges and five dumb hopper barges. The last had to be towed to and from the dumping ground. The fleet was worked as a whole, so that the various units could be dispersed or concentrated according to the necessities of the respective docks. While the bulk of the work, and particularly that at the more exposed western ports, was tackled in the summer months, some dredging work had to be done all the year round. It was a never-ending task, entailing considerable expense, for which there was no direct return; but without the dredging the docks could not have accommodated the ships which carried the enormous volume of imports and exports dealt with year by year.

For the most part the work went on with monotonous regularity, day after day, but occasionally obstructions were met with, as, for instance, when a bucket ladder got entangled in a piece of wire rope which lay unsuspected on the bottom of the dock, or perhaps a ship's lost anchor might foul the steadily moving line of buckets. Such incidents were the cause of considerable extra expense, owing to the damage they did to the dredging craft.

In late 1933, the GWR's old dredger "Baroness" was sold for breaking up. This was replaced by the purchase of the dredger "Foremost 49" in 1934. This vessel, which was built in 1928, was a bucket dredger of the non-self-propelled type. She had a dredging capacity of 1000 cubic yards per hour, which was greater than any other of the GWR's dredging fleet except the "Peeress". "Foremost 49" had a registered tonnage of 563 gross and 407 net, and her measurements were length 157ft 5in, breadth 33ft 1in and mean draft 8ft. A feature of this vessel was that the

Plate 215 In March 1934, the GWR installed a new train indicator in the centre of the Lawn. This imposing structure was built of polished teak, and had eight panels showing arrivals, with departures being listed on the other side. It can be seen that trains running late is not just a recent phenomenon.

bucket ladder had been specially lengthened to enable dredging to be carried out at a depth of 50ft.

1934 DEMOLITION OF A ROAD BRIDGE

Road widening and improvements by the Wiltshire County Council necessitated the demolition of a road bridge over the GWR near Dauntsey station. The bridge consisted of a brick arch of 25ft span and box wings, having a road width of 20ft.

It was decided that the most expeditious way of demolishing the bridge would be to blow it up with explosives. Once the overburden had been stripped off the bridge to expose the arch rings, fifteen holes in rows of five, were drilled two-thirds through the arch at the haunches and key, and each was charged with one pound of explosive. On a Sunday morning, when the railway traffic was minimal, the track was covered over and the charges were fired electrically and the arch destroyed. The rubble was then cleared away and the track protection removed, to allow traffic to be reinstated.

1934 RECONSTRUCTION OF PADDINGTON STATION

The selection of Paddington for the London terminal station of the GWR was sanctioned by an Act of 1837 which allowed the extension of the GWR line from Action to "ground adjoining the basin of the Paddington Canal in the Parish of Paddington". This Act provided for the northward diversion of Harrow Road near the Westbourne turnpike gate, and the making of sundry bridges, including a wide road bridge in place of the existing footbridge over the Paddington Canal close to the intended depot of the railway and over the railway itself from the Harrow Road to Spring Street (now Eastbourne Terrace), whence a new road was to be made by the GWR in lieu of the footpath known as Bishop's Walk to Black Lion Lane (Queen's Road and Porchester Road). This new road became Bishop's Road.

The original intention was to build the passenger station on the site which it occupies today, and to use the land north-west of the new bridge for the goods depot and engine shed. There was no time, however, after the passing of the Act to build the permanent station without delaying the opening of the line, and the space intended for the goods depot was taken for a temporary passenger station; later on, a wooden goods shed was erected on the east side of the bridge in the corner between it and Eastbourne Terrace, or Spring Street as it was then. This arrangement lasted for sixteen years, from 1838 to 1854.

In 1851 it was proposed to construct a new passenger station on a site beyond the goods shed to the east of Bishop's Road Bridge, and a new merchandise shed north of the existing passenger station. It was also proposed to build an hotel and refreshment rooms. In 1852, it was proposed to add general offices, goods offices and warehouses, and an engine house. In 1853, a permanent passenger arrival

Plate 216 New arrival side buffet adjoining the Lawn.

shed and platforms were proposed. The departure side of the new station was brought into use in January 1854, the arrival platforms in May 1854, and by February 1855 the station was complete. Paddington Hotel was opened in June 1854. In 1861, mixed gauge track (4ft $8\frac{1}{2}$in added to the original 7ft $0\frac{1}{4}$in) was introduced to provide a passenger service to the Midlands and the North. In 1863, Bishop's Road station was opened to provide a connection between the GWR and the Metropolitan systems, through trains being worked over the latter to Farringdon Street. The Hammersmith & City Railway opened in 1864 and became the joint property of the GWR and the Metropolitan Companies in July 1867. In June 1878, an extra arrival platform No 9 was brought into use, necessitating the construction of a cab approach by means of a bridge from the goods depot approach. Early in 1880 the goods lines were diverted through a short tunnel to make room for extra platforms at Westbourne Park. In 1881, a milk arrival platform was provided at the back of No 9 platform line near its outer end. In 1884, an additional platform was provided in place of carriage sidings under the original roof. In 1887, a subway was constructed to give direct communication between Paddington and the Praed Street station of the Metropolitan, which had opened in 1868. Broad gauge finally passed in May 1892. In 1893, another additional platform was provided in lieu of carriage sidings. The locomotive depot at Old Oak Common was brought into use in March 1906, and soon afterwards the large building adjoining Bishop's Road Bridge for the Goods Department was completed. In 1908, No 1A down excursion and milk platform was completed as an extension to the main No 1 departure platform, beyond Bishop's Road Bridge. The total length of the platform faces of the 1854 station was 3,500ft, but by 1911 the length of platforms had grown to 8,825ft, exclusive of the milk arrival platform behind No 9 line.

Brunel's station of 1854 thus proved to be basically sufficient for traffic requirements for well over 50 years. However, additional accommodation became necessary and an important programme of extensions and improvements was drawn up in 1906, and from 1909 to 1916 work was continuously in progress. The chief works in this programme were the replacement of the old brick arch road bridges across the line from Bishop's Road to Old Oak Common by long-span steel girder structures, so as to free the approach to the terminus for rearrangements to the permanent way, and the extension of the arrival side of the station by the addition of platforms Nos 10-12, No 12 being for inwards milk and parcels traffic. This arrival side extension added 2,500ft run of platform face. It necessitated heavy engineering works, the most notable of which were the setting back of London Street, the construction of a new goods approach on the site of an old coal yard, and the erection of a new wide-span roof of the same dimensions as the middle span of the main station. During this period, the Bakerloo line tube of the London Electric Railway was pushed westward under Paddington station and beyond to Queen's Park, and a booking office and entrance from the main GWR station were constructed.

The reconstruction of Paddington station was one of the main items proposed for inclusion in the list of works to be undertaken on the GWR under the arrangements of the Development (Loan Guarantees and Grants) Act of 1929. Although the number of platforms in the main part of the station was not increased the majority were greatly improved (as discussed earlier). In the existing

Plate 217 The new taxi rank was situated between platforms 8 and 9, with access by the ramp visible at the end of the line of taxis. This photograph, taken in September 1934, shows taxis waiting for business. In the 1930s, it was reported that on average 2,500 taxis passed through the station daily. Apart from the taxis, the horse-drawn cab in the foreground and the Associated Daimler delivery lorry to the left of the taxi ramp, may be noted; also the cobbled roadway.

Plate 218 No. 1 platform at Paddington station, showing the position of the clock.

station, the area between the buffer stops and the GWR Royal Hotel, known as the 'Lawn', was used for parcels traffic. Business had extended beyond what could be comfortably handled in that area, and in any case the space for passenger circulation there was too small. There existed however beyond the main line departure platform No 1, the old 1A platform, used for excursion trains and as a berth for incoming empty stock for platforms Nos 1 & 2. It was a very long platform extending to beyond Westbourne Bridge, a favourite haunt for photographers, since all departing trains, expresses and suburban alike, left on the one down running line. At that time, Bishop's Road station handled only trains to and from the Metropolitan, some of which worked between GWR suburban stations and the City, changing from steam to electric traction at Bishop's Road.

The complete scheme of alterations at Paddington station included the following work:

Plate 219 The three dials of the clock, one of which may be seen from any platform.

1. Remodelling of the whole of the permanent way leading up to Paddington over $^3/_4$ mile (see A on the general plan)
2. Resignalling, by power operated and colour light signals (already discussed).
3. New parcels depot and offices on the down side, with a subway under the station approach road from Bishop's Road (see B on the plan).
4. The reconstruction of the portion of Paddington station known as the 'Lawn', and the construction of two large office blocks (see C on the plant).
5. Alterations in the neighbourhood of Bishop's Road station (see D on the plan).

In summary, the old platform 1A was closed to the public and converted for handling parcels traffic, together with provision for efficient depots for handling parcels and for cartage. The removal of parcel traffic from the 'Lawn' enabled that area to be reconstructed as a spacious circulating area for passengers, and with the provision of new office buildings, refreshment rooms and other offices, the area at the head of the platforms was transformed into a dignified concourse. All main line platforms, except No 1, were lengthened and the track layout modified to suit. At the same time, Bishop's Road station was completely rebuilt to provide a terminal point for GWR suburban trains as well as through platforms for trains to and from the Metropolitan line. This provided easy interchange between electric trains on the Hammersmith & City line and steam-hauled suburban trains of the GWR. The alterations at Bishop's Road involved the building of new goods and cab approaches, and these were works of considerable engineering magnitude. The old tunnel leading to the Metropolitan had to be demolished for part of its length, to provide the necessary width for four platform roads, and the enlarged entrance was built as a covered way. With this reconstruction, the name 'Bishop's Road' was discontinued and the new four platforms were designated Platforms Nos 13 to 16 of Paddington station itself. Included with these reconstructions in Paddington station and its approaches was the scheme for complete resignalling with power-operated points and colour light signals of the searchlight type (as discussed earlier).

The Lawn, removed of the need to handle parcels, was converted into a spacious circulating area, covered with a new steel glazed roof, and surrounded by a new buffet and tearoom, the seat registration office, cloak room and lost property office. There was also a new entrance to the Underground and Tube railways by wide staircases to the subways, as well as a new entrance to the Post Office tube railway. The walls of the staircases and subways were panelled with tiling. Adjoining the Lawn end of No 1 main departure platform, the subsidiary booking office was reconstructed and a new waiting room provided, panelled in polished hardwood. There was a refreshment counter in this waiting room, a feature not usually found in railway waiting rooms. A new train departure and arrival indicator was fixed in the Lawn.

Two new blocks of offices were built at the eastern end of the station, one on the arrival side and the other on the departure side. Between the two a low range of buildings was built, at right angles to the main block, across the Lawn, and providing some of the accommodation mentioned above. This block had a mezzanine floor over the whole length. It was designed to be able to carry a possible future extension of the hotel.

The two new blocks of offices were steel framed, that on the departure side having seven storeys and housing in its basement the oil-fired boilers for heating both blocks of offices and providing hot water for the lavatories. The building on the arrival side had eight storeys. The method of construction was to use a skeleton steel framework, the beams and girders being planned to suit the varying floor loads and accommodation required, and the stanchions were spaced with due regard to room requirements and architectural features. The total weight of the structural steel in the arrival side block was 475 tons, and it was erected in the short space of five weeks. The new building had a frontage of 118ft to the approach road, the eight floors including the ground floor with a partial basement. Emphasis was given to the 'vertical' line, with wide spaces between the pilasters filled in with flat bay windows and metal panels, thus providing a maximum amount of window area and consequently natural lighting.

Plate 220 A view of the GWR Royal Hotel after modernisation carried out at the same time as the general improvements to the station. As well as upgrading of the interior, substantial work was done to the outside of the building. Almost all the Victorian iron work and decoration was stripped off and layers of grime removed. The old porte-cochere was removed and the basement area in the front filled in so as to allow a new entrance road to be created for motor cars. On the left is the last of the new office blocks built at Paddington; this building mirrored another new construction completed in 1933 in the arrival side.

The building rose upon a plinth of polished granite, with walls and pilasters faced with 'Victoria' patent stone backed with brickwork. The roof was of the Mansard type, constructed of concrete and steel framing, and had large dormer windows on either side. The lettering on the front of the building was in black Victoria stone, and was illuminated at night by flood lighting. The ground floor of the main block was occupied by the buffet and tea room already mentioned, with a service room between. The total area on platform level was 7,990 sq ft. This covered the accommodation provided for cloakrooms and the seat reservation office, part of the former and the whole of the latter being in the low range of new buildings across the Lawn. A basement for stores, service, etc in connection with the buffet and tea room was provided.

The upper floors of the main block had an area of about 6,000 sq ft each and were served by a broad staircase and two electric lifts. These floors were fitted up as offices, with metal partitions glazed in the upper potion. Special attention was given to ventilation, which was obtained by air trunks and fans. The staircase was of pre-cast concrete supported on steel stringers; the risers, treads and landings being faced with terrazzo. The dados were treated similarly in colours, with painted plaster walls above. The buffet had a marble dado around the walls and marble tiling to the floor, the counter front and back fittings were of walnut. The tea room walls were panelled in walnut to a height of 9ft, with 'Stuc' plaster above. The pilasters in the buffet and tea room were faced with marble and had bronze caps and bases.

The three-faced clock on No 1 platform at Paddington Station is well known. Originally it had its own clockwork mechanism. However, as part of the modernisation of the station, its mechanism was changed from clockwork to the 'pul-syn-etic' system of electric clocks and became just the outward visible sign of the inward working of a small electric master clock situated in the station master's office. This master clock now also controls and synchronises the working of all the clocks at Paddington, being

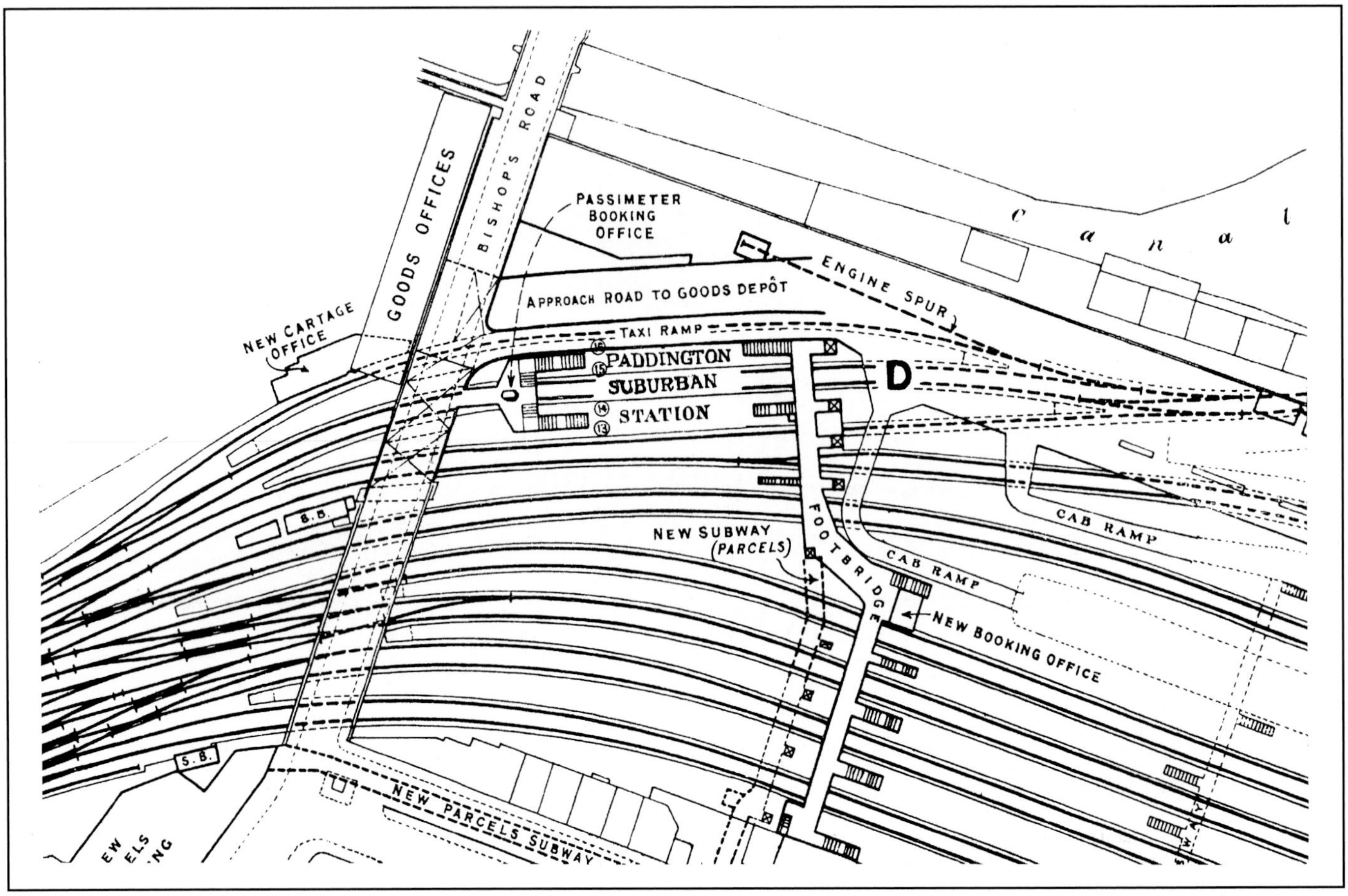

Map 41. A plan of the scheme of alterations at the Bishop's Road end of Paddington station.

Plate 221 In August 1930, excavations began at Paddington for the complete rebuilding of the old Bishop's Road station. The tunnel of the Metropolitan Railway was situated in the foreground of this photograph and it can be seen that the canal was uncomfortably close. Paddington's main platforms were to the left of this scene, and parallel to the canal. In the course of this rebuilding the terminus expanded sideways to occupy this location, to form the suburban side of the terminus (platforms 13-16).

Plate 222 This illustration shows how the work of demolition could only creep along and the new work be built a piece at a time. On the left is the screen wall of Bishop's Road station, and in the centre is the site of the new platform.

checked each morning by the 1000 hours 'time' signal, although so fine and accurate were the adjustments that the margin of error was only about a second a week.

Another new building was a new parcels depot constructed in Bishop's Road. Its purpose was to overcome increasing difficulties in handling parcels traffic in the area of the 'Lawn' and to prevent delays to road vehicles gaining access to the station. Use of the new premises also obviated much of the occupation of the station by barrows of parcels, because the new depot was connected to the platforms by a subway and lifts. This convenience was effected by the construction of a new subway under the arrival approach road, connecting with the parcels subway which previously existed at the

Plate 223 A portion of the concrete brick-faced wall which was found to be so hard that in order to split it up, hydraulic 'cartridges' had to be employed.

Plate 224 The old Bishop's Road station in course of demolition. New cab approach road on the right, with goods station approach beyond.

west end of the station and extended to connect with platforms 6,7 & 8. Access from the subway to all platforms, as well as to the new footbridge leading to Bishop's Road station, was gained by electric lifts. Above the new parcels platforms, which extended westwards from Bishop's Road bridge, was constructed a parcels receiving office on the street level, with a two-storey block of offices above, and to which independent road access was afforded from both Bishop's Road and Orsett Terrace A new footbridge was constructed, connecting all the platforms with Bishop's Road station. At the eastern end of the station, the GWR offices were given a seven-storied extension.

Bishop's Road station, with its two platforms, was demolished, and on the site were built two island platforms to form a part, if somewhat distant, of Paddington station itself. The new platforms were intended to take a larger share of the suburban traffic, as well as the electric services to and from the Hammersmith and City line. This section of the scheme involved extensive engineering work. For example, the goods offices, adjoining Bishop's Road bridge, had to be maintained in position while brick supports, upon which a portion of the higher building rested, were removed and steel girders substituted. Another interesting engineering feat was the placing of a steel girder to fill the gap caused by the demolition of 300ft of the rail tunnel leading to Edgware Road station. This girder was 130ft long and weighted about 125 tons. After being assembled some 45ft away from the tunnel it was finally moved into its permanent position. The platform extensions and the reconstruction of Bishop's Road station (this name was dropped from then on, as it was considered a part of Paddington station), necessitated some remodelling of the permanent way for a distance of $\frac{3}{4}$ mile immediately outside Paddington station.

Turning to the alterations in the neighbourhood of Bishop's Road station, in September 1933 this station, as such, ceased to exist, and in its place were four platforms about 600ft long, designated Nos 13, 14, 15 & 16 of Paddington station, each pair of platforms being served by a luggage lift.

Alterations to a station and approach lines in continuous use necessitate careful preparation of the works programme. For the old Bishop's Road station, the work was planned in the following stages:

1. Preparing for the up City line, which was carried round at the back of the old Bishop's Road station, and providing just sufficient of the new platform No15.

2. Traffic diverted to this new line, to free the old up City line, so that that line and platform could be demolished to enable the remainder of the new up platform to be built. This eventually became platform No15, but for the time being it was used for the down line.

3. Down trains diverted over platform No15 line, freeing the old down line and platform, the latter then being demolished. This gave a site for the new down platform No 13 and part of No 14.

4. Once the permanent down platform No 13 was ready, down trains were diverted from No 15 line.

5. Line No 15 was then altered for up traffic; the temporary portion constructed in timber, required when used as a down platform, at the east or City end, being removed. This released the site for platform line No 14 and allowed all four platforms to be brought into use.

Referring to the plan of the scheme of alterations at Bishop's Road station, it will be seen that the first stage required a slice to be cut off the goods offices to make room for the new up City line. This necessitated demolition of nearly half the length of a brick screen wall about 33ft high alongside the railway, leaving only the stanchions carrying the roof. Next, five braced wooden towers were erected between a pair of stanchions, to carry the roof principals and allow the main roof girders on which they rested to be removed and re-erected further back. The principals themselves were cut back, new steel ends and bracing being added as required. Afterwards, a new screen wall was built to match the portion remaining. Next, the goods invoicing office and cartage office were demolished, the invoicing office being re-erected on a new site, while the cartage office was rebuilt on the old site, only further back.

Continuing eastwards towards the City, the next work was the removal of a reinforced brick pier carrying the corner of the large block of office buildings which came on the site of the new up City line. This was accomplished by placing new steelwork alongside, and after making careful calculations as to the weight of the building and what deflections should be produced, placing hydraulic jacks on the new steelwork and applying pressure until the weight, as calculated, was transferred to the new work. Next, steel wedges were inserted and the jacks removed. The old pier was then removed. The results were successful, as not the minutest cracks could be discerned in the old building.

Next came the bridge over Bishop's Road. This could only be reconstructed to a small extent at this early stage, as the pier carrying the new bridge was on the site of the old up City line; but one

Plate 225 On the left is seen the new steelwork put in to replace the brick pier that carried the block of offices seen above.

new abutment was built and a way cut through for a single line of rails, with temporary second-hand girders carrying the roadway overhead.

Working still eastwards, the new line cut through the main approach road down to the Paddington goods depot, which was in continual use during the whole twenty-four hours. This old roadway was a ramped approach carried on brick arches, under which was stabling for 120 horses, and room for these had to be found elsewhere. Passing to the far east end, the four lines converged into the two old lines. The old tunnel was enlarged on one side to form a 'bell-mouth'. This work was accomplished by cutting away a short length of half the tunnel arch and side wall, and then rebuilding the side wall further back and constructing a half-arch to the larger span, to join up with the portion left remaining. This was done with the service of electric trains running every six minutes underneath, the clearance being only a few inches. When the width to be provided became too great for this method, the whole tunnel was taken down, girders and jack arches being provided in place. A shield under the tunnel arch protected the traffic running underneath while the arch was taken down and steelwork took its place. The shield was formed of five thicknesses of 5/8in boards, bent round and nailed together to conform to the curve of the inside of the tunnel, in short sections which could be taken out from behind and led forward as the work of demolition proceeded. This leading forward could be done only at night, during the short

Plate 226 The shield constructed under the tunnel arch to protect traffic running underneath while the arch was being demolished.

Plate 227 The steel work which replaced the brick tunnel.

period when the electric current was cut off.

Some of the concrete put in to strengthen the old tunnel, during alterations carried out in 1912, was found to be so hard that in regard to its removal the general contractors had to consult specialists, who drilled holes about $4\frac{1}{2}$ in diameter in the concrete, and in these they inserted hydraulic 'cartridges' which consisted of five small hydraulic jacks. These together exerted a force of about 150 tons, causing the concrete to split up in layers, which could then be dealt with in the usual way.

In designing the superstructure to carry the roadways over the line at this end of the station, considerable difficulty was experienced in obtaining any positions where stanchions could

Plate 228 The 126-ton girder completely riveted up ready to be traversed over the running lines into its final position. Old rails laid on their sides to form tracks for the balls used as rollers, can be seen at either end.

Plate 229 The girder in place across the tunnel, before being lowered on to the stanchions.

be placed. The solution adopted was to place one stanchion at the end of platforms Nos 15 & 16, and another on platforms Nos 13 & 14, with a large girder placed horizontally in the roadway above. A girder in this position was possible, as there was a line of kerbing dividing the vehicles for the passenger station from those for the goods station. This girder was 133ft long and weighed 126 tons. The magnitude of this girder was because it had to support a large area of roadway (4520 sq ft) and consequently a heavy load with vehicles. It was understood at the time to be the heaviest 'plate' girder in England. The girder was assembled alongside, and riveted up. Cradles were then inserted underneath at each end, running on 3in hard steel balls, which, in turn, rolled along steel rails laid on their sides. On these the girder was traversed sideways a distance of about 35ft across the old tunnel. This was accomplished in the short time of 20 minutes, and it was then lowered about nine feet on to the new steel stanchions.

The work included under the third item, that is the new parcels depot and offices on the down side, with a subway under the Bishop's Road approach (see B on the general plan), can now be considered. While there was a good gravel bed for the work in the neighbourhood of Bishop's Road just discussed, on the site of the parcels depot to be there was a clay filling to a depth varying between 14 and 22ft, below which was a thin layer of black soil marking the original ground surface, and below this yellow clay gradually changing to hard mottled clay. The top clay was considered to have come from the excavations when the railway was originally made. Under test, this geological strata was found not to be able to carry the intensity of loading required, and therefore the foundations would have to be piled.

The parcels subway was to start at Bishop's Road and continue down under the station approach road on a falling gradient of 1 in 29, then turn at right-angles to join up with the previously-constructed subway commencing under platform No 1. An opening under Bishop's Road already existed, and this, with some small alterations, was used to form the subway. Immediately to the east, two old arches at right-angles were encountered and had to be demolished. These arches were built on an incline and were lined underneath with a second separate arch of tiles. They were considered to have formed part of the original approaches to Paddington station. The next 260ft was constructed of cast iron segments to form a tube with an internal diameter of 13ft $1\frac{3}{4}$ in of similar design to that adopted on the Underground Railways. The length of tube was not sufficient to warrant the provision of a tunneling shield, so a length of 3ft 4in just sufficient for two lengths of cast iron segments, was excavated at a time, the ground being temporarily supported with timber until the iron lining was put in. No difficulty was experienced in carrying out the work, although the top of the tunnel was only 8ft below the road surface on which vehicles continued to pass, except that some of the top timbers had to remain in permanently. The inside was lined with concrete. Two shafts for ventilation were provided, necessary where petrol motors were expected to be working. This length of subway was found to be very noisy under traffic, so baffles were formed of thick canvas leaving rectangular openings, which reduced the noise.

An interesting part of the work was where it passed under the old office building. As usual in such alterations, there were several essential services which had to be moved first, including boilers heating the main offices and an electric lighting centre. The old foundations carrying the main offices were heavily loaded. The subway was therefore aligned as far as possible to miss these; there was, however, no alternative to going under the main outer wall. The first procedure was to put down piles clear of the old foundations, on either side of the wall. The perspective sketch shows the piles with their reinforced concrete caps. A hole on each side of the site of the subway was then cut under the main wall and a lintel girder inserted, bearing at either

Plate 230 A striking view of the large girder after being traversed over. It is here seen packed up on stanchions ready to be lowered into its final position.

Plate 231 The free space that was obtained underneath by the use of this large girder.

end on a group of piles. Then the two main girders, one on either side of the wall, were placed in position. Afterwards, small lengths of wall were cut away, commencing at each end, and steel joists inserted, the old wall being well wedged up on these. In this manner the whole length of wall over the subway was underpinned.

The new parcels depot level was some eight feet below the basement of the houses on the east side of Westbourne Terrace, some of which had to be cut off diagonally. Before any portion of the old buildings was cut away, a trench was cut through at basement level and new foundations put in and the outside wall built up, the old cross walls only being

Plate 232 A view showing the state of the work at Bishop's Road station in September 1933, with all four lines nearly ready for use.

cut away as the new wall rose higher, floor by floor. On reaching the top floor, when the house was practically already cut in two, a start was made in demolishing the portion of the old buildings to be removed. The perspective sketch shows the method adopted to transfer the load carried by the main steel framework of the parcel office building to the pile foundations. In order to minimise the disturbance to the adjoining premises, the main piles were constructed on the outer side of the adjoining house wall. The few inner piles required to give balance were constructed so as to be under the basement passage, and they were connected through 2ft square holes cut at intervals in the house wall. The sketch illustrates the inner and outer piles and the bridge pieces connecting the inner to the outer piles. These bridge pieces also carried the old house wall at each point where they passed through the wall.

Westbourne Terrace bridge had to be extended to allow a 50ft roadway and a 40ft wide platform underneath. Owing to the Terrace being on an incline there was not sufficient headway for a bridge in one span, so a steel pier was provided near the edge of the platform and another in the centre of the parcels depot roadway. Girders about 14ft apart, running longitudinally with the Terrace, were carried on these. The brick abutment carrying the large 232ft span girder bridge over the railway was already fully loaded, and the

Plate 233 The outer up line of the new suburban station (the enlarged renamed Bishop's Road station) showing the windows of the mess rooms beneath the goods approach and the underside of the new cab approach road above.

Plate 234 The site of the new parcels depot. In the background is Westbourne Terrace Bridge, and on the right the large girder bridge over the railway, which was reconstructed in 1908.

Plate 235 The site of the parcels depot between Westbourne Terrace and Bishop's Road.

Plate 236 The completed parcels subway, with cloth screen at intervals to deaden the noise.

requirements of the parcels depot necessitated the abutment being kept to the smallest size possible. The method adopted of carrying the new bridge is shown in one of the sketches. On the back of the old abutment were projecting brick piers (counterforts), and after the earth filling between these had been removed, piles were constructed, so placed with regard to the load to be carried that the brickwork built above, which filled up the intervening space, should have a tendency to tilt back against the old work. On top of this brickwork, girders were placed to span the projecting portion of the old abutment, and on these the ends of the main girders carrying the Terrace roadway rested. In this way no additional weight was put on the old foundations, nor was the overall width of the abutment increased.

Another job carried out at this time at Paddington, although not part of the

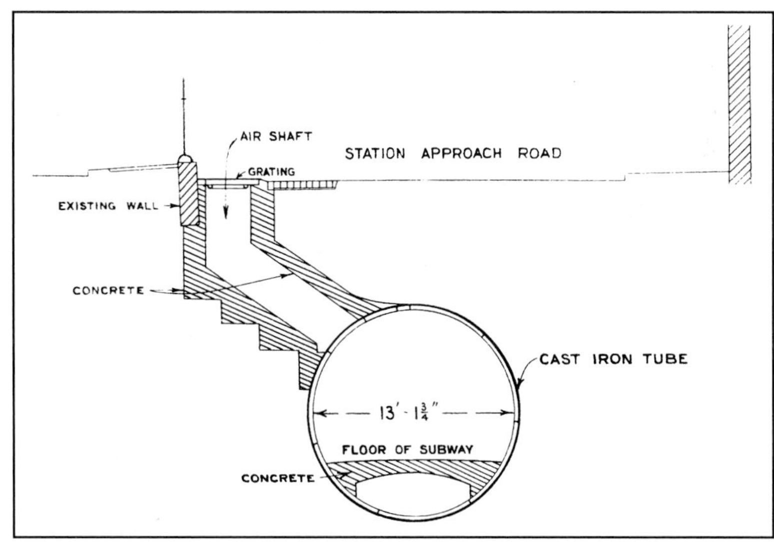

Fig 10. Cross section of subway, showing the ventilation shaft.

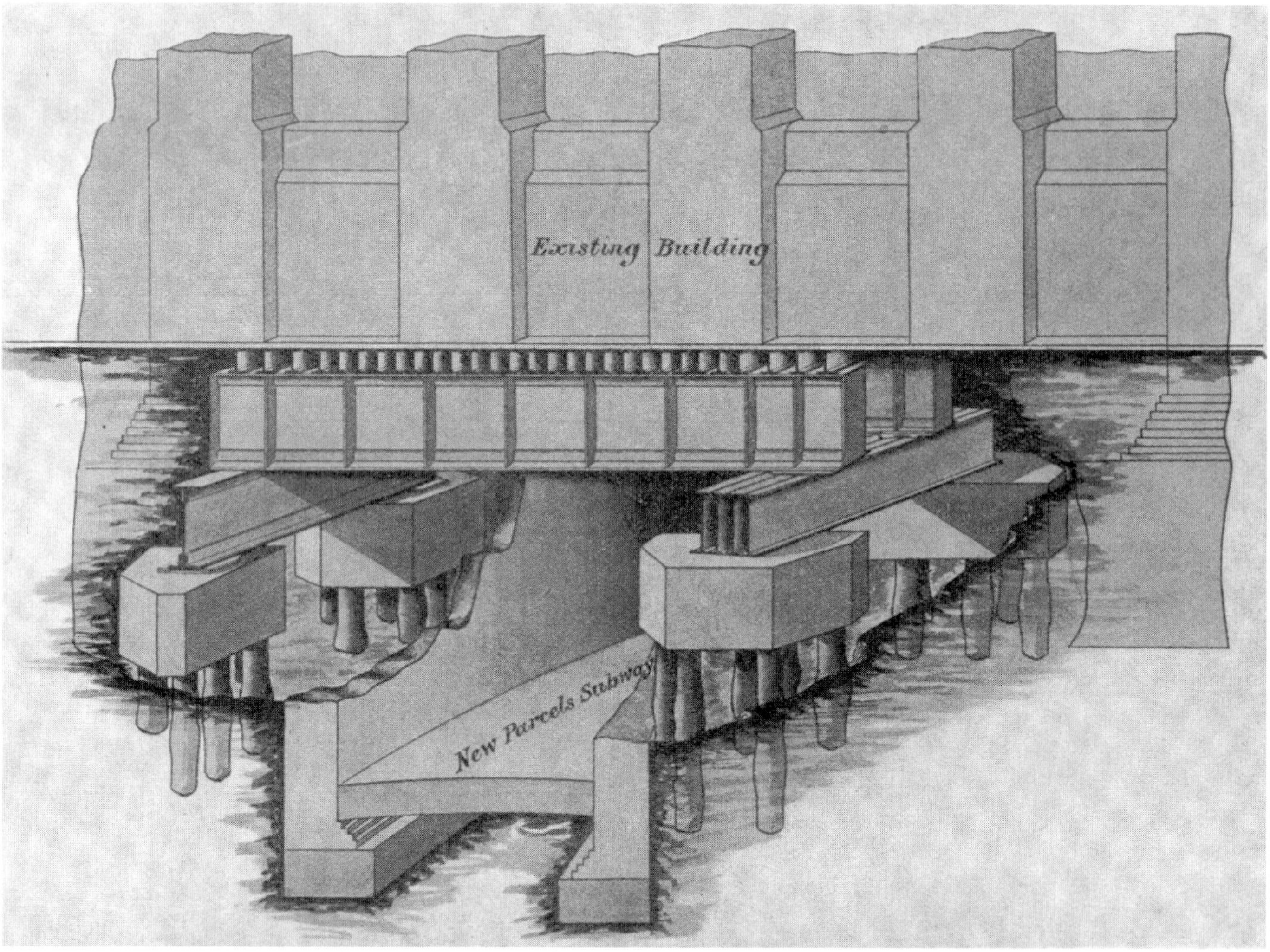

Plate 237 Groups of piles and concrete caps, lintel girders resting on these, main girder over subway, and cross needle girders under wall. All the girder work was encased in concrete.

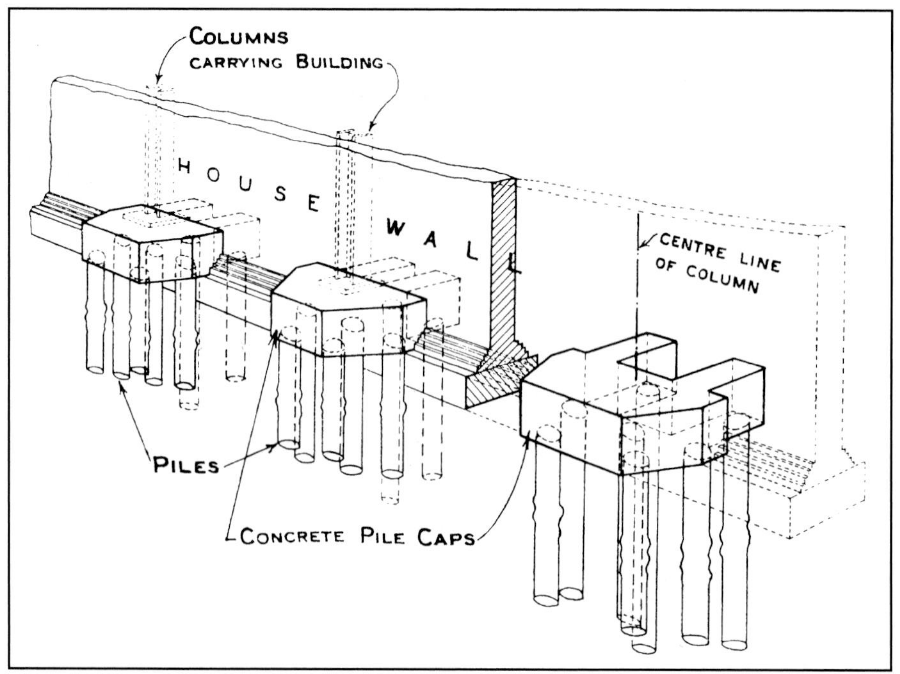

Fig 11. Perspective sketch, showing pile caps, with bridge pieces passing through house wall to piles on the inside.

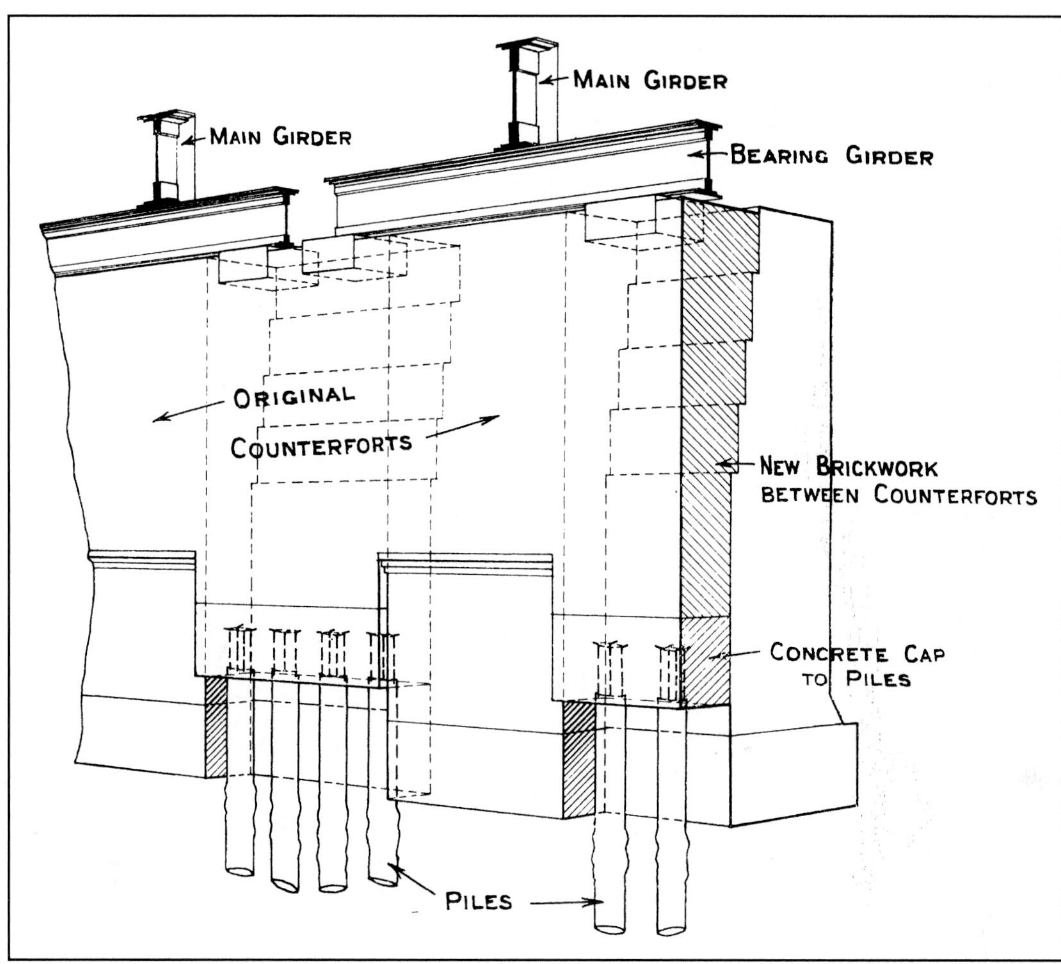

Fig 12. The abutment of Westbourne Terrace Bridge, showing new work and diagrammatically girder above to relieve the old brickwork of any additional weight.

Developments Act work, was the renewal of the glass wind screen at the west end of the roof. It was found necessary to renew the outer arched rib of the roof of the No 2 span. This rib was part of the original structure erected by Isambard Kingdom Brunel and was then about 80 years old. It was the first important member of the roof to require renewal.

The taking down of the old rib and the erecting of the new one presented a number of difficulties, chiefly because the span was 102ft and its highest portion 56ft above the level of the railway. Five platform lines passed underneath this span, and it was not possible to use cranes for the operations. Therefore, the old rib was cut into five pieces by oxy-acetylene gas and lowered by differential blocks and tackle. The whole was supported by tubular scaffolding, one frame being erected on either side of the rib. The new steelwork was delivered in five pieces, which were placed into position separately by similar means as were used for the taking down of the old rib. The sections were then riveted together.

1934 PASSING OF BRUNEL'S LAST TIMBER VIADUCT

Collegewood Viaduct, near Penryn, on the GWR Falmouth branch was built by Brereton after Brunel's death and opened in 1863. It was a strengthened version of those on the main line, the wooden superstructure being the latest design, the strongest, designated subsequently by engineer P.J. Margary as Class A2. It was the last viaduct on the line into Falmouth and was built on a sweeping downside left-hand curve. Its 15 spans were carried on 14 masonry piers, all fully buttressed and spaced at 66ft centres. The superstructure consisted of horizontal beams laminated from 12in by 14in timbers, with raking legs supporting the beams at 15ft 4in centres, with centre legs of 14in square timber. The linking spans were 20ft long, while the 30ft landward spans comprised the usual queen post trusses in the parapet. The total length has been quoted at 927, 954, 957, 964 and 974ft, the last being the official figure given by the GWR in 1934. Its height was given as 100ft.

In late 1933, work started on constructing masonry piers for a new replacement viaduct on the downside. When finished in 1934, the new structure had masonry piers, brick arches and reinforced concrete parapets. It was put into service in July 1934, the original timber unit then having completed a service life of 71 years, and was then the last Brunel timber viaduct to have remained in use.

1934 NEW DESIGN OF BRIDGE AT OXFORD

A bridge was required in 1934 to carry the Oxford Northern by-pass (now A40) over the Didcot to Aynho line near Wolvercote junction just north of Oxford city. This bridge was of a new design, the steelwork for which consisted of seven steel frames, each 96ft long.

Plate 238 The Great Western Railway New Parcels Receiving Office and Depot at Paddington, situated at the junction of Bishop's Road with Eastbourne Terrace.

Plate 239 A portion of the parcels yard, with ramped approach from Bishop's Road on right.

Plate 240 A portion of the reconstructed Paddington Goods Shed.

Plate 241 Workmen renewing the outer arched roof rib of No 2 span of the wind screen at Paddington station.

Plate 242 Brunel's original timber trestle Collegewood Viaduct, near Penryn, on the GWR Falmouth branch, the last to be in service in the west of England.

The horizontal portion and the two haunches of each frame were rivetted up complete, and each piece thus joined was 96ft 2in long, and 13ft 1½ in deep, allowing for the curved ends. These great frames were conveyed from the Fairfield Engineering Co of Chepstow to the site, slung upon high packings placed over the bogies of GWR CROCODILE well-type wagons, with the curved ends riding between the frames of two other CROCODILE wagons, from which the floor boards had been removed. This permitted the ends to be loaded to within 4½ in of rail level, thus keeping the total height sufficiently low to clear all structures en route.

The steel legs of the frames were placed in position during ordinary week-day working hours, but the large pieces shown in the illustration were erected during special occupations of the line on Sundays, using a GWR 36-ton travelling steam crane for the purpose. Each piece was lifted complete and landed on the legs. The steel frames were then encased in concrete and the new road carried on a high embankment on either side of the railway. Although the frame-type of bridge had been used fairly extensively in France and America, the new bridge at Wolvercote was believed to have been one of the first of the type built in the UK.

1934 IMPROVEMENTS AT CARDIFF

In the spring of 1930, an extensive scheme of improvements was started at Cardiff, which with consequent road works, involved an expenditure of nearly a million pounds (when money was really worth something!). This work, which was undertaken by the GWR as one of the schemes under the

Plate 243 The arches for the new College Wood viaduct being constructed. The old Brunel wooden viaduct can be seen behind.

Plate 244 The new masonry Collegewood Viaduct in the last stages of construction. It was opened in July 1934. The original Brunel timber viaduct can be seen through the arches of the new viaduct.

Plate 245 One of the seven bridge frames already in position, and the second about to be unloaded.

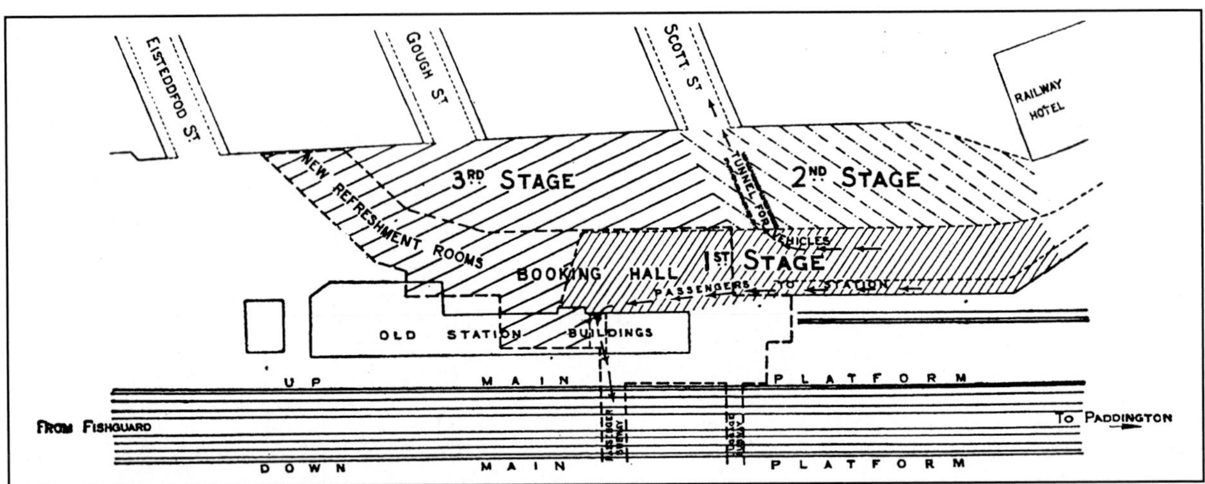

Map 42. This Diagram shows the stages in which the approach road lowering on the north side of the station was carried out. Note the temporary tunnel exit road to Scott Street at the completion of the first stage.

Development (Loan Guarantees and Grants) Act of 1929, was completed in 1934. The project involved the complete rebuilding of Cardiff General station and the adjacent Riverside station, the latter becoming virtually part of the main structure. Other principal features were the provision of additional and longer platforms, independent through running lines, storage accommodation for rolling stock, quadrupling of the lines to the east and west of the station, and other extensive alterations to the permanent way, bridges and depots in the vicinity, together with the introduction of colour light signals and electric power signalling (the last already described earlier in this book).

The new main station faced northward and eight platform lines were provided, by four island platforms 40ft wide. Of these platform lines, four were 1000ft long for the main line traffic, two 800ft long for the Taff Vale line traffic and two 600ft long, on the site of the old Riverside station, for the Barry line traffic. Approach to all platforms was from a new subway, which necessitated lowering the approach roads on both the up and down sides of the

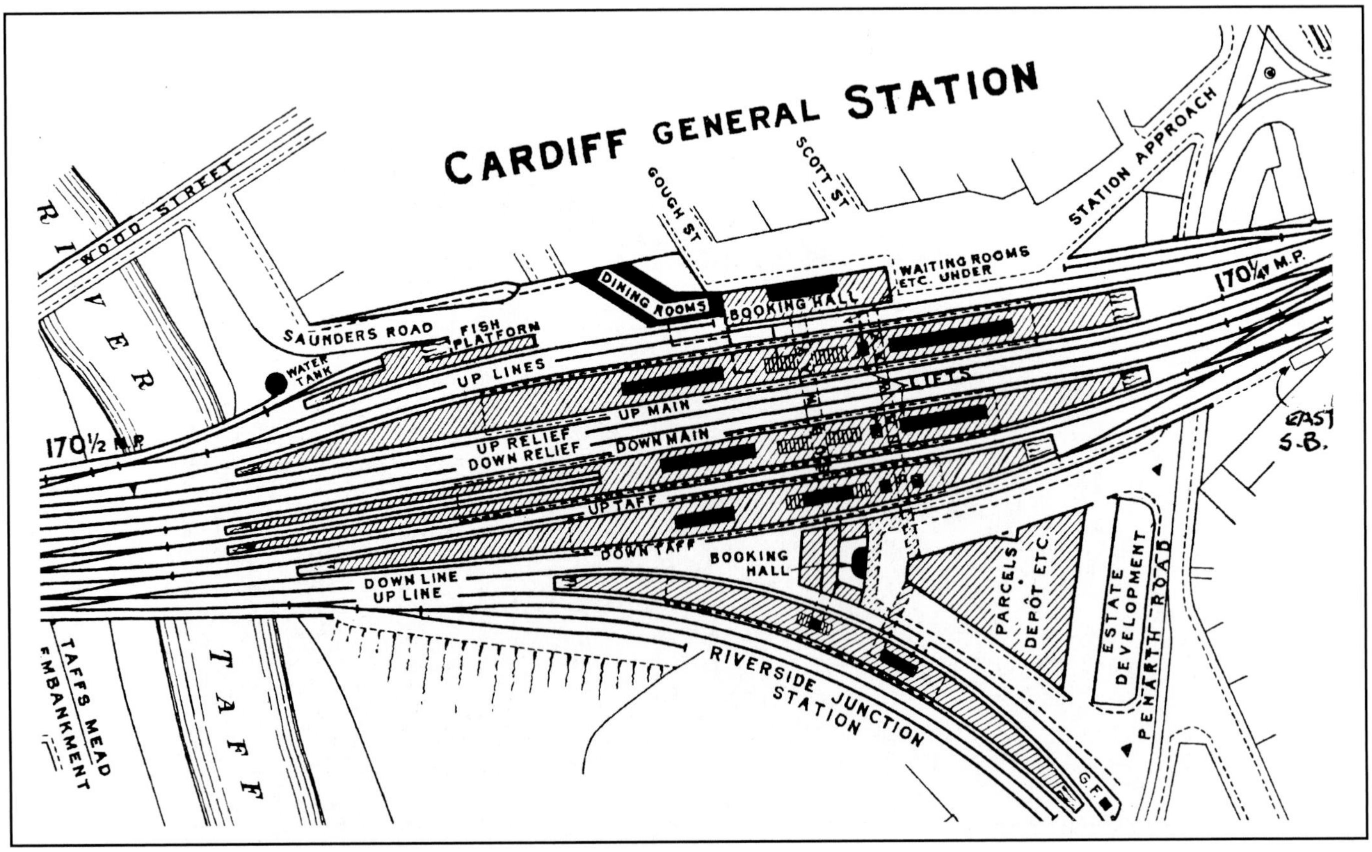

Map 43. A general plan of the lines, platforms, and buildings of the new Cardiff General Station.

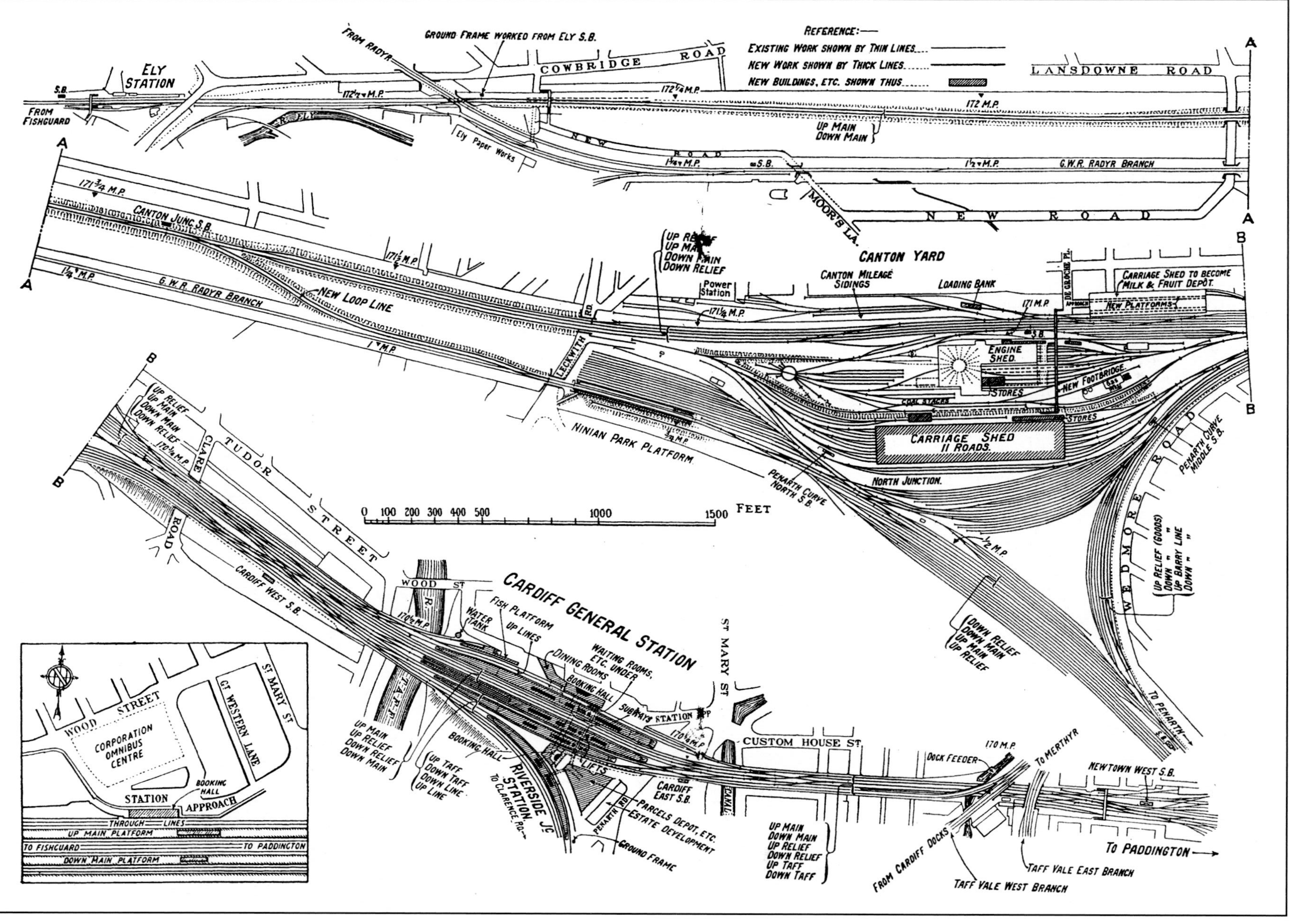

Map 44. A diagram showing the GWR Cardiff General station, as reconstructed, together with adjacent works. The inset in the bottom left corner shows the new road layout in front of the station after the Corporation had set up the new bus centre. This had the incidental advantage of opening up a better view of the new station frontage.

Plate 246 The first stage of the road lowering on the north side of Cardiff General station.

Plate 247 The old south side approach road to Cardiff General station before the alterations, when it was at platform level.

Plate 248 The new approach road to the south side of Cardiff General station after the alterations, when it became fifteen feet below platform level.

station. As a result, a portion of Saunders Road, between St Mary Street and the station, was lowered to subway level, and access was obtained from Wood Street, as well as from St Mary Street, on a through route. The western portion of Saunders Road was retained at its existing level as access to a new 430ft fish platform, which was constructed on a site adjacent to this section of the road. The new 16ft wide subway connected all the passenger platforms. The existing subway was converted to carry parcels and luggage traffic, connected with the platforms by lifts. Access to the platforms from the passenger subway was by two stairways to each platform. The greater part of all the platforms was placed under cover.

Turning to more details, in connection with the rebuilding of the station, the approach roads on the north and south sides were lowered to subway level, twelve feet below rail level. The extensive excavation that was necessary on the north side was carried out in three stages, as illustrated in the diagram. The new main booking hall was erected on this lower level, practically on the same site as the former one, which was at rail level. The facade of the new building, faced with natural Portland stone with Cornish granite plinth, presented an imposing appearance. When the City Corporation subsequently cleared the house property immediately between the station and Wood Street for a bus centre, the new building was given a dignified setting.

The interior of the new hall was 186ft long by 62ft wide, and impressively high, with walls which consisted of granite bases, above which was panelling of Devonshire green marble. The pilasters, which ran to the underside of the roof, were capped with Ashburton black marble. The walls between the marble panelling and the cove were finished with lined stucco. An effect of natural sunlight was given by amber glass in the glazing overhead, which covered the major length of the hall. The new booking hall featured large ticket windows, and recesses beneath them to accommodate the hand luggage

Plate 249 Up main platform of the reconstructed Cardiff General station showing the platform buildings.

Plate 250 View in the other direction of the up main platform of the reconstructed Cardiff General station, showing the platform buildings with Doulton's glazed stoneware. The station name was modelled on the face of the glaze ware and glazed in bronze colour.

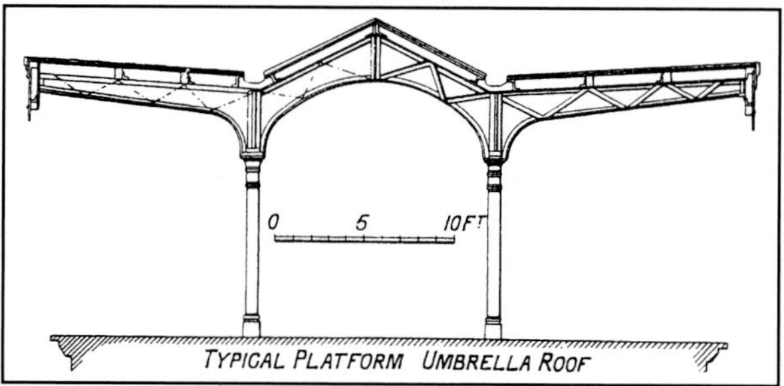

Fig 13. Typical platform umbrella roof.

of passengers while obtaining their tickets. Leading from the west end of the booking hall was a commodious dining room, handsomely panelled with laurel wood, with stucco above, the floor being of oak blocks laid in herringbone pattern. Adjoining the dining room was a refreshment room 72ft long by 20ft wide, panelled in oak.

The former subway was converted solely for luggage purposes, and lifts were provided to each of the platforms. A new passenger subway, 16ft wide, was built giving access by means of broad staircases to the eight station platforms, as stated earlier four 1000ft main line, two 800ft Taff Vale and two 600ft Riverside. There was also a bay platform

Plate 251 One of the new platform buildings, showing the general effect of the Carrara ware blocks on a granite plinth.

facing the down (or Ely) direction, and a new fish platform on the north side of the station. The new subway was lined with cream-coloured tiles, and brown panels made to size for the display of posters and notices. Each panel was provided with separate lighting.

In consequence of the somewhat restricted width of the four platform islands, the buildings could not be constructed of the usual brick or stone, and a new material of less thickness yet of substantial nature, had to be introduced. This was so-called Carrara glazed blocks, 5in thick, produced by Messrs Doulton Ltd, which were specially manufactured in blocks of the required size. Below the Carrara blocks the buildings were given a plinth of grey granite. The interiors of the buildings, which included waiting, refreshment, staff and other rooms, were panelled. The platform roofs, of the umbrella type, covered about 60% of the total platform area. Under the roof, the platforms were surfaced with 1in asphalt on a concrete base, while for the uncovered portion, concrete paving slabs were used. At the southern

Plate 252 The new passenger subway at Cardiff General station, showing the glazed tiling and advertisement panels.

Plate 253 Exterior of the new parcels depot and warehouse from Riverside platform, Cardiff General station. Road entrance to parcels depot on right.

Plate 254 Interior of the new parcels depot, showing the reception side with wooden bins provided for sorting parcels into delivery districts. Note roof lighting and overhead heating radiators.

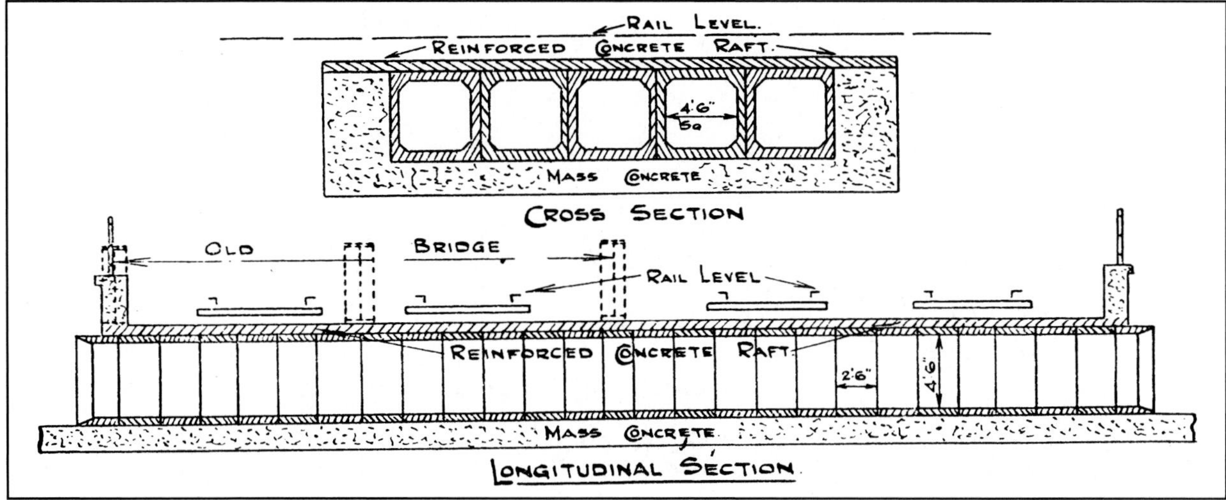

Fig 14. Detail of the reinforced concrete culverts which carry the Dock Feeder under the main lines, replacing the former bridge.

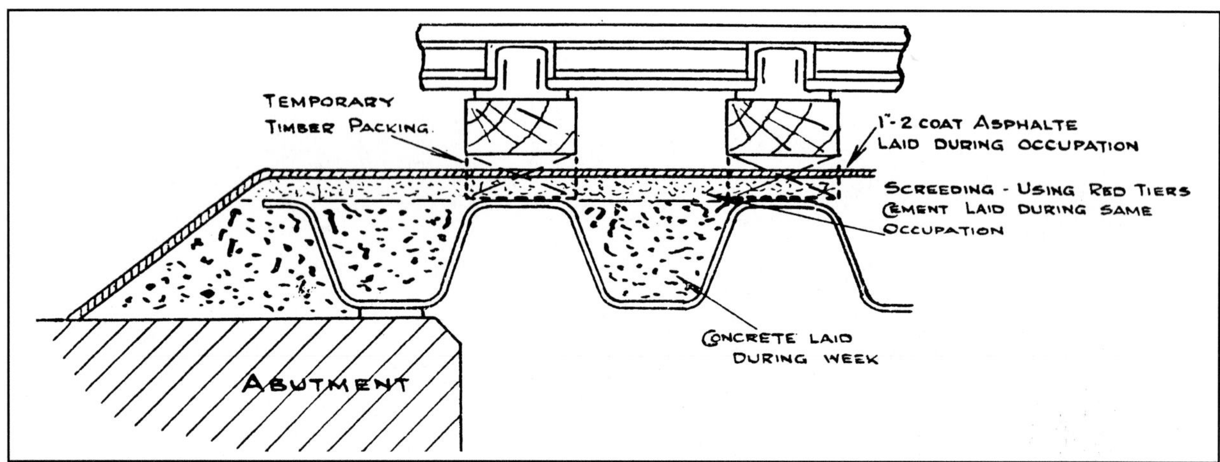

Fig 15. A sketch illustrating the interesting method employed to save time in bridge reconstruction.

Plate 255 Types of concrete retaining walls, constructed in connection with the quadrupling of the lines.

Plate 256 Widening of the Taff River Bridge on the south side, showing temporary coffer dams for construction of piers in the river bed.

Plate 257 The new bridge carrying the main line over Leckwith Road. Beyond the bridge may be seen the gates of the superseded level crossing.

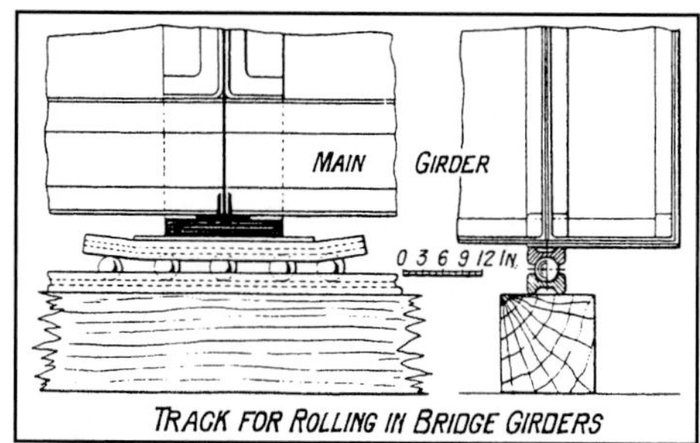

Fig 16 Track for rolling in bridge girders.

(or Riverside) approach to the station, which led out of Penarth Road, a second booking hall was provided, plus various offices for station staff. Within the triangle formed by the Taff Vale and Riverside platforms and the Penarth Road, a large new building was erected. The major portion of the ground floor was a new parcels depot and office, the smaller part being staff offices. The first floor was let to Messrs W.H.Smith & Son Ltd as a showroom and warehouse. This parcels depot was well placed for both road and rail access.

The quadrupled lines commenced from Newtown Yard on the eastern side of Cardiff, and continued through the station to a point just short of Canton Junction signal box, a distance of $1\frac{3}{4}$ miles (see plan). A noteworthy feature of the work was that no fewer than eighteen bridges had to be reconstructed. Commencing from the eastern end, the first was a footbridge near Newtown West signal box. This comprised two spans, one 75ft on the north side and one 30ft on the south side. Owing to the altered layout of the track, the bridge had to be reconstructed with the spans in the reverse order. About 300ft westward of this footbridge were four bridges very close together as will be seen from the plan. These were the Taff Vale East and West bridges, the Dock Feeder, and the Taff Viaduct bridge. The work of erecting the new East branch three-track bridge, which was about double the span of the old one, was complicated by limited occupation periods. The new bridge was erected on temporary trestles alongside its predecessor, and rolled into position after the old bridge had

Plate 258 New bridge east of Cardiff General station carrying the Taff Vale station over the main line.

Plate 259 Fruit and milk depot (formerly the carriage shed) on right, Canton locomotive depot in the centre and new carriage shed on extreme left.

Plate 260 The commodious new carriage shed in Canton Yard, with overbridge access on the right for staff and materials.

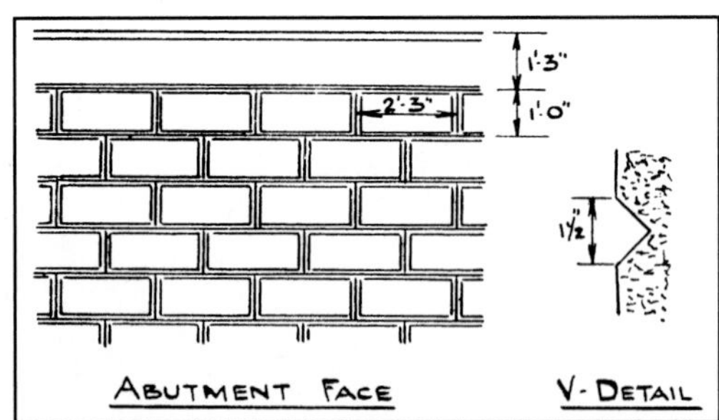

Fig 17. Face to mass concrete abutments. The sketch on the right shows indentations left by V-shaped battens.

been taken out piecemeal. In connection with the next bridge, which carried the three tracks of the West branch over the main line, the spacing of the main lines permitted the erection of a trestle, so that the new bridge was of two spans. It was possible to take each of the three West branch tracks out of use for a few weeks, and this facilitated the reconstruction of the bridge in three sections. Immediately to the west of this bridge was a low bridge was a low bridge by which the main lines spanned the Dock Feeder, a stream the name of which indicated its purpose. Renewal and maintenance of this bridge had always been difficult, as the water was only 2ft 7in below rail level. To obviate these difficulties, pre-cast reinforced concrete culvert sections were used, providing five culverts, each 4ft 6in

Plate 261 Rear view of the concrete arch retaining wall in course of construction. The right-hand sketch given in Plate 255 shows a front view of the wall.

Plate 262 A pre-cast reinforced concrete 'crib' retaining wall in the course of erection.

square inside, with 6in walls. The culverts were set in mass concrete and covered by a reinforced concrete raft. On the same site was the Taff Viaduct bridge, which carried the railway between Cardiff General and Queen Street stations. In order to carry out this work, together with the reconstruction of portions of four other bridges between the Viaduct bridge and the station, the lines between the General and Queen Street stations were closed for a week. Seven cranes were employed. The trough flooring was filled with cement concrete and asphalted, a special cement that would set in one hour being used, so that the asphalting could follow on without delay. A sketch shows the procedure followed. At the immediate west end of the station was five-span brick-arch bridge over the River Taff. The extension of the station platforms necessitated widening this bridge over the river on both sides, increasing its former width of 78ft to 175ft. The pier extensions were made independent of the old piers so that closed coffer dams could be used, and only joined to the old piers above the water level by small arches. Throughout the scheme, all bridge abutments and extensions to existing abutments, were carried out in mass concrete. A pleasing effect of ashlar work was obtained by nailing V-shaped battens to form rectangles on the face of the shutters, as shown in the illustration.

To the west of Canton Yard, two level crossings, which carried Leckwith Road and Grosvenor Street across the main line, were replaced by 50ft and 40ft bridges. This work was carried out by a slight diversion of the railway and the building up of embankments to raise the lines sufficiently to make bridges practicable. The adjoining bridges which carried the Radyr branch lines over Leckwith Road and Grosvenor Street were correspondingly widened. The level crossing at Ely Paper Works was replaced by a footbridge, and the bridge at Moor's Lane widened to a 24ft span.

Between Canton Junction and Ninian Park Halt, a useful new loop line was constructed, linking up the main line and Radyr branch lines. To provide additional and more convenient accommodation for locomotives and carriage stock, the Canton yard was completely remodelled. A new carriage shed 810ft long capable of holding 150 coaches was constructed. This had eleven tracks, five of which were constructed with pits to facilitate examination and cleaning. The new shed was a steel-framed structure, covered with Robertson's corrugated protected metal, with roof glazing. The old carriage shed was converted to a milk and fruit depot, and road access provided from De Croche Place. A new coal stage and locomotive stores were provided at the nearby locomotive depot, as well as a 65ft Mundt turntable. A footbridge 436ft long connected the carriage shed to De Croche Place.

To the south-west of Canton Yard, connected with the Penarth-Radyr line, the Ninian Park platform was extended from 350 to 500ft, and an additional platform provided. Also, in addition to the up main and up relief lines, a second up main platform line was provided. This enabled two up line trains to be at the platforms at the same time. A further track improvement was the provision of engine spurs both to the up and down sides, which contributed to the effective utilisation of the running lines.

Plate 263 A general view of the new station platforms. From left to right; the fish platform, up main platforms, down main platforms, Taff Line platforms and Riverside platforms.

Plate 264 The new 'Mundt' type turntable installed at the GWR Canton depot in Cardiff. The upper photograph shows the turntable itself and its relationship to the running lines. The lower photograph shows enginemen turning a Castle 4-6-0 on the new turntable. Exact central balance was unnecessary, as part of the weight was borne at the ends of the table.

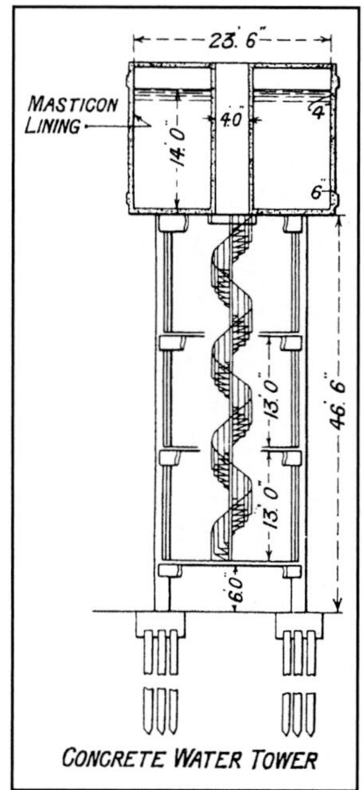

Fig 18. Concrete water tower.

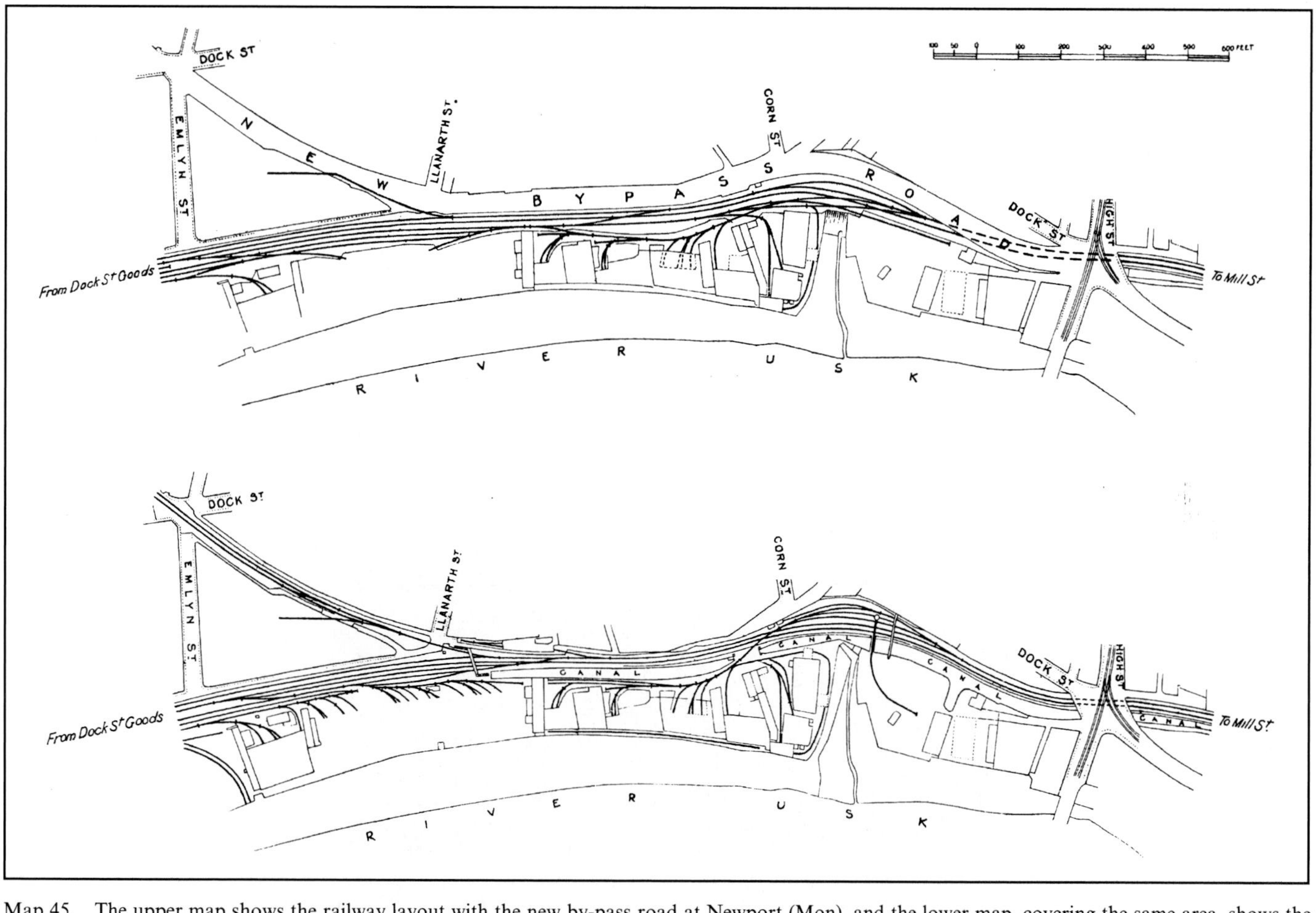

Map 45. The upper map shows the railway layout with the new by-pass road at Newport (Mon), and the lower map, covering the same area, shows the positions of the railway and canal before the changes were made to the railway and canal and the new road constructed.

Plate 265 A view looking towards the High Street road bridge, showing the railway line running underneath and the canal alongside, before alterations were commenced.

1934 NEW BY-PASS ROAD AT NEWPORT

The Newport Corporation promoted a Bill in Parliament in 1930 for the construction of a new by-pass road which involved filling in a portion of the Monmouthshire Canal and the deviation of nearly half a mile of the Eastern Valleys section of the GWR near Newport (High Street). The work of moving the railway lines was undertaken by the GWR, while the work of constructing the new road was carried out by the Newport Corporation.

The water passing through the canal was necessary to supply various wharves, and so it was transferred to a 3ft culvert. A portion of the railway was diverted on to the former site of the canal, and a portion of the new road was laid upon the site where the railway previously existed. The railway at Moderator Sidings, near Corn Street, had to be slewed, which involved an entire rearrangement of the permanent way and signals. The old signal box was removed and a new box, with 21 levers, was substituted near the old site but alongside the new up line. A two-lever ground frame and a protecting signal was provided at Llanarth Street to work the points leading into the works at this spot. The trailing connection in the down main line at Cross Street crossing, near Emlyn Street, was carried forward 20 yards, and this necessitated moving the Cross Street crossing signal box. The aerial telegraph and telephone wires were taken down and replaced by an underground cable for about 520 yards.

The new road, about 1/3rd mile long, was built to run from High Street railway bridge to the junction of Emlyn Street with Dock Street. To join up with the level of High Street, which carried over the GWR line, it was necessary to built a portion of the new road on a viaduct. The total width of the road was 50ft, the width of the carriage-way being 30ft and that of the footpaths 20ft. The surface of the road was mastic asphalt, laid on a foundation of reinforced concrete. It cost about £100,000 at the time.

1934 IMPROVEMENTS AT SWANSEA

The old Swansea High Street station had three platforms, one 360ft and the other 580ft long and a 70ft bay. An extensive scheme of improvement was carried out, including reconstruction of the station buildings, together with improvements to Ivey Place, the square in front of the station. The new station has four 900ft platforms and a 600ft bay, with an approach from Ivey Place which has been greatly enlarged.

Existing property on the south side of Ivey place was acquired by Swansea Corporation, which disposed of part on which was built the Grand

Plate 266 A view from the same point, showing the new by-pass road on its viaduct over the railway, but with the canal diverted.

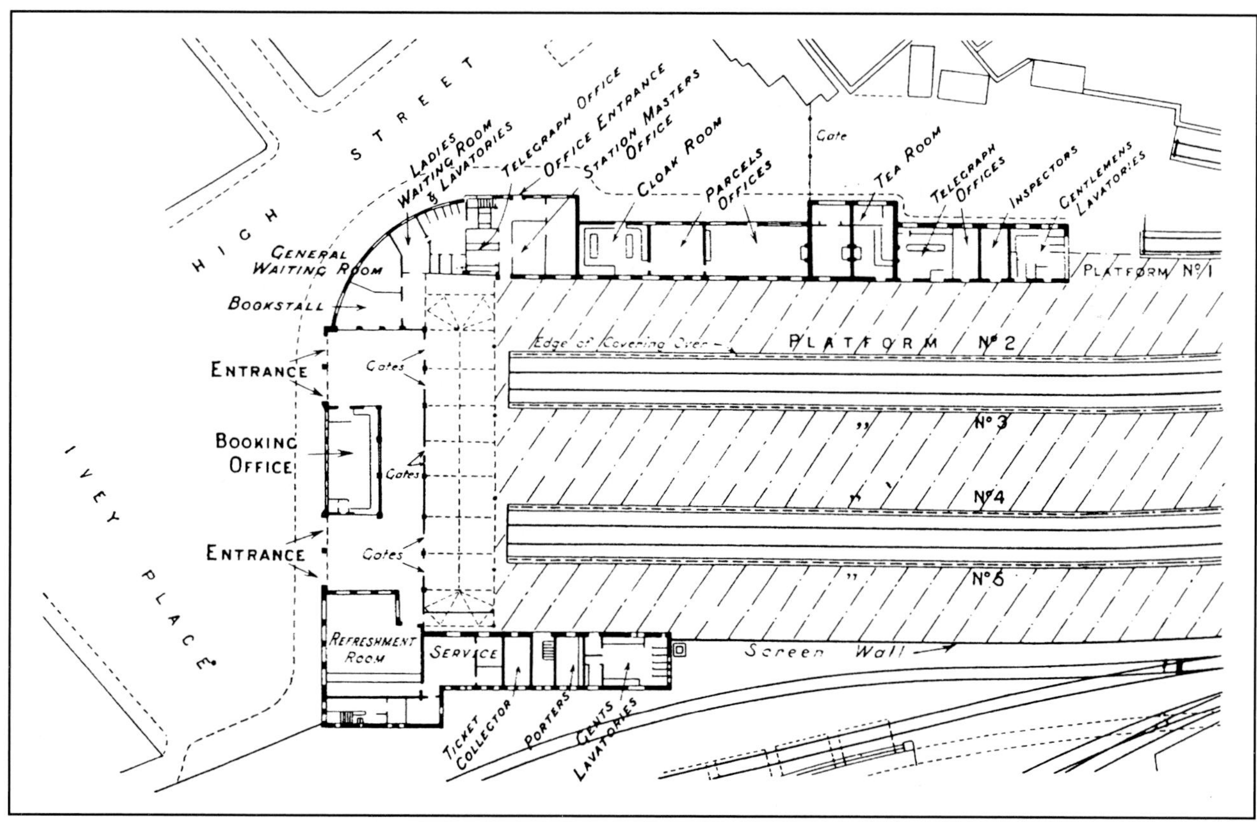

Map 46. The layout of the offices and other facilities at the new Swansea High Street Station.

Plate 267 The front of the reconstructed GWR station at Swansea High Street, showing the Portland stone façade, as well as an array of vintage taxis.

Plate 268 The passenger concourse at the new Swansea High Street Station, showing the booking hall on the left, the platform entrances on the right and the bookstall at the far end.

Hotel, while 35ft was added to Ivey Place; this together with 20ft added by the GWR through setting back the station buildings, provided a spacious station approach. The new Swansea High Street station buildings marked another step forward in the progress of station architecture. The main façade facing Ivey Place was faced with Portland stone said at the time to be in the character of modern Renaissance, giving the whole a dignified and pleasing appearance. Passengers entered from Ivey Place through two gateways sheltered by a glazed verandah. These led direct to the concourse, in which was situated the booking office, a self-contained unit. On the right was a refreshment room where lunches and snacks were served. To the left were waiting rooms and a bookstall, whilst straight ahead were the entrances to the platforms. The remainder of the rooms at this level were mostly for use of station staff. The station buildings were on two floors, with a third floor over the portion forming the main entrance. These upper floors consisted entirely of offices for GWR staff.

Beyond the station, extending along the side of the Swansea Canal, a large retaining wall was built and the low-lying ground between this and the railway filled up to enable sidings to be laid down for the storage of stock. Here, also, the carriages were to be cleaned and provided with fresh water, gas, etc. Altogether, over $1\frac{1}{2}$ miles of sidings were provided for traffic and goods purposes. All the permanent way work outside the station was remodelled, and an additional line laid down leading to the junction near Landore. Previous to the alterations, main line trains were booked to stop at Landore, and coaches for Swansea were there detached and afterwards taken into Swansea by a special engine. On completion of the new lay-out and platform extensions, this system of working was abandoned and Swansea station virtually became on the main line, as main line trains could now run direct into the station, set down and pick up passengers; and after an engine had been attached to the rear, the train could proceed in the direction of Fishguard.

A vast amount of work was involved to accomplish these extensive improvements, the site being hemmed in on the south-east by the Strand and the line down to the docks, and on the north-west by rising ground and house property; also quite a network of streets had to be crossed. A large amount of property around the station had to be acquired, new houses provided, and the site cleared for the railway extensions. Several streets had to be altered or diverted. The first was Pottery Street, the 1 in 6 gradient of which was so steep that the paving stones of the footpath were laid as shallow steps. It was therefore not much public hardship to close this street for vehicular traffic; a 10ft wide subway for pedestrians under the railway being all that was necessary. Next, Powell Street was diverted into Jockey Street, so that both passed as one under the lines and platforms. Jockey Street, Bargeman Row and the Strand, all converged under the railway, and were bridged over by some very peculiar and extensive archwork.

On the west side, the GWR's 900 ft long private road from High Street to the goods yard ran alongside the platform and line, and in order to make room for the widening work, a new site had to be found for this, which was across the valley to the Prince of Wales Road, a continuation of High Street. The new roadway was carried on an embankment on the site of Bethesda Street as far as the crossing of Bargeman Row, which was spanned by a reinforced concrete bridge; and that the Strand and Corporation Yard were crossed on a two-arched bridge at a height of 30ft above the Strand level. The pier carrying the later bridge on

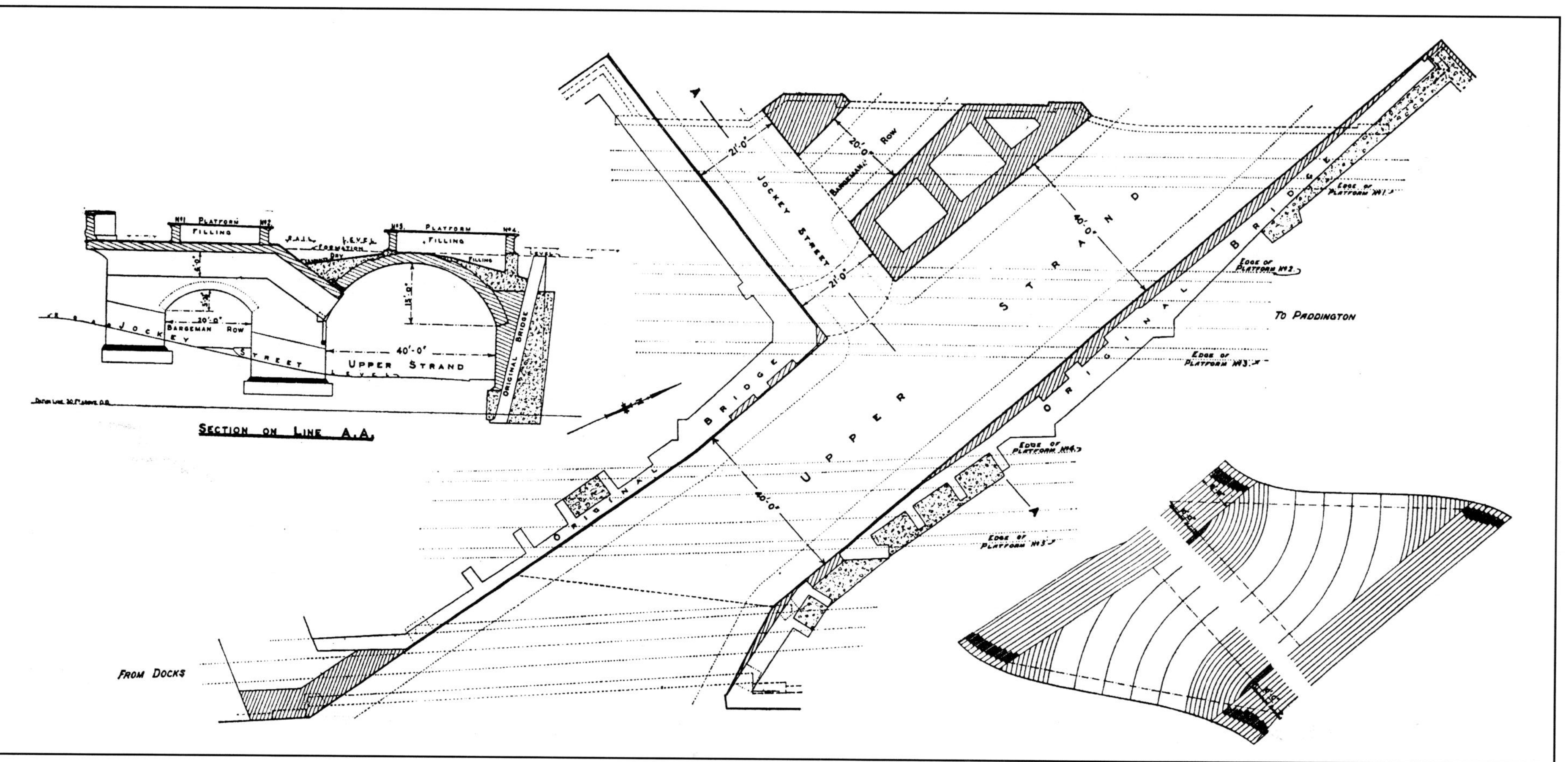

Map 47. Structural alterations at Swansea High Street station. The main plan view shows the relationship of the platforms and dock line to the underlying streets. The sectional view on the left shows the bridge over Upper Strand. The right-hand inset shows the curved surface of the underside of the arch when developed flat.

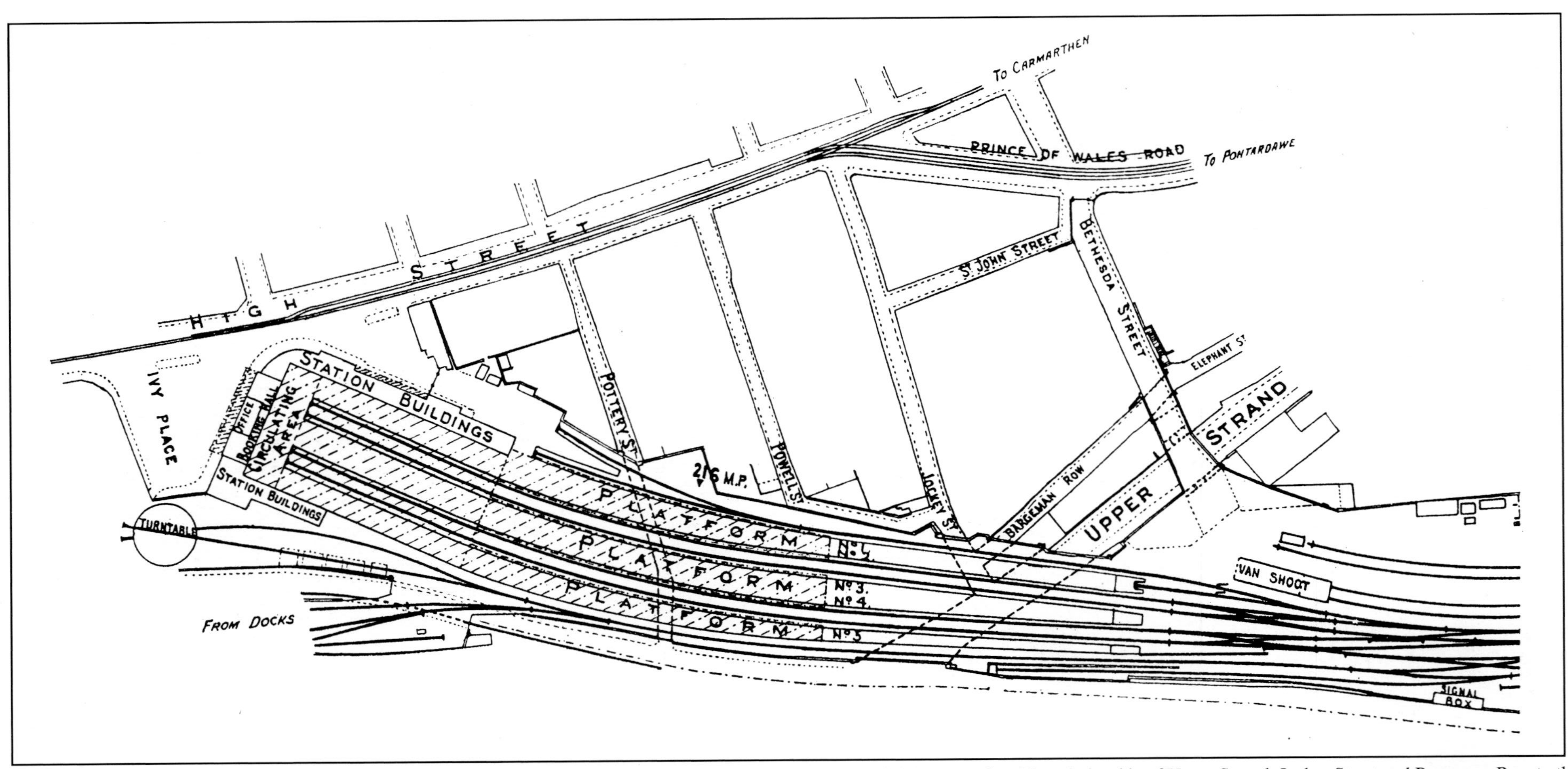

Map 48. A plan showing the approach roads, the new platforms, and permanent way at the reconstructed Swansea High Street station. The relationship of Upper Strand, Jockey Street and Bargeman Row to the station platforms is also apparent.

Plate 269 The north end of the bridge over the Upper Strand. Bargeman Row is on the right, behind the lamp-post. Inset is a view looking under the Strand bridge. Note the curved portion on the right-hand side of the arch, curved outwards so as to provide more supporting material.

Plate 270 A view looking down Jockey Street, the lower street being the Strand, while Bargeman Row enters on the left.

Plate 271 A view from the centre of the Strand under the main arch looking up Jockey Street, with Bargeman Row entering Jockey Street on the right.

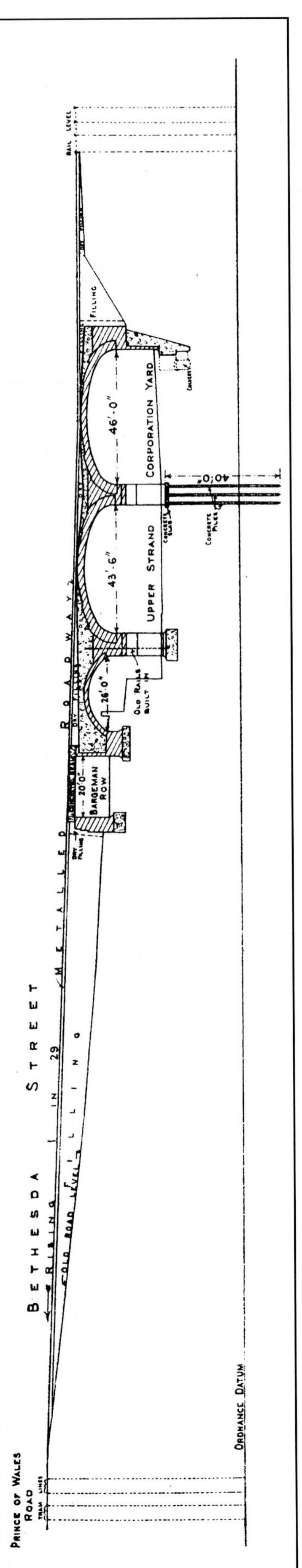

Fig. 19 Sectional view along the centre of the new road approach to the goods yard at Swansea, running from Prince of Wales Road, over Upper Strand to the yard.

one side of the road had to be carried on a piled foundation to a depth of 40ft, since at some time deep excavation had been made to obtain clay and later filled with very indifferent material. The goods yard over the remainder of the Corporation Yard was carried on a reinforced concrete substructure.

The bridge over the Strand was of noteworthy construction. Jockey Street entered the Strand almost at right angles and Bargeman Row entered Jockey Street in a similar manner. In the first case, the arches intersect one another, and in the second, one arch entered below the other. As the MoT Inspector reported, the most difficult piece of work was the widening over the Strand and its junction with Jockey Street and Bargeman Row. There was a very clever piece of arching here in five rings, passing from square construction to a spiral arch on a skew face. With regard to the Strand widening, the square span was a 40ft arch of seven rings, on the skew, springing from a straight arch with special granite blocks, which, on the west side, were in addition curved outwards. This was considered probably unique for arching in railway work. The Strand continued to widen and it was necessary to construct a girder bridge of 105ft span to carry the line which ran down to the docks. The bridge was erected on trestles alongside, and on the old bridge being dismantled, was rolled in during an occupation of the line.

Included in the overall scheme was a new warehouse, which consisted of a steel-framed concrete building, 200ft long by 52ft 6in wide outside dimensions, with three floors, providing 9000 sq ft internal floor space on each of the three floors. The warehouse was served by two electric lifts from the goods shed, and the first floor was provided with a spiral gravity shute in addition. To make room for this structure, a part of the old shed had to be taken down, together with the covering over the platform extension.

1935 IMPROVEMENTS AT BRISTOL TEMPLE MEADS STATION

The GWR Bristol Temple Meads station was opened in 1841, with a Tudor style façade and a train shed roof with a span of 74ft across four broad-gauge tracks. A few weeks before, the Bristol & Exeter Railway had begun running trains, with its own station close to that of the GWR but at right angles to it. In 1845, the lines were

Plate 272 The south end of the Strand bridge, Swansea, showing the 105ft girder bridge for the line down to the docks. It will be noted that the road bent round to the left while still under the arched portion. Along the Strand, in the distance, was the bridge for the approach road to the goods yard, and on the right of the picture are the five 30ft arches let into the old retaining wall with the parapet cantilevered out above. This method was adopted to obtain an additional width of 5ft at rail level without having to rebuild the retaining wall or reduce the width of the road.

joined by an 'express curve' with one narrow platform. The Midland Railway gained access to Bristol by its acquisition of the broad-gauge Bristol & Gloucester Railway and in 1854 standard gauge lines were laid. The extra traffic became a problem with the then existing facilities and various schemes for a joint station were considered. Finally, it was decided to develop accommodation on the 'express curve' and from that decision stems the impressive curved sweep of Temple Meads station today. It was stipulated that there should be no interruption to traffic, so work took several years. The down main platform was opened in 1874 and the remainder by 1876, the year in which the GWR took over the Bristol & Exeter and so the new station became joint GWR and Midland.

The gauge conversion in 1892 made possible the addition of an extra platform and also a down bay platform. Various other works were carried out with the object of relieving the ever-increasing traffic through the station, such as loop lines between North Somerset Junction and Dr Day's Bridge Junction, opened in 1886, and relief lines between East Depot, Marsh Junction and Pylle Hill Junction, bypassing the station for non-stop expresses such as the Cornishman, opened in 1892.

Bristol Temple Meads station was by then roughly in the shape of a letter 'V', with an entrance facade near the apex. The roof dominated with a curved sweep over the platforms. Through the main entrance was the booking hall with separate booking offices for the GWR and Midland Railway. On the left was platform 5 the Midland departure platform, and on the right platform 4 the main GWR up platform. Platforms 2 & 3 were islands. Platform 2, some 350ft long, dealt with Midland arrivals and interchange traffic. As stated, the other island was added in 1892 to cope with increased traffic. Platform 4 ran with platform 5. A subway led to platform 7 on the opposite side of the line, while a footbridge connected platforms 6 & 8 which ran through into the old train shed.

Under the arrangements of the Development (Guaranteed Loans and Grants) Act of 1929, it was decided to enlarge Bristol Temple Meads station, and also to facilitate the working of traffic to and from the West of England by providing two additional running lines between Filton Junction and Stapleton Road; Dr Day's Bridge Junction and Temple Meads; and Temple Meads and Portishead Junction; giving at least four running lines between Filton Junction and Portishead Junction, a distance of $6^1/_2$ miles. These works necessitated the reconstruction of Horfield and Ashley Hill stations, to the north-east of Bristol, and Bedminster and Parson Street stations, on the western side, also widening a number of bridges in the vicinity of Temple Meads. New carriage sidings were provided at Malago Vale, between Bedminster and Parson Street stations, and a new locomotive depot provided near the western end of Temple Meads station at Bath Road.

Very heavy and intricate engineering works were entailed in these alterations. The quadrupling of lines on either side of Bristol necessitated extensive earthworks and the recon-

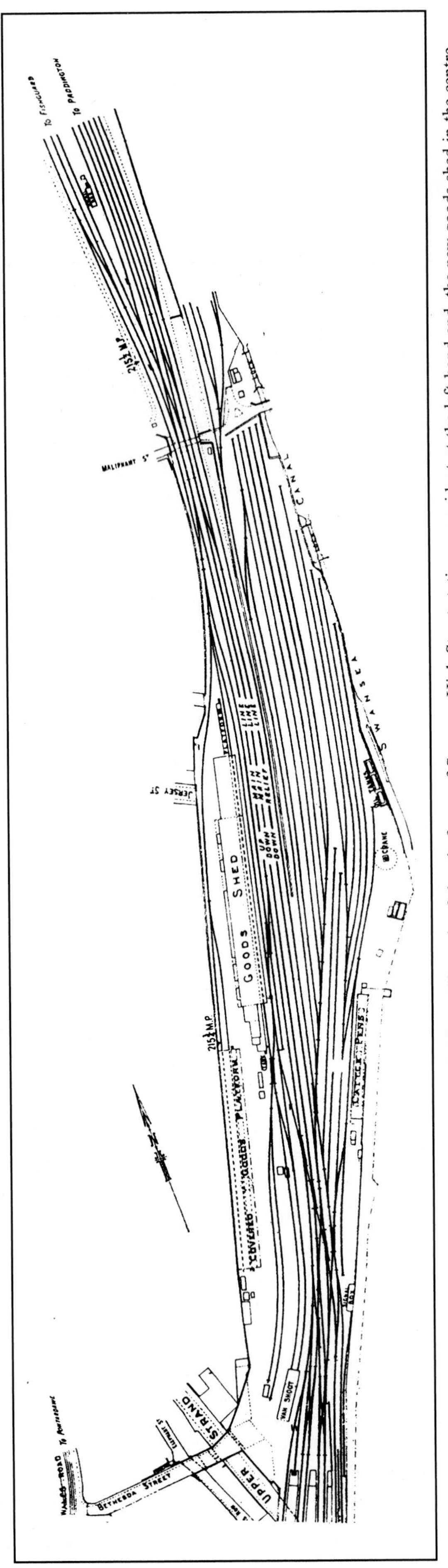

Map 49. A general plan of the lay-out of the main lines and sidings. The ends of the platforms of Swansea High Street station are evident at the left-hand end, the new goods shed in the centre.

struction of numerous bridges, as well as the rebuilding of Horfield, Ashley Hill, Bedminster and Parson Street stations, while many miles of permanent way had to be laid in and much of the old realigned. Owing to Temple Meads station being situated between the River Avon New Cut and the Floating Harbour, the bridges over these waterways had to be extensively widened. The bridges over the New Cut and Cattle Market Road had to be reconstructed, and were made 312ft wide, or more than five times their former width. The Floating Harbour bridge was extended by about 130ft, that is to about twice its previous width. Another noteworthy work was the erection of a new bridge of 190ft span carrying the Bath Road over nine lines of railway track, at the west end of the station. The reconstruction of this bridge was exceptionally difficult because of the necessity not to disturb the regular service of two lines of tramcars and heavy flow of other vehicular traffic over the bridge.

In connection with the quadrupling of the line between Stapleton Road and Filton Junction, the removal of an arch bridge of 68ft span was necessary. The structure was an old one, 13ft in width, built of brickwork in lime mortar, 3ft 3in deep throughout. Prior to the demolition, the earth and clay, together with the spandrill walls, were cleared away, down to the bare arch itself. Then fifty-four charges of gelignite were laid. Each consisted of two 4oz cartridges of gelignite, making a total of 27lb. The charges were arranged in seven rows and drilled to an average depth of 2ft 3in. They were placed not less than 2ft from the edge of the arch and not more than 2ft apart. To prevent damage to surrounding buildings, torpedo netting, timbers and brushwood were piled over each row of charges, and the windows of the booking office of Horfield station, some 40ft from the bridge, were boarded over. Two lengths of rails and sleepers were removed from each line of track immediately under the bridge. The charges were fired by two electric detonators, one being connected to 37 charges and the other to 17. The explosions were simultaneous, and the result was quite successful. The arch dropped clear at springing level and the debris was well broken up. A six-ton steam travelling crane, with engine attached, moved up immediately afterwards, and the clearing of the debris was taken in hand.

Plate 273 The new three-floored steel and concrete warehouse built over the existing goods shed platform.

The up road was connected up in four hours time, and the down road two hours later.

Regarding Temple Meads station itself, the enlargement increased its size to more than twice its former area, widening it by 230ft, with fifteen platforms, the longest of which was 1340ft against the previous longest of 920ft. A platform was built along the wall supporting the 1878 roof and two islands were also built; as the face of one was extensive, the platform was divided and provided with scissors crossovers giving the station an additional six platforms. With the additional use of a bay at the Exeter end of the main platform, the total number of platforms was increased from eight to fifteen. Under the existing roof, the original four platforms were entirely altered to give two very long platform faces, the running lines of which were divided centrally by scissors crossovers, allowing each platform to carry two numbers and for trains to depart independently through the central lines. The new platforms were numbered from the down side to the up side. Platforms 1 to 6 were outside the former station on the down side, and were built on the so-called Cattle Market site acquired by the GWR for this purpose some years previously. Platforms 7 to 10 were built partly under the former station roof. Platform 11 was a bay adjoining platform 10 at the western end, used for the Portishead trains. Platforms 12 to 15 were the unaltered dead-end platforms of what was still known as the 'old station', that is the original GWR terminus, and these were used for LMSR expresses and local services and the Avonmouth lines.

The coverings of the new platforms were of the GWR standard 'umbrella' and 'arcade' type. The platform buildings, which included refreshment, waiting, staff and other usual rooms, were constructed of Carrara glazed blocks (described elsewhere) on a grey granite plinth. A new refreshment room was provided to serve platforms 3, 4 & 5 platforms, also another new refreshment room on platform 6. In addition, the existing refreshment room on the old up main platform was modernised. The walls of the refreshment rooms to dado height were lined with Napoleon and Botticino marble. The panelling above the dado was of Indian silver-grey wood with quartered veneer panels; an inlaid border added to the beauty of the panelling. Black marble skirting and chromium-plated fittings, also a pale yellow semi-gloss ceiling, finished the decoration. Facing the main entrance to the station, under the clock tower, was provided a modern booking office, with seven large windows, five for GWR and two for LMSR bookings. The site of the former booking office was added to the circulating area in front of the ticket windows. A new cloak room was built, accessible on one side from the approach road and on the other side from platform 10. The old overbridge was demolished and a new subway constructed. All platforms were served by the main subway, which was 300ft long and 30ft wide. There were broad stairways from the subways to the platforms for passengers, and electric lifts for luggage. A branch subway gave access to the station from Cattle Market Road, and a booking office was provided at the junction of the branch and main subways.

A new parcels depot was erected on the site of the old carriage sheds and sidings. The ground floor of the depot was a covered area for collection and delivery work, connected by a lift with a warehouse on the first floor. A special

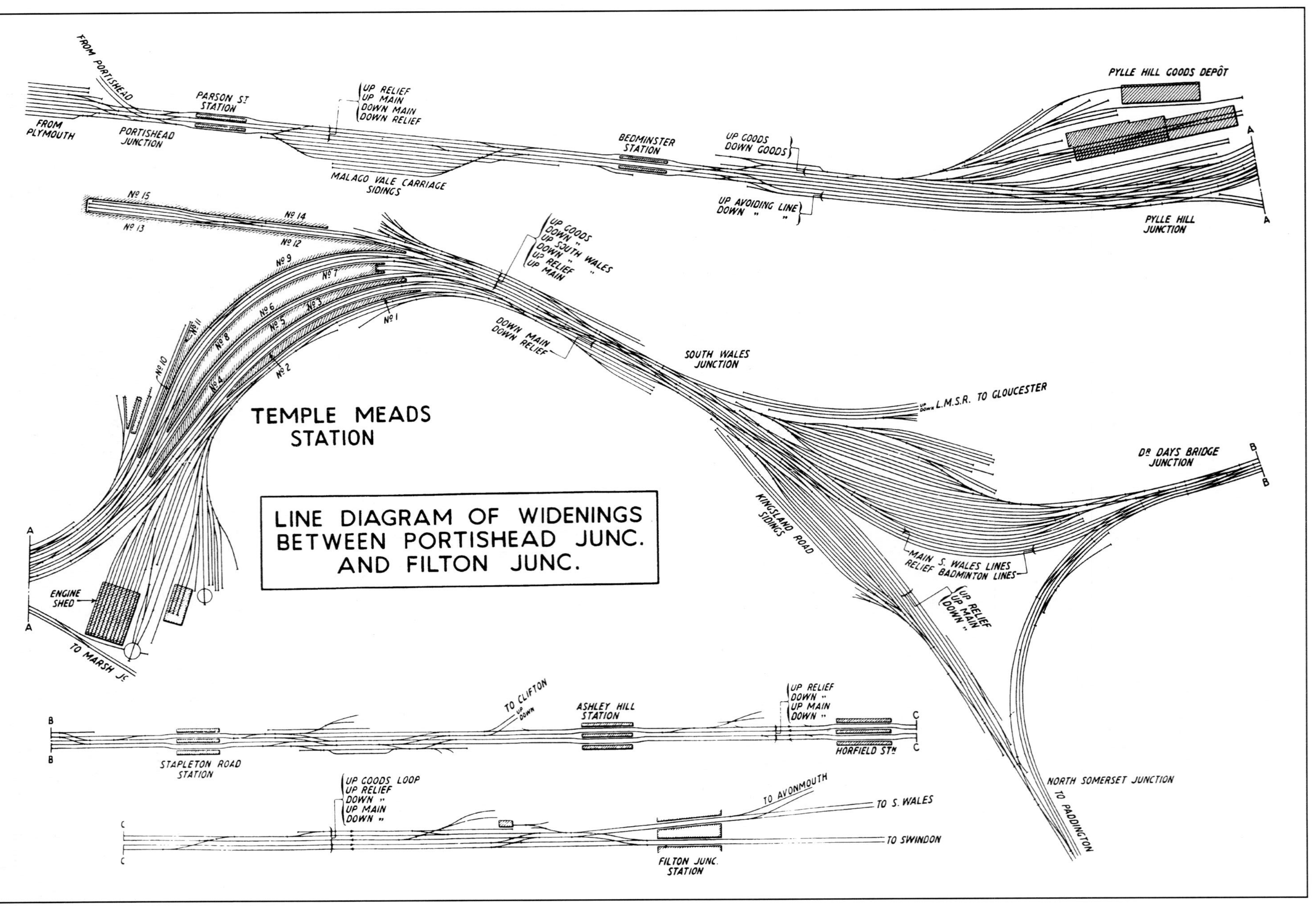

Map 50. Line diagram of the widened track between Portishead Junction and Filton Junction.

Plate 274 Lockleaze bridge, showing the sand drags on the up London line.

Plate 275 Reinforced concrete footbridge and the LMSR bridge.

Plate 276 The reconstructed Horfield station on the newly quadrupled running lines, also showing the new double-arch bridge.

Plate 277 Another view of Horfield Road bridge from the other direction, with Horfield station behind it.

Plate 278 The reconstructed Ashley Hill station on the newly quadrupled running lines. The other pair of lines are on the right, out of sight, between the platforms.

Plate 279 The arch bridge near Stapleton Road, Bristol, as it appeared shortly before the explosive charges were detonated. Note the brushwood placed where the explosive charges were laid.

Plate 280 The arch bridge at Stapleton Road at the moment the charges exploded.

subway, with lifts, was provided for parcels traffic between the depot and all platforms, and electric trolleys were brought into use to facilitate transport. On the Temple Gate front of the parcels depot was a parcels receiving office, above which were offices and messroom accommodation.

A new colour light signalling system was installed, replacing the old semaphore signals, operated by two new power signal boxes, Bristol East and Bristol West, with another box to work the locomotive depot points and signals. The advantages of all the alterations, from a traffic operating viewpoint, were considerable. The old troubles of long trains fouling the points giving access to an adjoining road, and also trains having to pull up twice at a platform because it was too short, vanished, while the broader platforms facilitated station work. The loading banks and run-round

Plate 281 Debris on the embankment and permanent way after the demolition of the bridge at Stapleton Road.

Plate 282 Excavating on the Filton to Stapleton Road widening scheme.

Plate 283 The widened approach from Bedminster station to Pylle Hill junction.

Plate 284 The new Bedminster station on the newly quadrupled lines, with its long platforms.

Plate 285 The new station at Bedminster.

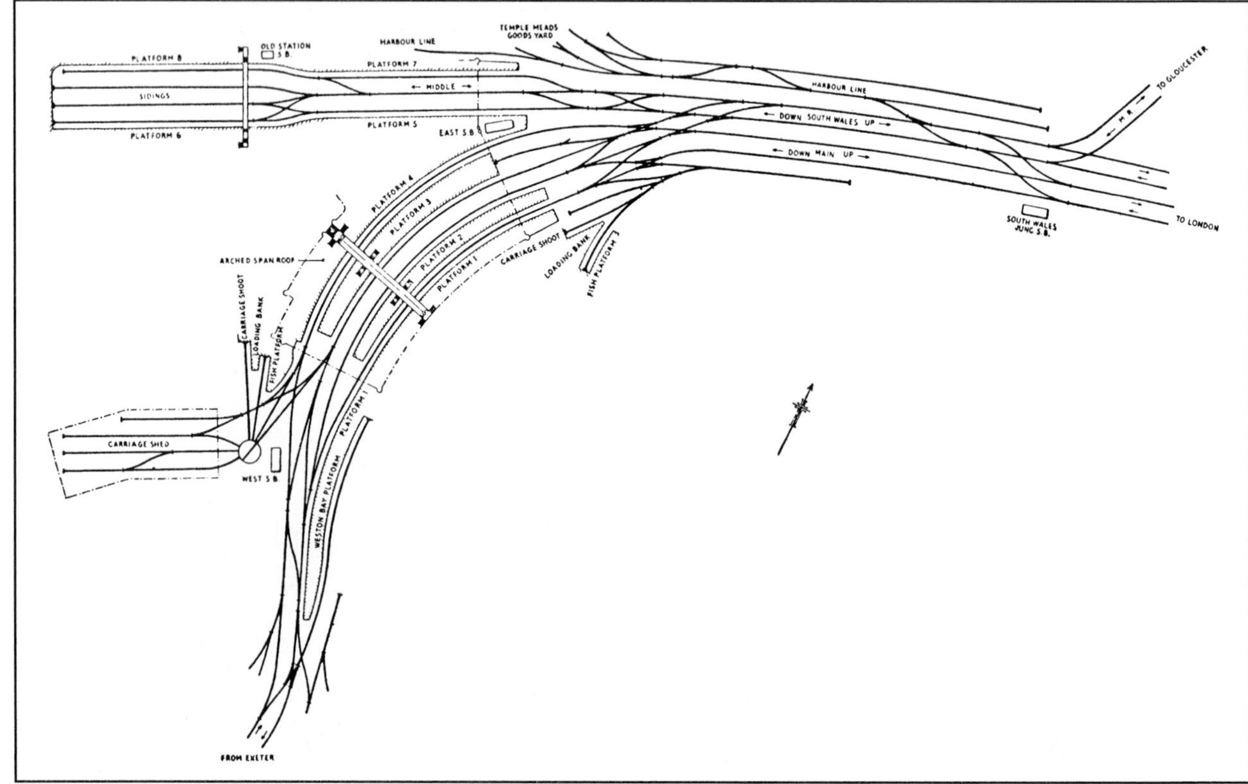

Map 51. Bristol Temple Meads station layout as it existed before reconstruction.

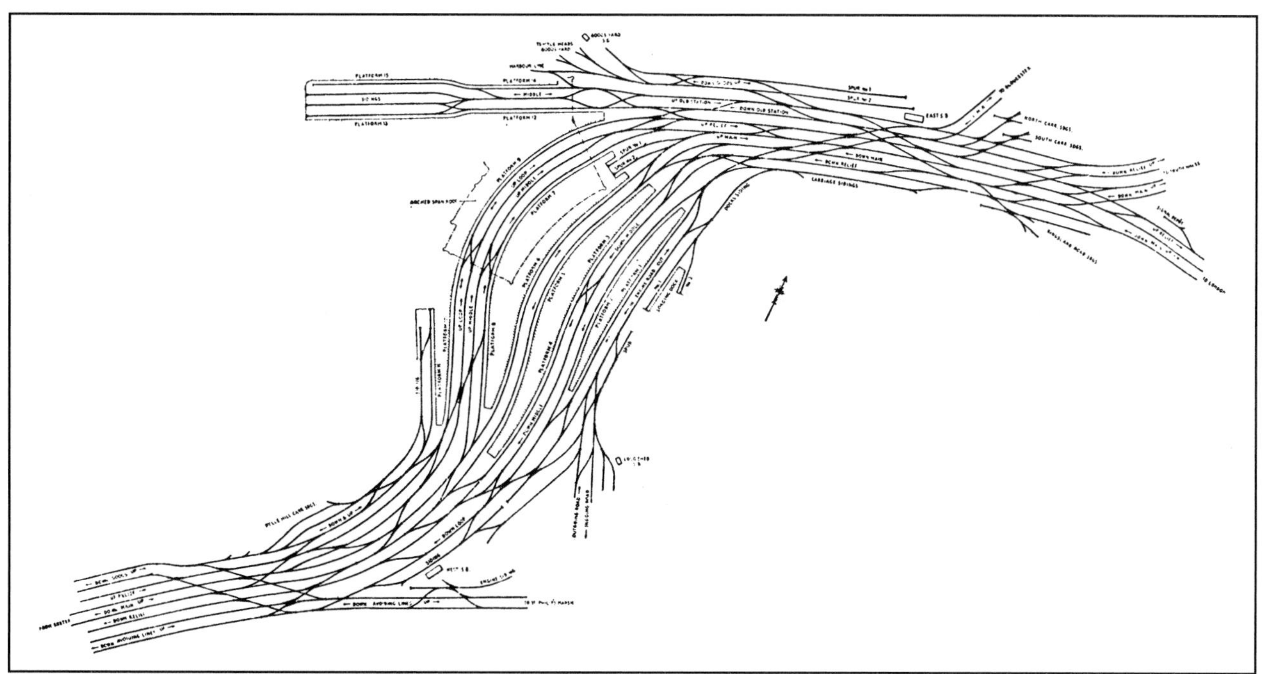

Map 52. The new layout at Bristol Temple Meads station.

roads on the up and down sides also helped operation. As against two pairs of running lines leading from the east end of the station, and a single pair of lines at the west end, there were now three tracks available in each direction, so that three up trains could depart and three down trains arrive simultaneously.

As can be seen, the reconstruction at Bristol Temple Meads was on an elaborate scale, with a number of entirely new platforms east and south of the old station, widening the existing outside platforms, clearing the centre ones away, and providing four running lines from end to end. In all, the work extended over a period of six years, and the alterations to the permanent way were carried out in no fewer than 71 stages. The difference between the old and new layouts was most striking.

The complexity of the traffic, as it existed at the time of the reconstruction, was as follows, per day. Passenger trains starting from Temple Meads 150, passenger trains terminating 150 (both with allied movements to and from the carriage sidings at the east end or Malago Vale), through passenger trains 150 (most changed engines), trains amalgamated or divided 12, trains involving attaching or detaching vehicles 124, engines to and from Bath Road shed 270, goods trains to and from the goods station 9 and transfers to and from the goods station and Kingsland Road sidings 12.

The necessity for keeping the entire traffic moving during the six years of reconstruction made it essential to progress by stages that could be completed at weekends. There was no opportunity of diverting traffic to other routes and weekday possssion of large sections of the layout was out of the question. At the same time, preparations were going forward for the installation of power signalling with colour-light signals by the time the whole scheme was completed. Every change in permanent way entailed changes in signalling, and this had to be done irrespective of the new equipment being installed for the final job. Temporary mechanical signal boxes were constructed at Pylle Hill Junction, Bristol West and South Wales Junction to cover the stage work. These were quite large boxes, having locking frames of 160, 80 and 158 levers respectively.

The new power signalling boxes, at the east and west ends of Temple Meads station, were among the largest in the country at the time, with 368 and 328 levers respectively. The entire scheme was completed by the bringing into service of the East box in November 1935. On the outgoing side there were block sections to the Midland line, to Dr Day's Bridge Junction on the four-track line to Filton, and to North Somerset Junction on the main line to London. In addition, block working was in force between Temple Meads East and West boxes on the various platform lines through the station. In the East box there were no fewer than 23 block bells, each of a sufficiently different tone from the rest to enable a trained ear to know which one was ringing. Power was used for the operation of the points and controlling the colour-light signals, and it was used for interlocking, both between levers and through the track circuits.

1937 DEMOLITION OF PENYRHEOL VIADUCT

The Rhymney Valley coalfield was being explored and developed at the time the Barry Dock was opened, and thus the construction of the Rhymney branch of the Barry Railway was formulated with the object of getting coal down to the Barry Railway system and docks via a route which would be shorter, give speedier working, and a lower rate than then in operation. It was also designed to give improved facilities for import traffic from the Barry Docks by gaining access to the then LNWR.

The Rhymney branch was opened for traffic in August 1901. The line was $6\frac{3}{4}$ miles in length, and proceeded from Tynycaeau Junction on the Barry line,

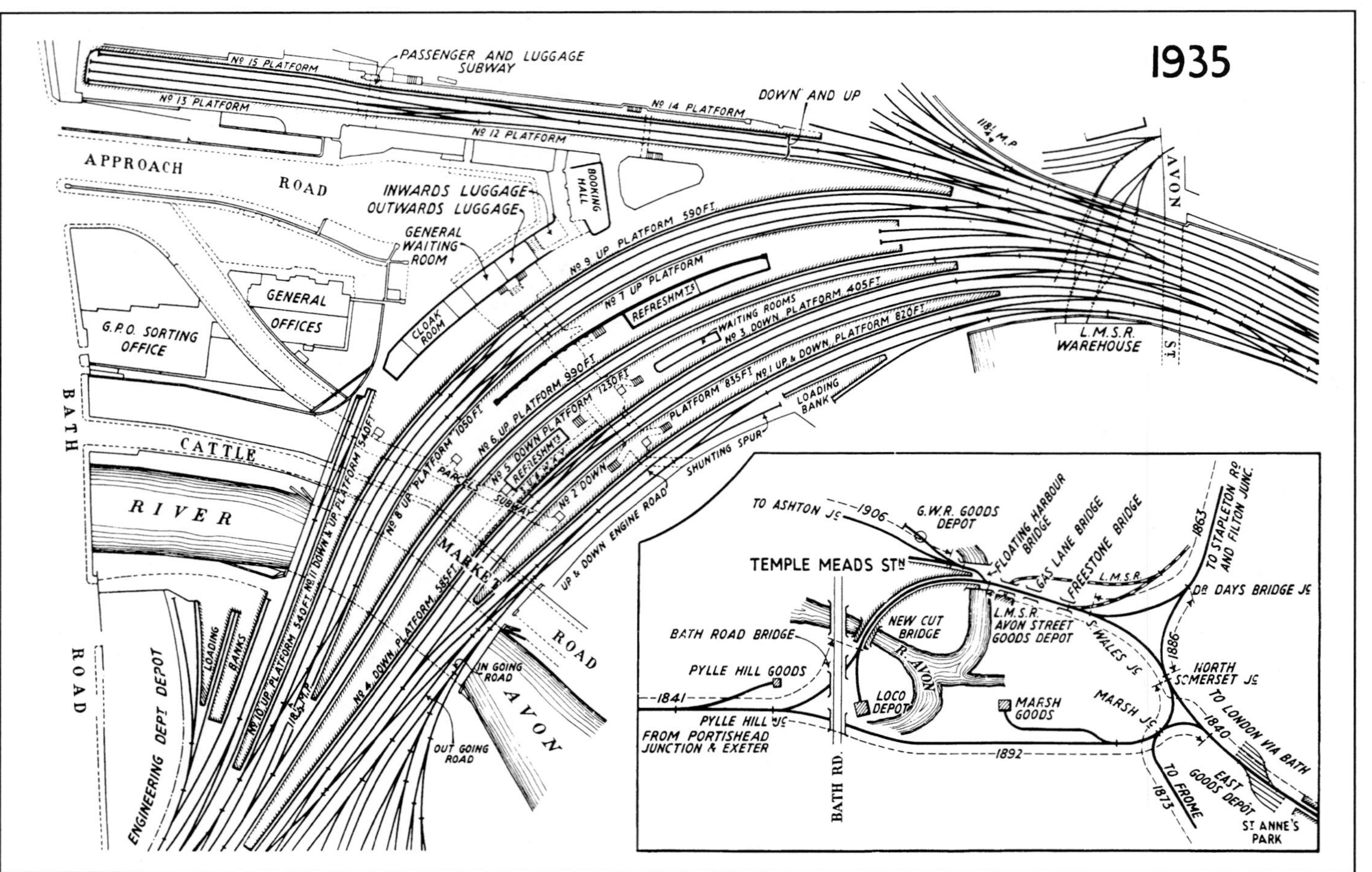

Map 53. Plan of the layout of the reconstructed Bristol Temple Meads station in 1935. The inset shows the rail routes in the area and the dates of construction.

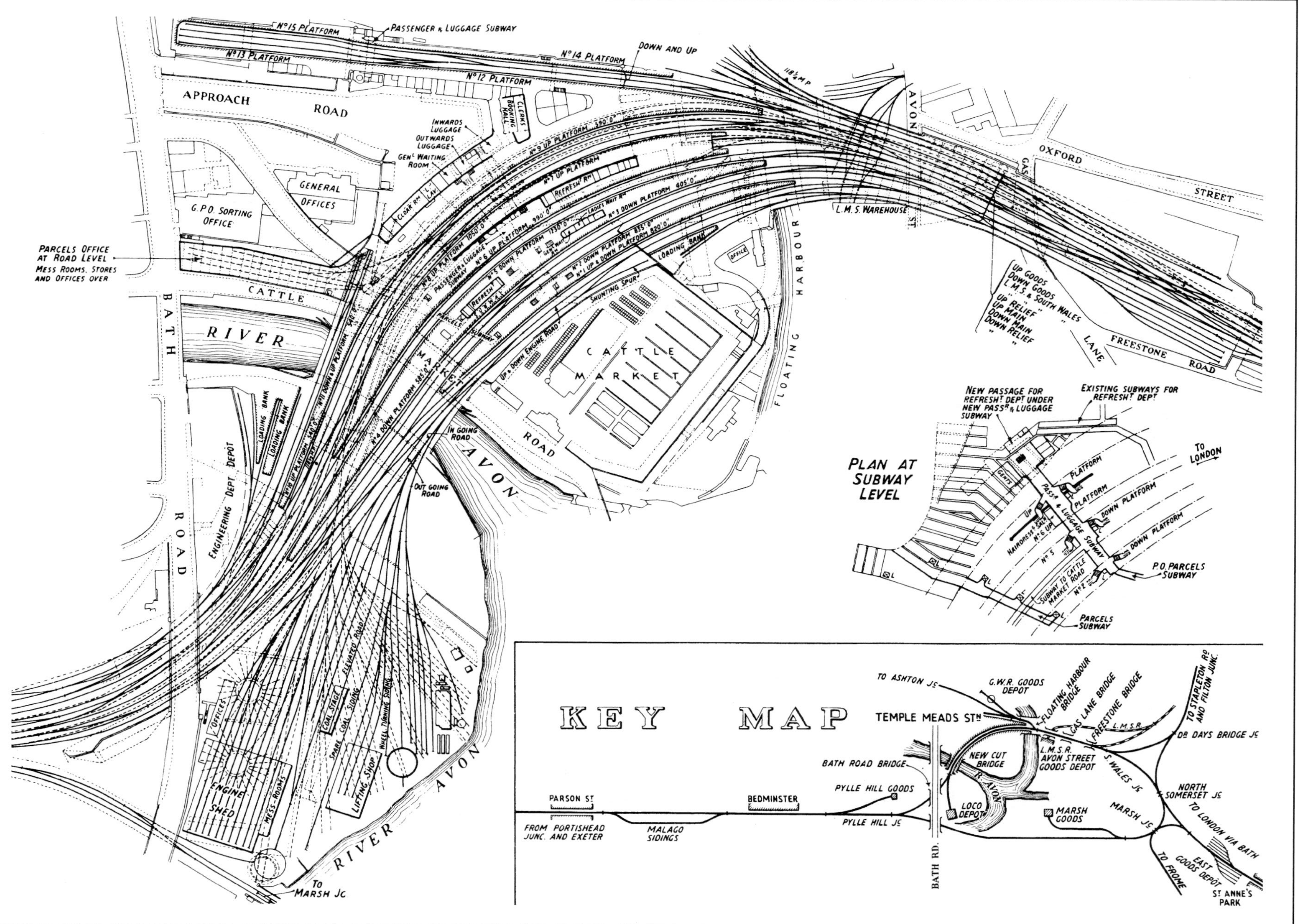

Map 54. Another version of the plan of the layout of the reconstructed Bristol Temple Meads station in 1935, showing a larger area. It also shows the previous layout in dotted lines, thus it gives more information but is more difficult to understand. It also shows a plan of the subway. The inset again shows the rail routes in the area, but without the dates of construction although with the advantage of covering a larger area.

Plate 286 A view at the west end of Bristol Temple Meads station before reconstruction. Note the cobbled stones between the rails.

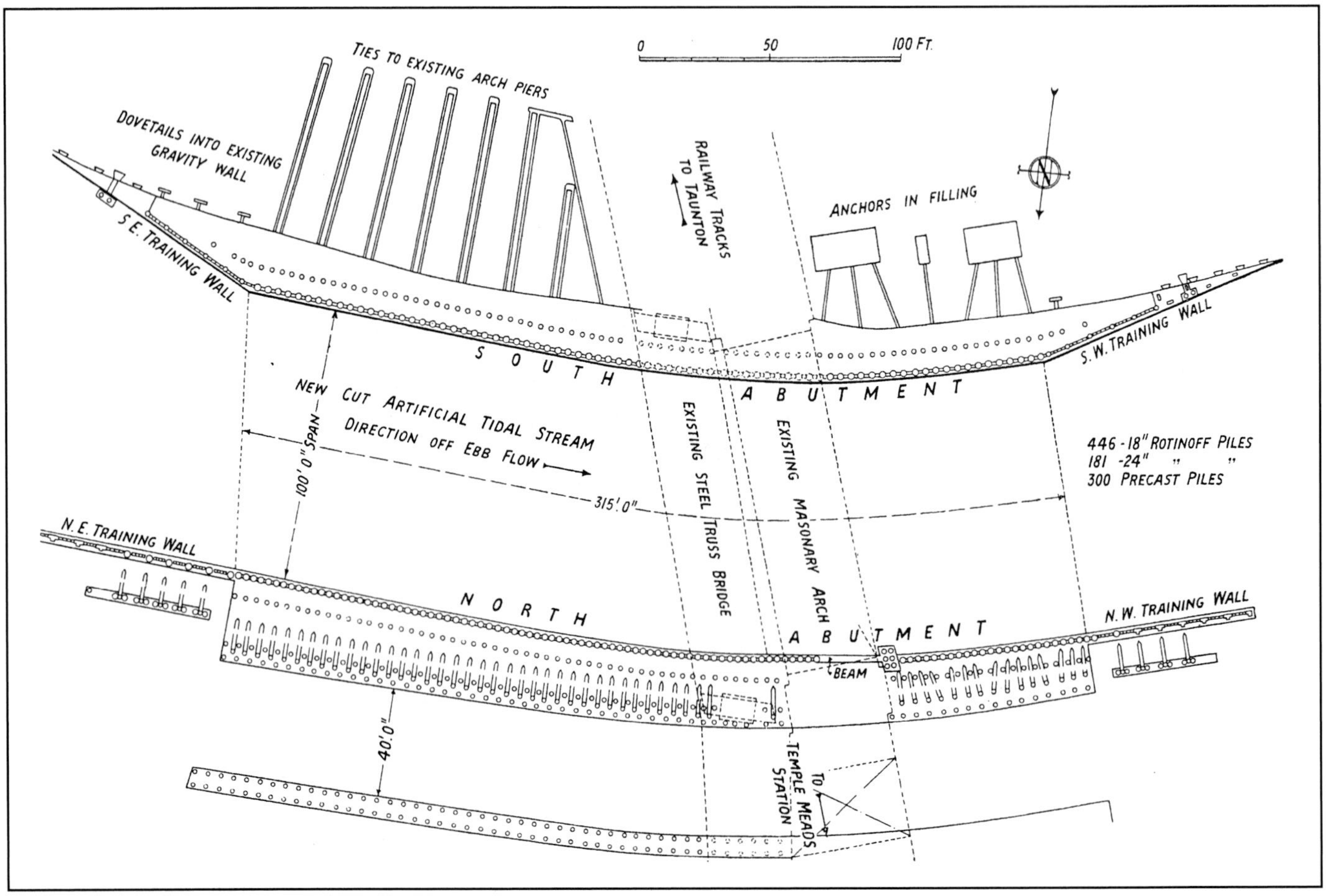

0 50 100 FT.
TIES TO EXISTING ARCH PIERS
DOVETAILS INTO EXISTING GRAVITY WALL
S.E. TRAINING WALL
RAILWAY TRACKS TO TAUNTON
ANCHORS IN FILLING
S.W. TRAINING WALL
SOUTH ABUTMENT
NEW CUT ARTIFICIAL TIDAL STREAM
DIRECTION OFF EBB FLOW
100'0" SPAN
315'0"
EXISTING STEEL TRUSS BRIDGE
EXISTING MASONARY ARCH
446 - 18" ROTINOFF PILES
181 - 24" " "
300 PRECAST PILES
N.E. TRAINING WALL
NORTH ABUTMENT
N.W. TRAINING WALL
BEAM
40'0"
TO TEMPLE MEADS STATION

Map 55. Abutments of the New Cut bridge at Bristol, showing a general plan of the piled abutments.

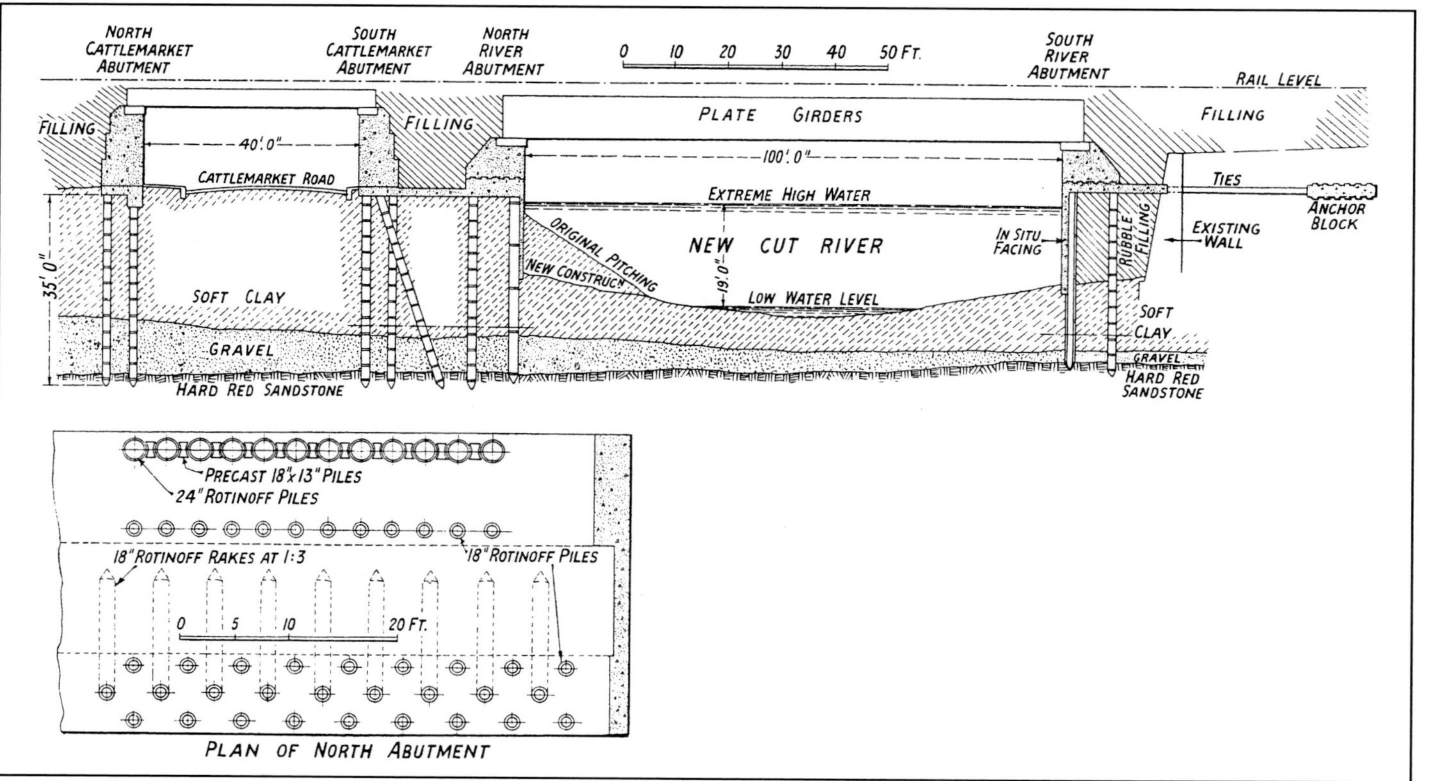

Fig. 20. Section through the Cattle Market Road and New Cut River bridges, showing details of the piled abutments, and on the left a separate detailed plan of the piling.

Plate 287 Constructing the abutments of the 300ft wide Temple Meads railway bridge at Bristol, the GWR adopted a combination of vertical and raked shell piles. This combination was said to have proved very efficient and showed a considerable saving over ordinary mass-concrete foundations. The front row of 2ft diameter piles were driven into the water, yet when the open bores were inspected before concreting, they were found to be dry. The inset shows the reinforced piles.

Plate 288 Piled abutment of the New Cut bridge, under construction.

near St Fagans Junction, crossing the valley at Walnut Tree by means of a hugh viaduct. The line ran parallel with the Walnut Tree branch of the Rhymney Railway on to Penrhos Junction, a point near the entrance to the Aber Valley. An extension crossing the Rhymney Valley to reach a point on the Brecon and Merthyr Railway just above Bedwas was subsequently opened in January 1905.

Under the unified control of the GWR, a portion of the Rhymney branch of the Barry line for a distance of $2\frac{3}{4}$ miles was found to be redundant, and the permanent way and bridges between Penrhos Junction and Barry Junction were therefore removed. This involved the demolition of Penyrheol Viaduct, and the steelwork was sold as scrap. The main girders were 101ft long, 11ft 2in deep and weighed some 35 tons each, which meant that they were far to unwieldy to lift and load into wagons directly. For this reason, after the decking had been removed, the girders were pushed off the tops of the piers, to fall into the valley below, a distance of some 50ft. The girders were then cut up by oxy-acetylene plant into convenient sizes and the material loaded into wagons by a crane standing on the remaining portion of the bridge on the adjoining line.

On the pier tops, jacks were used to give the girders an outward tilt, and a winch on the ground attached by a wire rope to the centre of the top boom gave a sufficient pull to make them overbalance. No difficulty was experienced with any of the girders and the felling of two, including the transference of the jacks and tackle, was accomplished in $\frac{3}{4}$ hour. It was interesting to note that the girders

Plate 289 Piled abutment of the New Cut bridge, showing the piles driven and backed with facing being placed.

Plate 290 Piled abutment of the New Cut bridge, showing the site of Temple Meads station widening.

turned a complete somersault so that the bottom flange finished furthest away from the piers.

1937 NEW GOODS STATION AT PENZANCE

This scheme involved moving the goods station at Penzance to Ponsandane, just outside Penzance, with the dual purposes of freeing the original site for the extension and improvement of the passenger station, as well as of improving and centralising the goods services.

The new commodious goods depot was situated on the up side of the line, adjoining the main road. In the new goods yard there were two mileage sidings, each holding about 60 wagons, flanked by roadways and stacking space, with siding accommodation for about 50 more wagons on either side of the new goods shed. This was an appreciable advance upon the yard accommodation hitherto available at Penzance. The goods shed, traversed by a single track, was 280ft long and held 14 wagons. Immediately adjoining the eastern end of it was an extensive warehouse 120ft long with a total floor space of about 400 sq yards. The shed platform was 30ft wide, with a continuous 15ft verandah covering the road side. There were six wide cartage

Plate 291 Construction work in progress showing the Bath Road bridge in the foreground, the entrance to the locomotive depot on the left, Temple Meads station with its old roof in the middle distance.

Plate 292 View of the construction work from the old station roof, looking towards Bath Road bridge and the locomotive depot on the left. In the foreground the new abutment of the New Cut bridge can be seen.

Plate 293 Construction scene viewed from the old station roof, but looking in the other direction, showing station widening work on the right.

Plate 294 The new platform 3, one of the new platforms at Bristol Temple Meads station, constructed on new ground on the down side of the former station.

Plate 295 The subway at the reconstructed Bristol Temple Meads station.

berths equipped with gates in the shed wall. The platform was particularly commodious and had natural lighting from extensive glazed roof areas. A one-ton overhead hand-operated runway crane system served practically all the shed siding, platform and cartage berths. Two $1\frac{1}{2}$ ton weighing machines were installed on the platform. At the west end of the shed were new offices, comprising a large general office, rooms for the agent and chief clerk, and messrooms.

Three new cattle pens were provided near the main roadway, and an end-on loading bank provided nearby. A new 20 ton Pooley weighbridge was installed just inside the main entrance, and the 6 ton yard crane transferred from its original position at Penzance to a convenient site in the new yard.

All the 'collected and delivered' goods traffic ("C & D" in Goods Department parlance) hitherto passing through Marazion station was concentrated on the new depot, the Penzance cartage services being

Plate 296 General view of the alterations at Bristol Temple Meads station. In the foreground, on the right, is the new signal box on the west side. In the centre is the new girder bridge carrying the Bath Road over the running lines. In the centre background are the old station building and the new platforms.

Plate 297 The new Bristol Temple Meads East signal box, which was brought into use following the complete reconstruction and enlargement of the station in 1935.

Plate 298 Part of the interior of Bristol Goods Shed, showing a Lister truck and petrol-electric mobile cranes in use.

extended to cover Marazion and district, so that Penzance served an area of about 100 sq miles by road lorries, the cartage service now being motorised. The heavy broccoli traffic forwarded from this area during the first three or four months of each year was dealt with at the loading banks already available at Ponsandane, and it was considered advantageos to have the whole of the goods facilities together.

1938 MOVEMENT OF PLYMOUTH SIGNAL BOX

Alterations in progress at Plymouth North Road Station involved widening the bridge carrying the railway over the road at the west end of the station and this necessitated moving Plymouth West signal box which occupied part of the site of the new lines which would pass over the widened bridge. The box, a timber structure on brick foundations measuring 38ft by 13ft, had been built about 34 years previously, and contained a heavy locking frame of 59 levers. To reduce interference with traffic operations to a minimum, it was decided to move the building as a complete unit to its new site, which was on the edge of a newly-tipped bank, into which timber piles had been driven.

Horizontal timbers were laid on the top of the piles to form a platform to

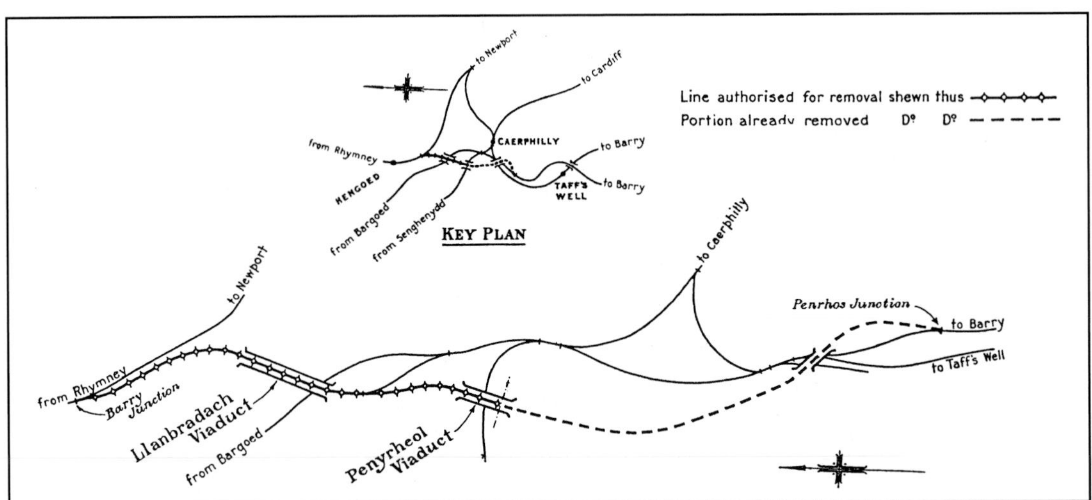

Map 56. Diagram showing the position of the Rhymney branch of the former Barry Railway, and of the line between Penrhos Junction and Barry Junction and of the Penyrheol Viaduct which was demolished.

Plate 299 Penyrheol Viaduct in course of demolition. One girder lies on the ground, ready to be cut up.

carry the box, and heavy timbers were laid to form a track from the old to the new site. A temporary hut was erected to accommodate essential electrical instruments for train working, and arrangements were made to work points and signals by hand where necessary. On 22 January 1938, the box was then taken out of use and dismantled, the whole of the locking frame and the heavier portions of the apparatus being removed, all parts being marked to facilitate reassembly. The next morning, the work of moving the box was begun, the structure being lifted by screw jacks and then lowered on to steel rollers. Twenty men then levered the box with the aid of crowbars to its new position, the actual traversal taking only $1\frac{1}{2}$ hours. The box was lowered on to its new foundations in its final position in another $3\frac{1}{2}$ hours. By 27 January, the whole of the equipment had been refixed and the points, discs and signals (except the distant signals) were coupled up to the frame, the distant signals being reconnected the next day.

1938 CONSTRUCTION OF NEW SEA WALL AT PENZANCE

Before 1920, the rail approach to Penzance station consisted of a single line carried on a viaduct of 51 spans, varying in length from 15 to 19ft. The viaduct was originally of timber construction, but was strengthened some years later by steel joists. It was supported on timber piles with the exception of nine spans at the Penzance end, where the supports were on stone piers. In 1920, the timber having come

Plate 300 Penyrheol Viaduct showing the second girder falling to the ground, bringing the edge of the top parapet with it.

Plate 301 The new Goods Shed and Offices at Ponsandane, Penzance, with motor lorries and trailers in the cartage bays.

Plate 302 Bodily removal of Plymouth West signal box. The left-hand photograph shows the box being lifted off its existing foundations by screw jacks, while the right-hand photograph shows the box being moved from its old site to the new site.

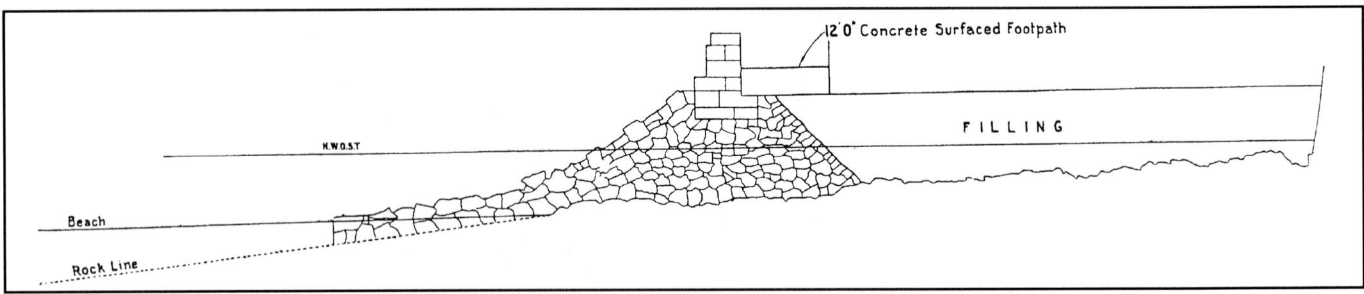

Fig. 21. Diagram giving a typical cross section of the sea bank and promenade under construction at Penzance.

Plate 303 The new sea bank at Penzance in the preliminary stages of construction, and the point at which the original sea wall was pierced.

Plate 304 Oxford Road bridge in Reading, showing the shield and some of the new main girders in position. The tram tracks reducing to a single track under the old bridge can also be seen.

Plate 305 Erection of cross-girders on the down side and demolition of the arch.

to the end of its life, it was replaced by a much wider stone-faced embankment carrying two lines into the station, as well as an engine line connecting with the locomotive depot at Ponsandane. This work involved the tipping of some 27,000 tons of stone.

As already discussed, the goods depot was transferred to Ponsandane, thus freeing space for the enlargement of the passenger station. To make possible the widening of the railway accommodation at the eastern end of the station, an area of the foreshore was reclaimed. On this land, together with some acquired from the Penzance Corporation, there was constructed a new sea wall about 1000ft long. This served a double purpose, as it was so designed as to give the additional amenity of a pedestrian promenade

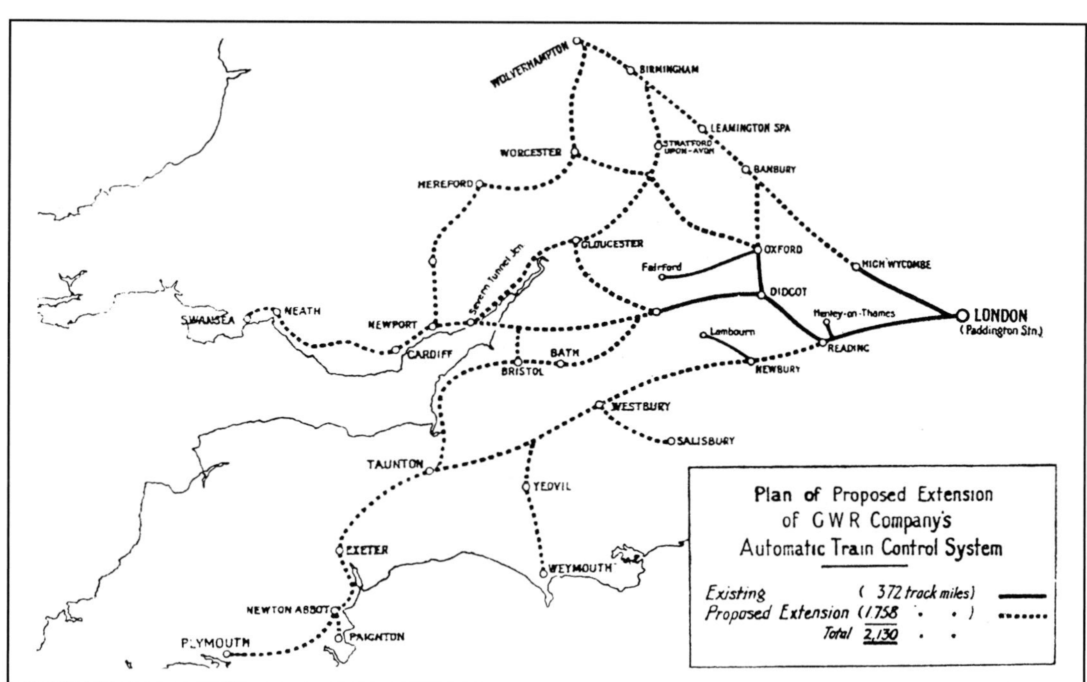

Map 57. Plan of the GWR rail system in 1930, showing the lines already equipped with ATC, and the extensions planned under the Loan Act.

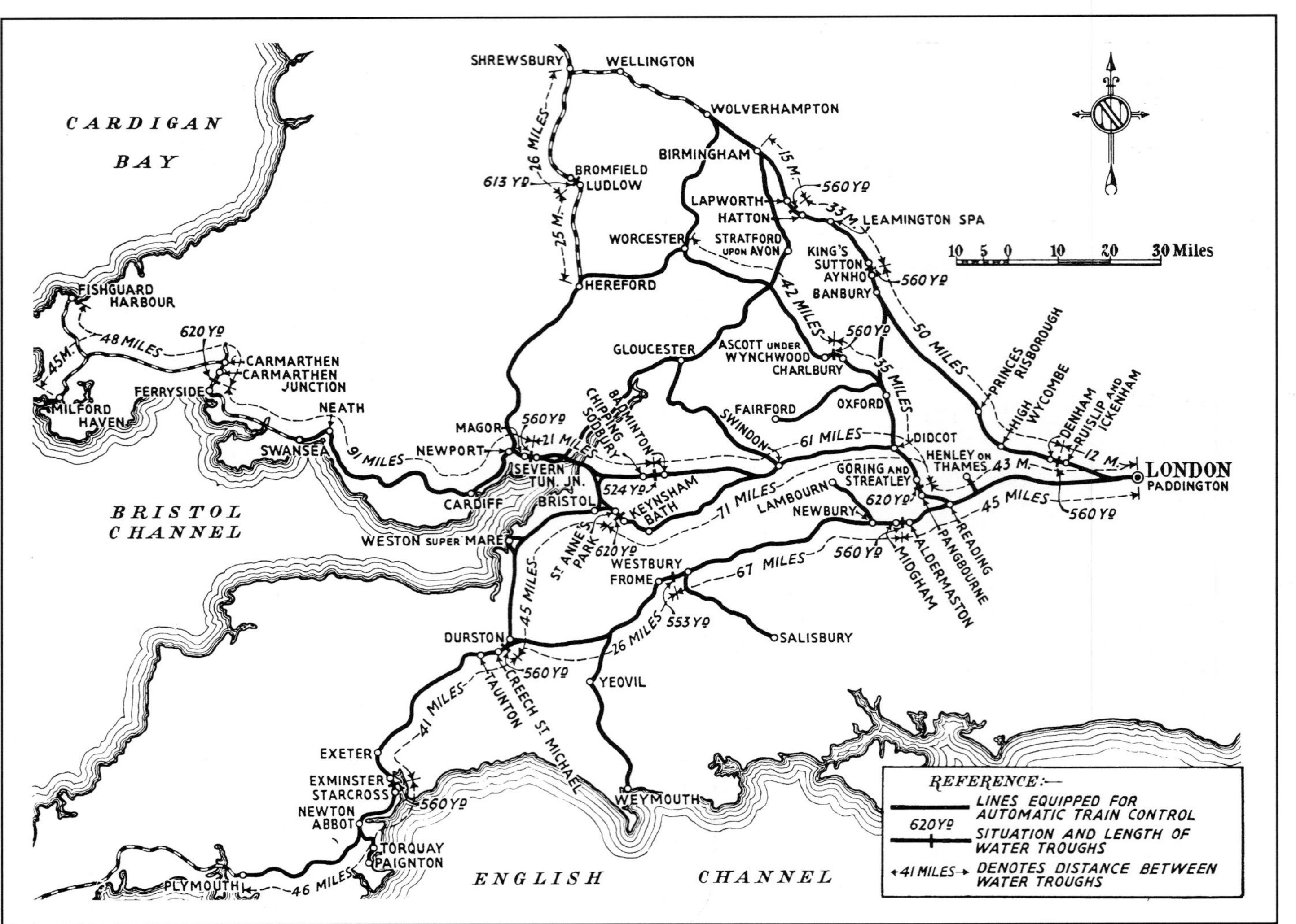

Map 58. Plan of the GWR rail system in the late 1930s, showing the lines equipped with ATC. It also shows the situation and length of the water troughs, and the distances between them.

Plate 306 Engine approaching ramp. The shoe is about to make contact with the ramp.

12ft wide. The Corporation cooperated by extending the promenade 200ft westward to Albert Pier and 400ft eastward to Chyandour Bridge.

To form the new sea wall, an opening was made in the existing masonry wall south of the railway, from which point an embankment was built up on which a temporary siding was laid. From this track, over 3000 wagons containing granite blocks, weighing from 5cwt to 5 tons, were unloaded by a travelling crane and placed in position to form a sea bank. Behind this stone barrier, some 20,000 tons of hard filling was deposited and levelled to provide a new formation. The sea bank was formed to a long sloping face, with large blocks of granite rubble projecting from the face to break up the force of rough seas. At the top of the slope of the sea bank, a cement concrete bed was laid to carry a heavy parapet wall of granite masonry, which was constructed high enough to prevent the sea washing over the railway. Behind the parapet wall was placed the promenade, separated from the railway by a strong fence.

This enabled the start of the scheme for the rebuilding and enlargement of Penzance passenger station and the provision of new office accommodation. The existing two short platforms which were unequal to the requirements of the longer trains arriving at, and departing from, the station during the summer months, were superseded by four platforms of nearly double the length and provided with ample overhead covering. To obviate the need to deal with fish and flower traffic on the passenger station, new loading banks were constructed. The permanent way and signalling were modernised and a new signal box brought into use.

1938 RECONSTRUCTION OF OXFORD ROAD BRIDGE IN READING

The purpose of the reconstruction of this bridge, carried out by the GWR in cooperation with Reading Corporation, was to provide sufficient headroom for trolley-bus vehicles to pass under the bridge and the greater width of road of 70ft for general traffic. The old bridge consisted of a six-ringed brick skew arch of 40ft span carrying the main Berks & Hants lines over the roadway, which had a single tramway track in the centre. The junction of the Berks & Hants line with Reading West curve was situated on the old structure, and in order to provide sufficient room for a centre girder, the connections had to be moved nearer to Reading, and the space between the up and down main lines increased.

Construction of the new abutments was started in December 1937. Temporary bridging was provided by 12in by 12in baulk timbers, 32ft long, to permit an 8ft trench to be sunk behind each of the existing abutments. The excavated material was taken out at the ends of the trenches and carted away to tip by lorries. The new abutments were then constructed in the trenches and completed by April 1938. A Locomotive Department 10in water main on the down side of the line was temporarily diverted to the outside of the up main track.

To facilitate the demolition of the old arch, on 19 June, a shield was erected under the arch to protect road traffic and to carry if necessary the weight of the lower rings of the arch during demolition. As the shield temporarily reduced the headroom by some 8in, the arch was carefully templated, and false kerbs provided, to ensure that vehicles kept to the centre of the road. The shield consisted of arched ribs made from old rails, carrying timber covering. As it was necessary to remove the tram wires, the tram service was terminated on either side of the bridge.

Occupation of the down main line was arranged during the week ending 26 June, and work in connection with the removal of the track proceeded, including dismantling the temporary bridging and the excavation of filling from over the arch. To retain the filling supporting the up main line, a temporary brick wall was constructed under the sleeper ends in the 6ft space between the tracks. As soon as the back of the arch was exposed, pneumatic and petrol-driven concrete breakers were set to work, and sufficient of the arch was removed to enable the outside girder to be placed in position. Occupation of the up line

Plate 307 This picture shows the actual contact of the shoe with the ramp.

was then arranged, and two new girders on POLLEN B wagons were brought alongside the bridge. Two 36-ton cranes lifted each girder (weighing 20 tons) and placed it in position. To save further occupation of the up line, the centre girder (40 tons) was also unloaded, and placed temporarily alongside the outside girder. Once this work was completed, the brickwork was then cut out and the centre girder was placed in its permanent position. The erection of cross-girders, rail bearers and floor plates followed, the track being subsequently replaced on packings and the line reopened to traffic on 27 June.

Next week, the water main was transferred to its permanent position over the new down line span of the bridge. Occupation was then arranged on the up main line, the track was removed, and excavation and demolition of the remainder of the arch proceeded. The new outside girder was erected and the cross-girders, rail bearers and floor plates fitted. The track was replaced on packings, and the line reopened to traffic on 4 July. The remaining work of rivetting, welding the floor plates, and demolition of the old abutments then took place during two 24-hour occupations on 10 and 17 July.

1938 AUTOMATIC TRAIN CONTROL

The primary object of the GWR type of automatic train control was to provide an audible signal in the engine cab corresponding to the position of the distant signal. If the signal was in the 'clear' position, a bell rang in the engine cab. If it was in the 'danger', or more correctly, in the 'caution' position, a siren sounded in the engine cab and at the same time the brakes were automatically applied. The application of the brakes and the sounding of the siren continued until the driver 'acknowledged' the signal by lifting a small handle on the apparatus in the engine cab.

While originally designed purely as an audible cab signal, to assist the working of trains in foggy or snowy weather, it was soon realised that the principle could be readily extended to a form of automatic train control, by arranging that the air valve, when opened, not only admitted air to the siren but also to the brake pipe, so that if no action was taken the train would be stopped. By December 1914, 180 miles of track and 90 locomotives had been equipped. By 1930, the system had proved its reliability on the main line from Paddington to Reading for 25 years, and no less than 372 miles of track were covered. Under the Development (Loan Guarantees and Grants) Act of 1929, it was proposed to extend the system over another 1758 track miles making a total of 2130 track miles in all, and to equip another 3000 locomotives.

The system worked as follows. A ramp was fixed between the running lines at or near each distant signal. The ramp consisted of a baulk of timber about 40ft long, on which an inverted tee-bar was mounted, the highest point being 3½in above the rail level. To the ramp was connected an electric battery, the circuit from which was closed and opened by a switch coupled to the lever in the signal box operating the signal. This switch was closed, thus energising the ramp, when the signal was in the 'clear' position; and was open, thus leaving the ramp electrically 'dead', when the signal was in the 'caution' position.

On the engine was an electric battery connected to an electro-magnet, which controlled a valve in the vacuum brake system. The circuit from this engine battery was closed and opened by a switch which was operated by a plunger fixed on the centre line of the locomotive. The plunger projected to within 2½in of the rail level, and was consequently lifted one inch each time the locomotive passed over a ramp. When the locomotive was not on a ramp, the switch was closed and electro-magnet was energised, keeping the brake valve shut. When the engine passed over a 'dead' ramp, the signal being in the 'caution' position, the plunger lifted, opened the switch, and broke the circuit. The electro-magnet was de-energised, and allowed the brake valve to open, admitting air to the brake pipe through the siren, and applying the brakes. When the locomotive passed over a 'live' ramp, the signal being at 'clear', the circuit on the

Plate 308 Part of the cab of a Great Western Railway engine, showing the automatic train control apparatus.

Plate 309 Interior view of the new carriage storage shed at Swindon.

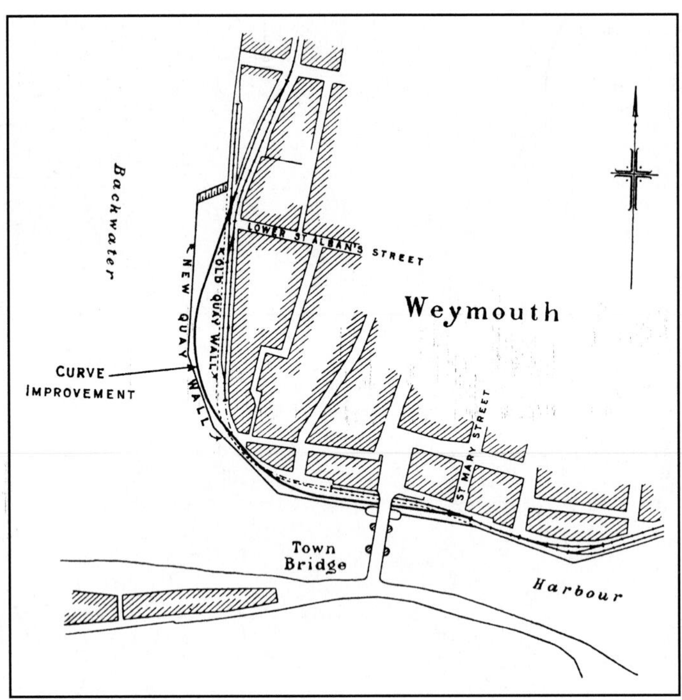

Map 59. Site of the new quay wall, showing the improvement to the curve.

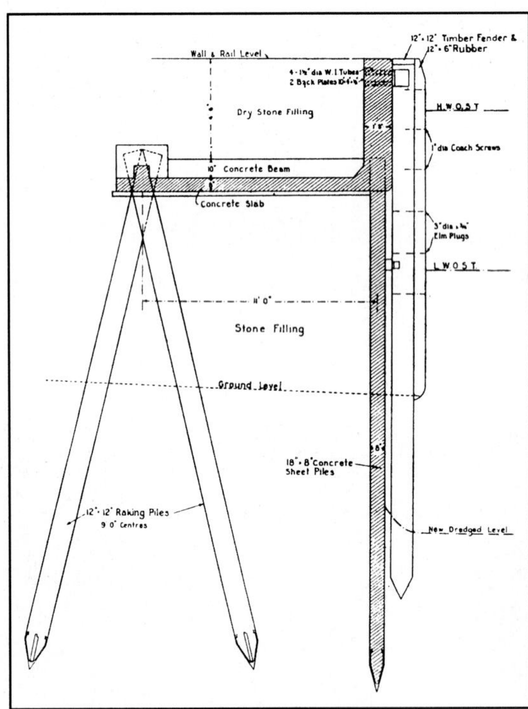

Fig 22. Typical section of piling and quay wall, showing the concrete slab joining the raking piles to the quay wall.

engine was broken, as before, by the movement of the shoe, but the current from the ramp was picked up by the plunger, and flowed through the electro-magnet, thus keeping the brake valve shut, and also causing relays to work and to ring a bell. The engineman thus received an audible signal in the engine cab at every distant signal, no matter what was the position of the signal, consequently the apparatus provided a location indication under all conditions. For single line working, special provision was made to ensure that only such signals were given on the engine as applied to its direction of travel. Failure of any portion of the apparatus either on the engine or on the track, resulted in a danger signal being given on the engine; and failures were therefore always on the safety side.

The extension authorized in 1930 provided for the equipment of the main routes from Paddington to Plymouth via Bath and via Westbury; Paddington to Wolverhampton via

Plate 310 The Royal Albert Bridge being repainted grey on 18 July 1938, as 2-6-2T 4598 crossed the bridge on an up local goods train.

Plate 311 A detailed view of one of the painters at work, more than 100ft above the Tamar. He was not wearing any safety line and the cradle itself was hung on a large hook beneath the pulley block only by means of a knot. The paint pot must have required frequent refilling, although quite how this was done is not apparent.

Plate 312 The painters, who appear to have worked with the minimum of safety lines, at work on top of one of the 455ft spans, whose tubes were nearly 17ft in diameter. The central railings were added sometime after the original construction of the bridge.

Plate 313 The inside of one of the tubes of the Royal Albert Bridge at Saltash. These tubes, which spanned 455ft, were 16¾ft broad and 12¼ft dep.

Aynho and via Oxford and Worcester, including Aynho to Wolvercote Junction and Handsworth Junction to Stourbridge Junction; Swindon to Swansea via Badminton and via Gloucester; Castle Cary to Weymouth; Westbury to Salisbury; Cheltenham to Birmingham; and Worcester to Newport via Hereford. The mileage equipped was equivalent to 54% of the total mileage of two or more tracks.

Because of the accident on the LNER at Castlecary in a blizzard in December 1937, on 22 March 1938, a special run was made from Paddington to Reading to demonstrate the working of the GWR automatic train control system. For the purpose of this test, a 10 coach train of 300 tons was made up, and hauled by Castle class engine No 5055 "Earl of Eldon". From the operating viewpoint the most significant of the tests was one made on the down journey approaching Maidenhead, where the distant signal was kept at caution and the driver instructed to ignore it and continue at full speed. On passing the signal at nearly 70 mph, the siren began to sound, but no acknowledgement was made, and with full steam still on the train was brought to a dead stand in 2700ft, all on dead level track. The ramp was 955ft ahead of the distant signal, and as that signal was 3100ft ahead of the home signal, the train was stopped 1355ft short of the danger point, an impressive demonstration.

1938 NEW CARRIAGE STORAGE SHED AT SWINDON

Authorised in 1936 under the Developments Act of 1929, the GWR built a large new carriage storage shed designed to hold new stock built in the shops during the winter months until required for holiday periods and summer traffic. This was sited on the south side of the line about a mile west of Swindon station, and to permit its construction, it was unfortunately necessary to demolish Newburn House which had been built in 1873 as a residence for the GWR Locomotive Superintendent (First Mr Joseph Armstrong, then Mr William Dean in 1877 and lastly Mr G.J.Churchward in 1902 until 1933 after which it was unoccupied).

Some 35,000 wagons of filling had to be deposited to bring up the level of the site to that of the main line. The shed columns were carried on concrete piers, varying in length up to 30ft, built up from the ground. The building was of light steel construction, covered on the sides with asbestos tiles and roofed with corrugated asbestos sheets. To avoid exposing to sunlight the coachwork of the vehicles in storage, only the north side of each roof span was glazed. The building was 1,800ft long and 122 ft wide, in two spans of 61 ft each; the height to eaves was 15ft and the total area under cover about five acres. The structure was capable of holding a total of about 260 coaches on its ten roads.

Plate 314 The old Houndiscombe Road bridge at Plymouth, showing the masonry construction and limited space for only two rail tracks and road traffic above. In the right hand side of the picture can just be seen part of the temporary access at the corner of the bridge.

Plate 315 Work in progress on the new enlarged Houndiscombe Road bridge, showing the concrete main beams with their stirrups left projecting at the top, and the new concrete trestle supports.

1938 IMPROVEMENTS AT WEYMOUTH QUAY

For many years considerable delay was occasioned to passenger stock working over the Weymouth Tramway to Weymouth Quay owing to the sharp curvature of the line, which necessitated detaching the couplings of vehicles and substituting special long couplings so as to avoid risk of damage to the undercarriages of rolling stock.

In 1938, work was carried out to increase the radius of the worse curve,

Plate 316 View of the existing Trenance Viaduct at Newquay from the roadway with reconstruction work in progress. Scaffolding is in place. The widening extensions to the piers can be seen, splayed back to avoid interference with traffic on the road. The new stonework is naturally lighter in colour than the existing stonework. Work has started on the top plinths of the piers. The photograph is marked in white to show where the first and second stage arches would be built.

Plate 317 The steel structure of the Trenance Viaduct viewed from the side. The left illustration shows the structure before the slewing operation, and the right illustration shows it after the slewing operation.

extending for a distance of about 1,100ft from Lower St Alban's Street, passing under the town bridge, to St Mary's Street, where it joined up with the existing railway. The reclamation of a portion of the harbour, to a maximum width of 70ft, was involved, together with the construction of a new quay wall of reinforced concrete sheet piling with a concrete capping. Behind this, some 22,000 cubic yards of stone filling was tipped. Having filled in the space, the sheet piles of the quay wall were anchored back to two raking piles by means of a flat floor slab.

1938 REPAINTING THE ROYAL ALBERT BRIDGE

In 1938, the Royal Albert Bridge was repainted, a grey colour being chosen at the request of the Air Raid Precautions authorities in anticipation of the war which was declared in September 1939. It was, of course, difficult to disguise such a prominent and characteristic structure, but presumably the grey colour was considered to render it at least slightly less obvious.

This bridge is nearly half a mile in length and rises 200ft above the River

Plate 318 The Trenance Viaduct viewed from above. The upper picture was taken before the slewing of the steel structure, and the lower picture after.

Plate 319 The frontage of the new station at Leamington Spa.

Tamar. The most difficult parts to paint were the two large tubular trusses which formed the centre spans. Each is 455ft in length. The men painting these and other parts of the structure difficult of access were let down from the top in boatswains' chairs. Three coats of paint were applied to the bridge and the total area that needed to be covered was about 350,000 square feet.

1938 PLYMOUTH (NORTH ROAD) STATION IMPROVEMENTS

In connection with the improvements which were carried out at Plymouth (North Road) station, an additional line was laid between Mutley and North Road stations. This necessitated the lengthening of the bridge carrying Houndiscombe Road over the railway between these points, leaving space for two possible future additional tracks. Complete reconstruction was decided upon, and the existing structure, which consisted of a masonry arch spanning the up and down tracks with a width of 22ft between the parapets, was demolished.

The Plymouth Corporation was advised of the GWR's intention in

Plate 320 The down platform, showing the refreshment room with its large windows.

Plate 321 The new large forecourt with space for parking cars.

respect of the bridge, in order that if widening of the road was required suitable provision could be embodied in the reconstruction work. The Corporation decided to increase the width between the parapets from 22ft to 45ft, the new bridge to carry a 27ft roadway and two footpaths each 9ft wide with provision for mains and cables under the latter.

The new bridge, which was of reinforced concrete, consisted of three spans supported on intermediate trestles, also of reinforced concrete, and founded on rock a little below formation level. The erection of the new structure was carried out in two stages so that road traffic was not interrupted, the reinforcement being so arranged at the junction of the two sections that when completed a monolithic construction was obtained.

The ribs of the main beams of the centre span, which was 44ft 3in between centres of trestles, were precast on a plot of ground alongside the track adjacent to the site, and after a period for maturing were hoisted into position by steam cranes. The stirrups

Plate 322 The steps to the down platform and the new subway to the up side. Note the tiling.

Plate 323 Exterior view of the Paddington Arrival signal box after the disastrous fire of 25 November 1938.

were left projecting at the top of the main beam ribs and were bent over the top reinforcement incorporated with that of the deck slab, after which the whole of the concreting of the deck was completed. The two small side spans over the space left for possible future tracks were 15ft 6in and 16ft 3in clear between the trestles and abutment face, the main beams being so arranged as to give continuity over the three spans; the whole of the concreting of the small span beams and slabs being carried out on the site. The parapets which were carried by the outer reinforced beams were constructed of masonry above the level of the footpaths to be in keeping with buildings in the vicinity. To enable the first section of the work to be carried out without interruption to road traffic, it was necessary, by means of a service girder and substantial timber decking, to provide temporary access at the corner of the existing bridge on the down side nearest North Road station.

1938 RECONSTRUCTION OF TRENANCE VIADUCT IN NEWQUAY

The continued growth of holiday traffic to Newquay rendered it desirable to improve the working facilities on the branch line from Par, including the reconstruction of the Trenance Viaduct. This viaduct was situated on the line from St Dennis Junction to Newquay, which was opened for traffic in 1849, becoming amalgamated with the GWR in 1896. The original viaduct was 98ft high and 630ft long, constructed of timber on stone piers and carrying a single line. In 1874, the structure was converted to a girder viaduct by raising the existing piers and adding buttresses to them. The dimensions then became 450ft long with a maximum height of 75ft consisting of nine 45ft long plate girders, from which

Plate 324 Interior view of Paddington Arrival signal box after the fire of 25 November 1938, showing how all the equipment was ruined.

Plate 325 Reversing a set of points with the emergency crank handle.

Plate 326 Groundmen setting points by hand to cross an engine into Ranelagh Bridge locomotive depot over No 2 carriage line, down main line and No 1 carriage line.

it would seem that the track level was lowered to give a shorter structure.

In 1938, the viaduct was reconstructed to the design of an arched structure in concrete with masonry facings, and widened to carry two lines of track, this widening was effected equally on both sides. The existing piers of local stone were first enlarged to the necessary size and strength by casing at each end in granite masonry backed with concrete. Special extensions to the piers, splayed so as not to interfere with the alignment of the road, were built on each side of the main road which passed under the viaduct. Subsequently the existing single line was slewed sideways some six feet to provide the necessary space in which to build throughout the half-width of the new arches. A single line of traffic was then carried over the half-width of the new arched viaduct and the old girders and track removed, thus leaving space to construct the remaining half-width of the new arches.

It was necessary to maintain the traffic during the reconstruction of the viaduct. The arches were built in two stages, the southern half being built first. To achieve this object, the whole of the existing steel superstructure was slewed simultaneously six feet northward on to brick piers which had been previously built on the north side from the new skewback level to form a bearing for the main girders when slewed over. The purpose of the slewing was to provide clearance on the south side to construct arches wide enough for a single line.

The road at each end of the viaduct was broken at 0630 hours and at 0700 the contractors commenced jacking up the girders by hydraulic jacks of from 35 tons to 50 tons capacity. By 0900 the whole of the superstructure had been lifted three inches; this enabled a steel plate $\frac{1}{2}$in thick, 8ft long by 6in wide, to be placed under each bearing in the direction of the slew, three $1\frac{1}{2}$in diameter steel rollers to be placed under the bearing plate, and a cover plate also of $\frac{1}{2}$in thickness, 1 ft 9in square, with its leading edge chamfered, to be put on the rollers. The girders were then lowered on to their respective plates.

At 1007, screw jacks for slewing the girders were in position between the main girders and short ends of rail, which had some time previously been fixed in concrete in the tops of the piers for this purpose. Slewing commenced at once. As the rollers cleared themselves from the back of each plate they were replaced under the leading edge of the cover plate, a spare roller being available so that the girder always had a bearing on three rollers. In less than two hours the entire length of 450ft of steelwork was traversed a distance of 6ft, care being taken to ensure that the whole structure moved at the same rate.

Once more the girders were lifted, this time to remove the plates and rollers, and when this was done the superstructure was lowered on to its new bearings. This work was completely by 1500 hours, slight adjustments being made to correct the alignment of the track. During the time the bridge steelwork was being slewed, the track at each end of the viaduct was also slewed to conform with the new alignment. On completion, the ends were coupled up, the Signal Engineer made good the track circuiting, and by 1600 the track was ready for traffic. The first train passed over the realigned track at 1625.

The building of the southern half of the arches was then proceeded with and on completion, the track diverted from the existing steelwork to a line over the new arches. The steelwork was then removed and the remaining half width of arches completed.

1938 RECONSTRUCTION OF LEAMINGTON SPA STATION

In 1937, it was decided that the Leamington Spa station buildings and platform coverings which were erected in 1853 should be demolished and replaced by new modern buildings. Features included a new subway, 15ft wide, between the up and down platforms, with electric lift services for luggage, the lowering of the original high level approach road to subway level, the provision of new approaches to the loading docks (one by means of a reincorced concrete horse-ramp) and increased covered platform areas. This reconstruction work had to be carried out in several stages, and was not finished until 1939, but the bulk of the work was carried out in the period under review in this book.

Much water was encountered during excavations below the platforms, and this led to the adoption of cavity wall construction throughout. All retaining walls under the platforms and the subway abutments were set back 6½in to allow for a 4½in brick lining separated from the walls by a 2in cavity. Some 6750 square feet were so lined, and drainage pipes were also laid through the walls below floor levels, connecting with additional drains under the floors, with access for inspection through manholes. Working space on the up side was very narrow, and on this side all surplus excavation and the materials recovered from demolition were removed by rail. The reconstruction of the platform walls enabled them to be raised to standard height. The new platforms were paved with precast slabs obtained from the GWR depot at Taunton.

The station's forecourt, or main approach, with an approximate area of ¾ acre, and separate entrance and exit, replaced the former combined high level and low level approach, over 27,000 square feet of new road surface being laid and giving ample parking space for cars. About 18,000 cubic yards of excavation were removed to form the forecourt. Direct access from the forecourt to the parcels office, cloak room, cycle store and refreshment room cellar on the down side was now available. These rooms were all on the left of the main entrance to the station. The booking hall, which was immediately inside the main entrance, led directly to the steps to the down platform and the new subway to the up side. The walls of the booking hall were lined with tiling above a polished granite plinth, which was a notable feature of the new station, being used extensively on the front elevation of the main building, and also at platform level on the whole of the building work on both platforms. The plinth formed an effective contrast to the Portland stone facing of the main building and entrance to the subway. The new buildings were steel-framed structures sheathed with brickwork faced with Portland stone, except on platform elevations. The roofs were flat and surrounded by low parapets. The platform coverings were of conventional design in steelwork on cast iron columns, the roof covering being zinc sheets on match-boarding, and glass adjoining the buildings.

1938 PADDINGTON SIGNAL BOX FIRES

On 25 November 1938 at about 0200, fire suddenly broke out in the electric locking frame in the Paddington Arrival signal box, and so rapidly did the flames spread that despite the efforts of the signalmen on duty, practically the whole of the locking frame was burnt out, together with the telephones, block instruments and other equipment. This box controlled the signalling covering the arrival lines into Paddington station, and also the Hammersmith and City lines between Paddington and Westbourne Park, and as a result of the fire all signals and points on these sections were put out of action. The signal lights in the departure box, and the telephones between there and Westbourne Bridge were also affected, but this trouble was quickly rectified and the departure box was able to resume normal working.

Within an hour of the Arrival box fire, the London division district inspectors were called up on the telephone and instructed to send all available district relief signalmen and signalmen to Paddington to act as groundmen. So well did they respond that soon after 0800 over thirty competent men arrived to act in this capacity. These men were divided into day and night turns in charge of an inspector; in all, twenty men were employed on each turn. By 0430 the responsible Traffic, Locomotive, Engineering and Signal Department officers, and representatives of the London Passenger Transport Board (LPTB) had assembled and a meeting was held by the divisional superintendent to decide upon a programme.

On the main line side, the block telegraph apparatus and telephones were included in the fire destruction, and "time-interval" working for the incoming trains was instituted between Subway Junction and the Arrival box, until the block telegraph was restored at 1700. Telephones were re-installed temporarily in the adjoining lineman's hut. The 38 motors working the points were operated by hand by means of the emergency ground levers, each motor having to be operated separately. All movements were controlled under a system which was described at the time as "interlocking by loud speakers", which were promptly installed by the Signal Department at all key points. The Arrival box signalman (housed in the lineman's cabin) on being offered a train, spoke to the chief groundman at a hut known as "GHQ" over the microphone. For example, his message might be "Up relief to 7"; GHQ passed this round to the groundmen by another loud speaker, and on receiving their hand signals indicating that the points had been reversed, clipped and padlocked, he replied to the signalman, "Right, Up Relief to 7"; this message was then repeated to all concerned, including the flagmen at the Intermediate and Inner Home signals, who then changed their red hand signals to green. For outgoing movements with coaches and engines, the signalmen informed the groundman in charge, for example "Next move, No 9 to Down Carriage Line", and similar procedure was followed. Special lights were provided to assist in point working at night, and Tilley lamps were found useful for ground illumination at the points themselves.

This hand signalling was in force from 25 November to 18 December, and not a single mishap or mistake arose; the total possibilities of such an occurrence were obviously considerable, and it was a very high tribute to the staff and organisation that nothing of the sort occurred. On a normal winter day over 5000 lever movements were made on the Arrival box main line locking frame, with over 300 in the busiest hour; all these movements were made by hand!

Signalling on the Hammersmith and City section was converted temporarily to automatic working by the LPTB, and in order to permit this, shunting of trains at the suburban station was discontinued. An emergency timetable providing for some reduction in local services was instituted, and a number of suburban trains that usually arrived and departed from Paddington suburban station terminated and started from Westbourne Park, the connecting services being by the Hammersmith and City Underground trains. Arrangements were also made with the LPTB whereby the Ealing and Central London trains were used to Lancaster Gate by passengers holding tickets from Ealing and beyond to Paddington.

Meanwhile, the Signal Department and other departments concerned were busy erecting a temporary signal box on the power house adjoining the burnt-out box. The LPTB kindly loaned three electric locking-frame sections to the GWR and a temporary frame with 141 working levers was erected and coupled up to essential points and signals, and this was brought into use for the Hammersmith and City lines on 13 December and for the main lines into Paddington on 18 December.

Just when the Traffic Department were hoping that they would have the use of something approaching full signalling facilities for the heavy Christmas traffic, unfortunately, a second although somewhat less disastrous fire occurred in the Westbourne Bridge box on 23 December. It was subsequently determined that both fires were due to electrical causes. There were 67 working levers in the Westbourne Bridge box, operating 17 points and 50 signals. Fortunately, a skeleton staff of groundmen had been retained at the Arrival box for possible emergencies, and these men proceeded at once to Westbourne Bridge with point clips, power point crank handles, etc ready to carry on operation. Westbourne Bridge box controlled the working on the down main line, No 1 carriage line, and No 2 carriage line and Ranelagh Bridge turntable depot and the parcels depot.

The telephone between the Departure box and Subway Junction remained intact, and time-interval working was not necessary. The signal Engineer took immediate steps to install the main line and carriage line block instruments in the ganger's hut, which became the "signal box". The main line block was ready at 1315 and that for the carriage lines by 1900. The Locomotive Department helped by closing Ranelagh Bridge depot on the day of the fire, and dealt with all engines at Old Oak Common, and thereafter sending only a limited number of engines to Ranelagh Bridge depot, 26 as compared with the normal 60. About 3500 lever movements were made at Westbourne Bridge box on a normal winter day, including 250 movements in the busiest hour.

As concluded at the time, the staff of all GWR departments displayed a splendid team spirit in coping with the emergencies arising from both fires, especially the groundmen, and this seems a good note on which to end this book.